ENGINEERING DESIGN
IN GEOTECHNICS

ENGINEERING DESIGN IN GEOTECHNICS

Fethi Azizi

University of Plymouth, UK

Published by F. Azizi

First published 2007 by F. Azizi
School of Engineering, University of Plymouth
Plymouth, PL1 8AA

British Library Cataloguing in Publication Data
A catalogue record for this book is available from the British Library.

ISBN 978-0-9555996-0-6 (hb)
ISBN 978-0-9555996-1-3 (pb)

Printed in Great Britain by T J International Ltd, Cornwall England

Le but de la science n'est pas d'ouvrir la porte de la sagesse infinie, mais d'imposer une limite à l'erreur infinie.

Galileo Galilei

Contents

Preface

Initially, I intended to write a comprehensive book on Geotechnical engineering that encompasses several aspects such as engineering geology, modelling of soil and rock behaviour and engineering design. I quickly realised that such an ambitious task cannot be achieved under the cover of one book, and so a decision needed to be made as to the best way to present these topics without watering down the content or the analysis. I also came to the conclusion very early on that writing one book in two volumes was not the answer; instead I have elected to write two separate books (with an almost identical preface), which can be read independently, but which can be complementary since they are written in the same style using the same philosophy: *Physical Behviour in Geotechnics* and *Engineering Design in Geotechnics*. The content of this second book relates to design methodologies covering topics such as slope stability, shallow and deep foundations (including the design of pile groups and laterally loaded piles), retaining structures, sheet piles, and tunnel design. The book is written in a logical congruent way, and I have endeavoured to make it enjoyable to read, but in this respect, only your judgement matters.

I am assuming that the reader has a working knowledge of engineering mechanics, especially on stresses and strains, Mohr's circle representation of stresses and strains, equilibrium equations in terms of moments and forces, elasticity and plasticity.

Although I have some sympathy with the view that an engineer should be literate and numerate, I do believe that a design engineer *must* be able to translate a physical behaviour into mathematical equations; after all that is what design *is* about. In this respect, I am aware that part of the analysis in some sections of the book may appear somewhat mathematically involved. In fact, you would be surprised to realise how easy they are once you have reread them: it is only by reading about it time and time again that an intellectual skill can be mastered. The book contains more than 50 worked examples and in excess of 320 state-of-the-art illustrations which are presented in a clear detailed way that can only enhance the understanding of the principles involved.

By the time you have read through this book, you would have hopefully understood, learned and mastered its content. In addition, you would have been able to satisfy some of your curiosity through some detailed derivations of formulae and equations which are otherwise presented as a *fait accompli* in other textbooks. You would have also noticed the rather lengthy process related to the detailed calculations of some worked examples. In practice, these calculations are almost exclusively undertaken numerically, since not only specialised software packages dealing with different themes in geotechnics are widely available, but a designer can always develop a software to suit his or her needs. So, do not despair if you find the hand calculations in some instances long and tedious because that was the feeling I had when I wrote them! However, as a learning experience, every example presents you with an opportunity to see how these details are handled, and more to the point, helps you develop your engineering judgement, in that the outcome of any computation always reflects the choice made vis à vis the soil parameters. One has to realise that geotechnics is not an exact science; rather, it can be described as an art in which the artist (*i.e.* the engineer) has to rely sometimes, if only partly, on his or her intuition (*i.e.* judgement).

Moreover, you will be able to appreciate that, although in practice calculations may be undertaken in a different way, the fundamental thinking is similar to what you would have learned throughout the book. If anything, once you have assimilated the basic knowledge and principles, you will find it much easier to make the *appropriate assumptions* with confidence. This reinforces the statement made earlier about mastering an intellectual skill; and so do not be put off if you do not fully understand what you have read: go through it again bearing in mind that the last reading *is* the one that matters.

This book is also meant to be useful to a postgraduate student who seeks a deeper understanding and a specialised knowledge about different design aspects in geotechnics. In addition, practising engineers may find the book valuable since most of the mathematical formalisms can be forgone, provided that the assumptions of the formulation are well understood, so that it is not used in a perfunctory way as a recipe: bear in mind this book is meant to make you think, then act.

Fethi Azizi
June 2007

Acknowledgements

Reasonable effort has been made to seek copyright permission and to include acknowledgements where appropriate, and any omission notified will be rectified at the earliest opportunity.

I am thankful to the many friends and colleagues who contributed, in their own ways, to the improvement of the content of this book.

List of main symbols

a	radius, area
A	air content, activity, area, porewater pressure coefficient
A_b	base area
A_s	shaft area
B	width, porewater pressure coefficient
B'	effective width
b	width
c	apparent cohesion
c_u	undrained shear strength
c_w	cohesion at soil/wall interface
C	compressive strength
C_g	coefficient of gradation
C_s	swelling index
C_u	coefficient of uniformity
C_α	slope of secondary consolidation graph
$D,\ d$	diameter, depth, depth factor, depth of embedment
$d_c,\ d_q,\ d_\gamma$	depth factors
$[D]$	elasticity matrix
e	void ratio, eccentricity, depth corresponding to zero net pressure
E	stiffness (elasticity modulus)
E_b	soil secant modulus
E_c	stiffness modulus of pile material
E_m	pressuremeter modulus
δE	work done by an external load
$E_p I_p$	flexural stiffness
F	force, factor of safety
f_o	correction factor
$\{F\}$	vector of nodal forces
g	acceleration due to gravity, depth corresponding to zero bending moment
G	shear modulus
G_s	specific gravity
$h,\ H$	height, total head, length of drainage path, lateral load
h_e	elevation head
h_p	pressure head
h_s	capillary saturation level

i	hydraulic gradient
i_{cr}	critical hydraulic gradient
i_e	exit hydraulic gradient
I	moment of inertia, rigidity index
I_c, I_q, I_γ	inclination factors
I/y	steel section modulus
k	permeability
K	ratio of horizontal to vertical effective stresses, bulk modulus, subgrade reaction modulus
$[K]$	stiffness matrix
K_a	coefficient of active pressure
K_e	length ratio
K_o	coefficient of active pressure at rest
K_p	coefficient of passive pressure
l_c	characteristic length
L	length
M	mass, moment
M_s	soil/shaft flexibility factor
m_α	slope constant
n_h	rate of increase of the subgrade reaction modulus
N	normal force, stability number
N_c, N_q, N_γ	bearing capacity factors
N_f	number of flow channels
N_d	number of equipotential drops
$[N]$	shape functions
OCR	overconsolidation ratio
p	mean stress, perimeter, reaction pressure, normalised volume loss
P	soil reaction per unit length
P_a	active thrust
P_p	passive thrust
$[P]$	permeability matrix
q	load, rate of flow, deviator stress
Q	load, rate of flow
Q_a	safe working load
Q_b	ultimate base resistance
Q_n	negative skin friction
Q_s	ultimate shaft friction
Q_u	ultimate loading capacity of a single pile
Q_{ug}	ultimate loading capacity of a pile group
R, r	radius
r_u	pore pressure ratio
R_e	Reynolds number
S	degree of saturation, sensitivity, spacing, total settlement
S_e	elastic shortening

s	reduced mean stress
s_c, s_q, s_γ	shape factors
t	time, reduced deviator stress
T	shear force per linear metre, characteristic length
u	porewater pressure, lateral displacement
U	thrust due to water pressure,
$\{U\}$	vector of nodal unknowns
v	velocity, specific volume, vertical displacement
V	volume, shear load along pile shaft
V_a	volume of air
V_L	volume loss
V_s	volume of solids, volume of trough per metre length of tunnel
V_w	volume of water
w	water content, weight, radial displacement
w_L	liquid limit
w_P	plastic limit
w_S	shrinkage limit
W	weight
δW	work dissipated per unit volume
y	lateral displacement
z	depth
z_f	neutral depth for negative skin friction
Z_{max}	length factor
β	soil slope behind a retaining wall
γ	unit weight
γ'	effective unit weight
δ	soil/structure friction angle, settlement above tunnel crown
ε	strain
η	ratio of total heads, efficiency factor, optimum angle of failure behind a retaining wall
θ	temperature
λ, Ω	wall inclinations
ν	Poisson's ratio
ξ	correction factor, strength ratio
ρ	density, sheet pile stiffness
σ	total stress
σ^e	tunnel face equilibrium pressure
σ'	effective stress
σ_a	active pressure
σ_h, σ_3	horizontal stress
σ_p	preconsolidation pressure
σ_v, σ_1	vertical stress
τ	shear stress
τ_{mob}	mobilised shear stress

υ	angle of dilation
ϕ	angle of shearing resistance, from factor
ϕ_p, ϕ_c, ϕ_r	peak, critical and residual angles of shearing resistance
Φ	stress function, velocity potential

Conversion factors

- **Multiplication factors**
  10^9 *giga*   G
  10^6 *mega*   M
  10^3 *kilo*   k
  10^{-3} *milli*   m
  10^{-6} *micro*   μ
  10^{-9} *nano*   n

- **Length**
  $1\,cm = 0.3937\,in$ $1\,in = 2.54\,cm$
  $1\,m = 3.28\,ft$ $1\,ft = 30.48\,cm$

- **Area**
  $1\,m^2 = 10.76\,ft^2$ $1\,ft^2 = 929\,cm^2$

- **Volume**
  $1\,l = 1000\,cm^3 = 61.02\,in^3$ $1\,in^3 = 16.388\,cm^3$
  $1\,m^3 = 35.32\,ft^3$ $1\,ft^3 = 0.02832\,m^3$

- **Mass**
  $1\,g = 0.0022\,p$ $1\,p = 453.6\,g$

- **Density**
  $1\,g/cm^3 = 1\,Mg/m^3 = 62.43\,p/ft^3$ $1\,p/ft^3 = 0.01602\,Mg/m^3$

- **Energy**
  $1\,J = 1\,Nm = 1\,kg\,m^2/s^2$

- **Force**
  $1\,N = 102\,g = 0.2248\,p$ $1\,p = 4.448\,N$

- **Pressure**
  $1\,N/m^2 = 1\,Pa$ $1\,bar = 100\,kPa$
  $1\,kN/m^2 = 20.89\,p/ft^2$ $1\,p/ft^2 = 0.04787\,kN/m^2$
  $1\,kN/m^2 = 0.1450\,psi$ $1\,psi = 6.895\,kN/m^2$

- **Angle**
  $1\,rad = 57.296°$ $1° = 0.017453\,rad$

- **Temperature**
  $°C = 0.555\,°F - 17.778$ $°F = 1.8\,°C + 32$

The Greek alphabet

Lower case	(selected) Capital	Name
α		alpha
β		beta
γ	Γ	gamma
δ	Δ	delta
ε		epsilon
ζ		zeta
η		eta
θ		theta
ι		iota
κ		kappa
λ	Λ	lambda
μ		mu
ν		nu
ξ		xi
ο		omicron
π	Π	pi
ρ		rho
σ (ς)	Σ	sigma (at end of word)
τ		tau
υ		upsilon
φ	Φ	phi
χ		chi
φ	Ψ	psi
ω	Ω	omega

CHAPTER 1

Engineering properties of soils

1.1 Physical properties of soils

On the basis of the grains size of different soils given in table 1.1, one would expect, for instance, a clay with solid particles of a size smaller than 2×10^{-3} *mm* to be much more compressible than a sand; similarly, a gravel would be much more permeable than a silt. These logical conclusions are closely related to the soil composition, whose behaviour is dependent on the type and size of solid particles and their volumetric proportion with respect to water and air, as well as on the soil stress history (*i.e.* the way in which it was deposited and its subsequent loading-unloading cycles).

Table 1.1: Grain size corresponding to different types of soils

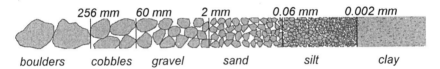

Consider the volume of soil depicted in figure 1.1a. Assume that a microscopic analysis revealed that water is not filling all the voids between solid particles and that some pockets of air exist within the soil matrix. Now imagine that the volume V of this *unsaturated soil* is rearranged in a (theoretical) way such that all solid particles are squeezed together so that no gap is left for water or air to fill (figure 1.1b). The remainder of the volume is therefore constituted of water and air, hence :

$$V = V_s + V_w + V_a \qquad\qquad (1.1)$$

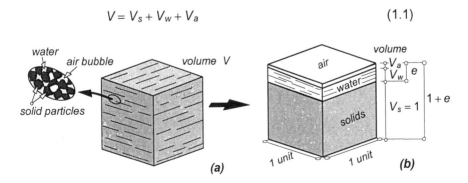

Figure 1.1 (a) Elementary volume of soil, (b) soil composition.

The volume V_s in the above equation is that of solid particles and the quantity $V_w + V_a$ corresponds to the *volume of voids* V_v. Notice that the total volume of soil V in figure 1.1b is selected so that V_s corresponds to one unit. This does not affect in any way the general aspect of the ensuing formulation. The following basic soil properties can thus be defined in a straightforward way:

- *the void ratio*:

$$e = \frac{V_v}{V_s} \tag{1.2}$$

- *the specific volume*:

$$V = V_s + V_v = V_s\left(1 + \frac{V_v}{V_s}\right)$$
$$= V_s(1 + e) \tag{1.3}$$

- *the degree of saturation*:

$$S = \frac{V_w}{V_v} \tag{1.4}$$

- *the water content*:

$$w = \frac{M_w}{M_s} \tag{1.5a}$$

or

$$w = \frac{V_w}{V_s}\frac{1}{G_s} \tag{1.5b}$$

and

$$G_s = \frac{\rho_s}{\rho_w} \tag{1.6}$$

The dimensionless parameter G_s in equation 1.6 refers to the *specific gravity* and represents the relative density of solid particles with respect to water. Typical values of G_s for soils are in the range 2.65 (sands) to 2.75 (clays). M_s and M_w correspond to the mass of solids and that of water respectively, and ρ_w refers to the density of water ($\rho_w = 1 Mg/m^3$). Equation 1.4 indicates that a *fully saturated soil* has a volume of water identical to that of voids because no air is contained within the soil matrix, in which case the degree of saturation is $S = 100\%$. On the other hand, a totally dry soil contains no water and therefore its degree of saturation according to equation 1.4, is $S = 0\%$. In practice, the water content is calculated from equation 1.5a in which the quantities M_w and M_s are measured in the laboratory in a very simple way. For a given volume of soil, the operator needs to determine the mass of soil in its natural state M_t, then its mass M_s after being thoroughly dried in an oven at 105°C for long enough (usually 24 hours) to ensure that all but the chemically bonded water has evaporated; the mass of water M_w is therefore $M_t - M_s$. Also, it is easy to show that, by substituting for V_v and V_s from equations 1.4 and 1.5b respectively, into equation 1.2, the following expression for water content can be established:

$$w = \frac{e\,S}{G_s} \tag{1.7}$$

so that for a fully saturated soil (*i.e.* $S = 100\%$), the latter equation reduces to $e = wG_s$. However, for a totally dry soil, equation 1.7 cannot be used to calculate the void ratio since, in this case, both w and S are zero. *Typical values* for the void ratio range from 0.5 to 0.8 for sands and between 0.7 and 1.3 for clays. Another useful property related to the void ratio and known as *porosity* is defined as the proportion of the volume of voids (that is air *and* water) with respect to the total volume (refer to figure 1.1*b*):

$$n = \frac{V_v}{V} = \frac{e}{1+e} \qquad (1.8)$$

The air content in a soil mass corresponds to the ratio of the volume of air to the total volume and, referring to figure1.1*b*, it can be seen that:

$$A = \frac{V_a}{V} = \frac{V_v - V_w}{V} = \frac{V_v}{V}\left[1 - \frac{V_w}{V_v}\right] = \frac{e}{1+e}(1-S) \qquad (1.9a)$$

Substituting for S from equation 1.7, it follows that:

$$A = \frac{e - wG_s}{1+e} \qquad (1.9b)$$

A relationship between the degree of saturation S of a soil and its air content A can easily be found were the void ratio in the above equation to be replaced by its value from equation 1.7, in which case:

$$S = \frac{1-A}{1 + A/wG_s} \qquad (1.10)$$

Equation 1.10 is markedly non-linear when the air content is larger than zero.

The soil *density* is defined as the ratio of the soil mass to its volume. Accordingly, the following useful relationships are easily established using equations 1.2 to 1.6:

- *the bulk density:* $\qquad \rho = \dfrac{M_s + M_w}{V} = \dfrac{G_s(1+w)}{1+e}\rho_w \qquad (1.11)$

- *the dry density (zero water content:* $w = 0$): $\qquad \rho_d = \dfrac{G_s}{1+e}\rho_w \qquad (1.12)$

- *the saturated density* ($w = e/G_s$, equation 1.7 with $S = 100\%$):

$$\rho_{sat} = \frac{G_s + e}{1+e}\rho_w \qquad (1.13)$$

A combination of equations 1.11 and 1.12 yields the relationship between the bulk and dry densities of a soil:

$$\rho_d = \rho/(1+w) \tag{1.14}$$

Furthermore, it is most helpful during a compaction process (which will be explained shortly) to relate the dry density to the air content of the soil. Thus, rearranging equation 1.1:

$$\frac{V_s}{V} + \frac{V_w}{V} + \frac{V_a}{V} = 1 \tag{1.15}$$

Making use of equations 1.3 and 1.12, it follows that:

$$\frac{V_s}{V} = \frac{1}{1+e} = \frac{\rho_d}{\rho_w}\frac{1}{G_s}$$

On the other hand, both equations 1.2 and 1.4 can be exploited:

$$\frac{V_w}{V} = \frac{V_w}{V_v(1+V_s/V_v)} = S\frac{1}{1+1/e}$$

Hence, substituting for the degree of saturation S from equation 1.7 and rearranging:

$$\frac{V_w}{V} = \frac{wG_s}{1+e} = \frac{w\rho_d}{\rho_w}$$

The last ratio in equation 1.15 corresponds to the air content (equation 1.9a). From whence, a straightforward substitution for the different ratios into equation 1.15 yields:

$$\frac{\rho_d}{\rho_w}\frac{1}{G_s} + w\frac{\rho_d}{\rho_w} + A = 1$$

or

$$\rho_d = \frac{G_s(1-A)}{1+wG_s}\rho_w \tag{1.16}$$

As will be seen later, the calculation of stresses are undertaken using the appropriate soil *unit weight* instead of the density, the two being related through the acceleration due to gravity $g = 9.81\,m/s^2$. Accordingly, the *bulk unit weight* of a soil is established from equation 1.11:

$$\gamma = \rho g = \frac{G_s(1+w)}{1+e}\gamma_w \tag{1.17}$$

γ_w being the unit weight of water ($\gamma_w = 9.81\,kN/m^3$).

Both the *dry* and the *saturated unit weights* are obtained in a similar way from equations 1.12 and 1.13 respectively:

$$\gamma_d = \rho_d g = \frac{G_s}{1+e} \gamma_w \qquad\qquad (1.18)$$

$$\gamma_{sat} = \rho_{sat} g = \frac{G_s + e}{1+e} \gamma_w \qquad\qquad (1.19)$$

When a soil is fully saturated (or submerged), its solid particles are subjected to a buoyancy due to the water in accordance with *Archimedes'* principle. In that case, the *effective unit weight* of the soil corresponds to the difference between its saturated unit weight and the unit weight of water:

$$\gamma' = \gamma_{sat} - \gamma_w = \frac{G_s - 1}{1+e} \gamma_w \qquad\qquad (1.20)$$

Example 1.1

A sample of sand occupying a total volume $V = 1000\,cm^3$ has a total mass $M = 1960\,g$. Once dried in the oven, the mass of the sample was reduced to $M_s = 1710\,g$. Assuming the specific gravity of the solid particles is $G_s = 2.65$, let us evaluate the different following quantities:

• *the water content:* using equation 1.5a, it is seen that:

$$w = \frac{M_w}{M_s} = \frac{1960 - 1710}{1710} = 14.6\,\%$$

• *the void ratio:* equation 1.2 yields $e = \dfrac{V_v}{V_s}$, where the volume of solids is calculated from equation 1.6:

$$V_s = \frac{M_s}{G_s \rho_w} = \frac{1710}{2.65 \times 1} = 645\,cm^3$$

Hence the volume of voids: $V_v = V - V_s = 1000 - 645 = 355\,cm^3$, and therefore the void ratio:

$$e = \frac{355}{645} = 0.55$$

• *the degree of saturation:* equation 1.4 is now used, and as $\rho_w = 1\,g/cm^3$, it follows that:

$$S = \frac{V_w}{V_v} = \frac{1960 - 1710}{355} = 70.4\,\%$$

- *the bulk density:* calculated from equation 1.11:

$$\rho = \frac{M}{V} = \frac{1960}{1000} = 1.96 \, Mg/m^3$$

- *the air content:* found from equation 1.9a:

$$A = \frac{V_a}{V} = \frac{V_v - V_w}{V} = \frac{355 - 250}{1000} = 10.5\%$$

If the sample of sand were saturated, then obviously the air content would be reduced to zero, implying that the volume of voids is equal to that of water: $V_v = V_w$. Accordingly, the mass of water becomes:

$$M_w = V_v \rho_w = 355 \times 1 = 355 \, g$$

thus yielding a water content (for the saturated sand) of:

$$w = \frac{355}{1710} = 20.8\%$$

The void ratio is defined as the ratio of the volume of voids to that of solids, both of which are unchanged, and hence, the void ratio remains constant. Knowing that the degree of saturation is in this case $S = 100\%$, equation 1.7 then yields:

$$e = wG_s = 0.208 \times 2.65 = 0.55$$

which is the same value as the one calculated previously. The density of the sand, however, increases to reflect the saturation and is calculated from equation 1.11 in which the total mass is now:

$$M = M_s + M_w = 1710 + 355 = 2065 \, g$$

Therefore: $\qquad \rho_{sat} = \frac{2065}{1000} = 2.065 \, Mg/m^3$

Example 1.2

A sample of compacted clay with a total volume $V = 7.85 \times 10^{-4} m^3$ has a moisture content $w = 15\%$, an air content $A = 8\%$, and a specific gravity $G_s = 2.7$. Required are: the degree of saturation, void ratio, porosity, and bulk, dry and saturated densities.
The volume of air is 8% of the total volume and thus :

$$V_a = 0.08 \times 7.85 \times 10^{-4} = 0.628 \times 10^{-4} m^3$$

Moreover, the volume of water as a proportion of the volume of solids can easily be calculated from equation 1.5b:

$$V_w = wG_sV_s = 0.15 \times 2.7V_s = 0.405Vs$$

Since the total volume is $V = V_a + V_w + V_s$, it follows that:

$$V = 0.08V + 1.405V_s$$

Hence:

$$V_s = \frac{0.92}{1.405}V = 5.14 \times 10^{-4}m^3$$

and

$$V_w = 0.405V_s = 2.08 \times 10^{-4}m^3$$

The degree of saturation is evaluated from equation 1.4:

$$S = \frac{V_w}{V_a + V_w} = \frac{2.08}{0.628 + 2.08} = 77\%$$

the void ratio and the porosity being calculated from equations 1.7 and 1.8 respectively:

$$e = \frac{wG_s}{S} = \frac{0.15 \times 2.7}{0.77} = 0.53, \qquad n = \frac{e}{1+e} \approx 0.35$$

Finally the bulk, dry and saturated densities are determined from equations 1.11, 1.12 and 1.13 respectively, in which the density of water is taken as $\rho_w = 1Mg/m^3$:

$$\rho = G_s\frac{(1+w)}{1+e}\rho_w = \frac{2.7 \times 1.15}{1.53} = 2.03\ Mg/m^3$$

$$\rho_d = \frac{G_s}{1+e}\rho_w = \frac{2.7}{1.53} = 1.77\ Mg/m^3$$

$$\rho_{sat} = \frac{G_s+e}{1+e}\rho_w = \frac{2.7+0.53}{1.53} = 2.11\ Mg/m^3$$

1.2 Particle size analysis

The mechanical behaviour of a given soil depends on the size of its solid particles, on the minerals it contains, as well as on its stress history. In particular, the resistance of a soil to any applied load or the ease with which water can flow through its matrix is governed by its *granulometry* (*i.e.* the range of solid particles it contains). Soils can be classified either as *granular* or as *fine-grained*.

- *Granular soils* such as sands and gravel have individual solid particles, most of which can be identified by sight. The strength of such materials results from the interlocking of solid particles which provides resistance through friction. Accordingly, the range of particle size present within the soil matrix and the way these particles interact are a key element to predicting the soil behaviour. The grain size distribution can be determined with the help of a technique known as *sieving*. This old technique, which applies to granular soils (*i.e.* soils that do not contain silt or clay), has the advantage of being simple and cheap. During the standard procedure (a detailed description of which can be found in any standard laboratory testing manual), the soil is sifted through progressively finer woven-wire sieves, down to a mesh size of 63 μm. The percentage *by weight* of material passing through each sieve is then plotted on a chart representing the particle size distribution such as the one depicted in figure 1.3. The shape of the curve thus obtained gives an indication of the distribution by weight of different sizes of solid particles within the soil. However, the graph in question does not correspond to the *true* weight distribution since the material retained in any sieve yields the weight of solid particles with an individual size exceeding that of the sieve mesh, including those (elongated) particles with only one dimension larger than the mesh size. Accordingly, the outcome of such a test depends on the time and method of operation: the longer it takes to undertake the test, the more likely that some (or in some instances all) elongated solid particles will fall through the sieve because of a change in orientation.

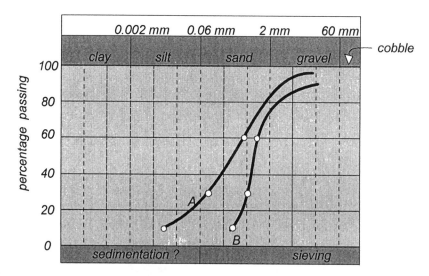

Figure 1.3: Particle size distribution for granular soils.

Assuming that these shortcomings are acceptable, then the two typical curves in figure 1.3 are indicative of different soil grading: the soil corresponding to curve A is referred to as *well graded* because the graph reflects relatively similar proportions of different particle sizes. For curve B, however, although there is no disproportion between the solid particles' size distribution, the graph is more compact than in case A, and the corresponding soil is known as *uniformly graded.* Moreover, if d_{10}, d_{30} and d_{60} are the solid particle sizes corresponding to 10%, 30% and 60% respectively of percentage passing, then it is useful to calculate the two following coefficients:

- *the uniformity coefficient:* $C_u = \dfrac{d_{60}}{d_{10}}$ (1.21)

- *the coefficient of gradation:* $C_g = \dfrac{d_{30}^2}{d_{10}d_{60}}$ (1.22)

The higher the value of C_u, the larger the range of particle sizes contained within the soil matrix. Also, the coefficient of gradation of a well graded sand is usually in the range $1 \le C_g \le 3$.

Example 1.3

Calculate the coefficients of uniformity and gradation of the soils corresponding to graphs A and B in figure 1.3.

For soil A, it is seen that: $d_{10} \approx 0.01\,mm$, $d_{30} \approx 0.09\,mm$, $d_{60} \approx 0.55\,mm$.

Hence: $C_u = \dfrac{0.55}{0.01} = 55$, $C_g = \dfrac{0.09^2}{0.55 \times 0.01} = 1.47$.

For soil B : $d_{10} \approx 0.35\,mm$, $d_{30} \approx 0.6\,mm$, $d_{60} \approx 1.1\,mm$, and

$$C_u = \frac{1.1}{0.35} = 3.1, \qquad C_g = \frac{0.6^2}{1.1 \times 0.35} = 0.94.$$

Soil A contains a wide range of particle sizes, from gravel to silt (hence the large value of C_u), none of which is predominant. This is reflected in the value of the coefficient of gradation C_g. Soil B on the other hand has a uniform grading indicated by a grading coefficient value of slightly smaller than one.

- **Fine-grained soils** have solid particles with a size smaller than $0.063\,mm$, making the sieving technique impractical. Instead, the grain size distribution of such soils can be determined using other techniques such as *sedimentation.* This traditional method, which is only (realistically) applicable to grain sizes in the range 2 to $50\,\mu m$, is based on Stokes' law relating the terminal velocity v of a solid particle with an equivalent sphere diameter D_s, falling in water of dynamic viscosity η, to its weight (read diameter D_s):

$$v = \frac{(\rho_s - \rho_w)}{18\eta} gD_s^2 \tag{1.23}$$

where g is the acceleration due to gravity, ρ_s and ρ_w are the densities of solid particles and of water respectively, and $\eta = 1.005 \times 10^{-6}$ $Mg/m.s$ is the water dynamic viscosity at a standard temperature of 20°C. Equation 1.3 can therefore be used in a straightforward way to calculate the settling time.

Example 1.4

Estimate the time t that will take a solid particle with an equivalent diameter $D_s = 1\,\mu m$ and a density $\rho_s = 2.5\,Mg/m^3$ to settle a distance $h = 1\,cm$ in water at 20°C. Rearranging equation 1.23, it follows that:

$$v = \frac{h}{t} = \frac{(\rho_s - \rho_w)}{18\eta}g.D_s^2 \quad \Rightarrow \quad t = \frac{18\eta h}{(\rho_s - \rho_w)gD_s^2}$$

therefore:

$$t = \frac{18 \times 10^{-2}}{(2.5 - 1) \times 10^6 \times 9.81 \times 10^{-12}} \approx 12,200\,s$$

The time needed for this particle to settle a mere 1 cm (about 3.4 $hours$) is an indication that sedimentation of very fine particles is an exceedingly slow process. Knowing that Stokes' law uses an equivalent diameter D_s which assumes that the solid particle has a regular compact spherical shape, one therefore expects an irregularly shaped normal particle to have a larger surface area than its equivalent sphere, thus causing the settling to be even slower because of the increased drag. Consequently, the time calculated using equation 1.23 is likely to deviate substantially from the actual settling time. Furthermore, theoretical and experimental evidence indicate that for particles smaller than 2 μm in size, the gravitational settling calculated from Stokes' law is markedly affected by the Brownian movement (*i.e.* the irregular oscillations of particles suspended in water) which can induce an error of more than 20%. On the other hand, Stokes' law is no longer applicable for particles larger than 50 μm in size, the settling being turbulent. Therefore the range 2 to 50 μm mentioned earlier within which equation 1.23 can be applied under a strict temperature control since the water viscosity η is a temperature dependent parameter (it is useful to remember that a 1°C change in temperature will induce a 2% change in water viscosity). To offset these shortcomings, other sophisticated techniques have been developed and are slowly being adopted in soil mechanics laboratories, although their use was restricted until recently to the fields of clay mineralogy and sedimentology. These techniques include *photon correlation specstroscopy* which can be applied to measure particle sizes in the range $1\,nm$ to $1\,\mu m$ (that is $10^{-9}\,m$ to $10^{-6}\,m$). Because of their small size, these particles known as *colloids* are subjected mainly to a Brownian motion that scatters light. The principle of the method consists of relating the diffusion of particles to the auto-correlation function of the scattered light, and more details can be found in MacCave and Syvitski (1991) and Weiner (1984). *Laser diffraction spectroscopy* is another reliable technique that can be applied to measure particle sizes in the range $0.1\,\mu m$ to $2\,mm$. The method is based on the fact that the light diffraction angle is inversely proportional to particle size. The technique itself consists of passing a laser beam through a suspension and focusing the diffracted light on to a ring detector which senses the angular distribution of scattered light intensity. This distribution is then related to the size distribution of the suspension through an appropriate mathematical expression, the details of which can be found in Weiner (1979) and Agrawal and Riley (1984).

1.3 Statistical analysis of the grain size distribution: the Φ-method

The statistical analysis of the grain size distribution of a granular soil can be undertaken using several methods such as *a)* the arithmetic method of moments, *b)* the geometric method of moments, *c)* the logarithmic method of moments, *d)* the logarithmic (original) Folk and Ward graphical measures, *d)* the geometric (modified) Folk and Ward graphical measures. Details of these methods can be found in the paper by Blott & Pye (2001) for instance. In what follows however, only the logarithmic (original) Folk and Ward (1957) graphical measures method is developed due to its practical usefulness. The method consists of plotting the *"percentage sediment coarser than"* against *phi* (Φ) *units*:

$$\Phi = -\log_2 d \qquad\qquad (1.24)$$

where *d* is the grain diameter in millimetres, and $\log_2$ is logarithm to the base 2. The graph is then used in conjunction with size scale table 1.3 compiled by Friedman and Sanders (1978) to determine the precise composition of the soil in terms of percentage as well as type of grains. More importantly, the statistical analysis of the grain size distribution can be undertaken using the logarithmic Folk and Ward graphical measures method in accordance with tables 1.2. The statistical analysis consists of calculating:
- the average grain size through *the mean,*
- the spread of size around the average through *the standard deviation,*
- the degree of grain concentration relative to a normal distribution through *the kurtosis,*
- the preferential spread to one side of the average through *the skewness.*

Table 1.2a: Logarithmic (original) Folk and Ward (1957) graphical measures skewness and kurtosis calculations

Skewness		Kurtosis	
$S = \dfrac{\Phi_{16} + \Phi_{84} - 2\Phi_{50}}{2(\Phi_{84} - \Phi_{16})} + \dfrac{\Phi_5 + \Phi_{95} - 2\Phi_{50}}{2(\Phi_{95} - \Phi_5)}$		$K = \dfrac{\Phi_{95} - \Phi_5}{2.44(\Phi_{75} - \Phi_{25})}$	
Skewness	S	Kurtosis	K
very fine skewed	+ 0.3 to + 1	very platykurtic	< 0.67
fine skewed	+ 0.1 to + 0.3	platykurtic	0.67 to 0.90
symmetrical	+ 0.1 to - 0.1	mesokurtic	0.90 to 1.11
coarse skewed	- 0.1 to - 0.3	leptokurtic	1.11 to 1.50
very coarse skewed	- 0.3 to -1.0	very leptokurtic	1.50 to 3.0
		extremely leptokurtic	> 3.0

Table 1.2b: Logarithmic (original) Folk and Ward (1957) graphical measures mean and standard deviation calculations

Mean	Standard deviation
$M = \dfrac{\Phi_{16} + \Phi_{50} + \Phi_{84}}{3}$	$\sigma = \dfrac{\Phi_{84} - \Phi_{16}}{4} + \dfrac{\Phi_{95} - \Phi_5}{6.6}$
Sorting	(σ)
very well sorted	< 0.35
well sorted	0.35 to 0.50
moderately well sorted	0.50 to 0.70
moderately sorted	0.70 to 1.00
poorly sorted	1.00 to 2.00
very poorly sorted	2.00 to 4.00
extremely poorly sorted	> 4.00

It is useful to point out that in relation to the terminology used in conjunction with the kurtosis, the word mesokurtic describes a normal *S*-shaped graph, platykurtic describes a flat *S*-shape, and leptokurtic is used to describe an elongated *S*-shape.

Table 1.3: Friedman & Sanders (1978) size scale

Grain size		Type of soil	
phi	**d**		
-11	2048 mm		very large
-10	1024 mm	**Boulders**	large
-9	512 mm		medium
-8	256 mm		small
-7	128 mm	**Cobbles**	large
-6	64 mm		small
-5	32 mm		very coarse
-4	16 mm	**Pebbles**	coarse
-3	8 mm		medium
-2	4 mm	**Gravel**	fine
-1	2 mm		very fine
0	1 mm		very coarse
1	500 μm		coarse
2	250 μm	**Sand**	medium
3	125 μm		fine
4	63 μm		very fine
5	31 μm		very coarse
6	16 μm		coarse
7	8 μm	**Silt**	medium
8	4 μm		fine
9	2 μm		very fine
		Clay	

Example 1.5

Consider the soil in figure 1.4 in which the "percentage coarser than" is plotted against phi (Φ) units according to Folk and Ward "log-normal method". According to the size scale table 1.3, the sample consists of 24% gravel (2/3 of which is very fine), 24% very coarse sand, 16% coarse sand, 12% medium sand, 7% fine sand, 5% very fine sand, and the remaining 12% silt and clay.

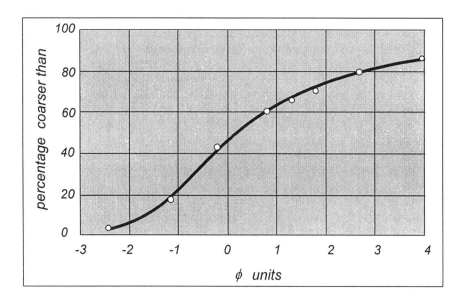

Figure 1.4: Folk & Ward Particle size analysis method.

The statistical analysis corresponding to the same figure 1.4, based on the "log-normal" method in tables 1.2 yields the following parameters:

- the mean:
$$M = \frac{\phi_{16} + \phi_{50} + \phi_{84}}{3} = \frac{-1.4 + 0.2 + 3.2}{3} = 0.66$$

- the standard deviation:
$$\sigma = \frac{\phi_{84} - \phi_{16}}{4} + \frac{\phi_{95} - \phi_5}{6.6} = \frac{3.2 + 1.4}{4} + \frac{7 + 2.3}{6.6} = 2.56$$

- the kurtosis:
$$K = \frac{\phi_{95} - \phi_5}{2.44.(\phi_{75} - \phi_{25})} = \frac{7 + 2.3}{2.44 \times (1.8 + 0.9)} = 1.41$$

- the skewness:
$$S = \frac{\phi_{16} + \phi_{84} - 2\phi_{50}}{2(\phi_{84} - \phi_{16})} + \frac{\phi_5 + \phi_{95} - 2\phi_{50}}{2(\phi_{95} - \phi_5)}$$

$$= \frac{-1.4 + 3.2 - 2 \times 0.2}{2 \times (3.2 + 1.4)} + \frac{-2.3 + 7 - 2 \times 0.2}{2 \times (7 + 2.3)} = 0.383$$

Referring to tables 1.2, these results correspond to a very poorly sorted ($\sigma = 2.56$), leptokurtic ($K = 1.41$), very fine skewed soil ($S = +0.383$).

1.4 Classification of fine-grained soils

Given the small size of its solid particles, a clay soil is characterised by a large *specific surface* (*i.e.* the surface area per volume of solid particles) and extremely small pores in comparison with sand. In fact, taking the sand pores as a reference, the clay pores in figure 1.5 (depicting the arrangement of perfectly spherical solid particles for identical volumes of sand and clay) are in reality at least twenty five times smaller than the ones shown in the figure. Accordingly, clays have a high *surface tension* which results in a high *capillary rise* (refer to Azizi, 2007 for instance); most importantly, the velocity with which water can seep through the pores, known as *permeability* is much lower for clays than for sands. Furthermore, the behaviour of a clay can be markedly affected by the types of mineral that it contains and their reaction to porewater. Of the three main clay minerals, kaolinite is the most stable *vis à vis* water so that practically no volume change occurs if water content changes.

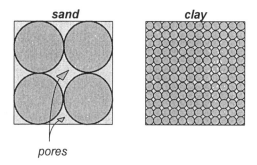

Figure 1.5: Theoretical arrangement of solid particles for sands and clays.

On the other hand, illite has a moderate reaction to water in that the changes in volume due to a variation in water content can result in modest swelling or shrinkage. However, montmorillonite is well known for its swelling and shrinkage properties so that a clay containing this mineral is bound to be subject to large volume changes in the event of water content variation. The water content of clay soils has therefore an effect on their mechanical behaviour, so much so that the empirical system of classification, based exclusively on the moisture content and known as the consistency limits is widely used to classify the type of fine-grained soil. Hence, the *liquid limit* w_L corresponds to the moisture content of the soil as it changes from a plastic state to a slurry type material. The *plastic limit* w_P on the other hand is the water content when the soil changes from plastic to friable state as per figure 1.6. In practice, both liquid and plastic limits can be determined using a cone penetrometer test. The apparatus sketched in figure 1.7, consists of a 35 *mm* long, 30° cone of stainless steel. The standard test corresponds to a cone and a sliding shaft with a combined mass of 80 grams. The actual test consists of lowering the cone so that it just touches the surface of the soil (contained in a $55\,mm$ diameter, $40\,mm$ deep cup), locking it in its support, then releasing it for a period of $5\,s$, and recording its depth of penetration. The procedure is repeated four to five times, using the same sample but increasing its moisture content each time. The (logarithm of) penetration is thereafter plotted against the moisture content, and the liquid limit w_L corresponds to the moisture content at a penetration of $20\,mm$ as illustrated in figure 1.7.

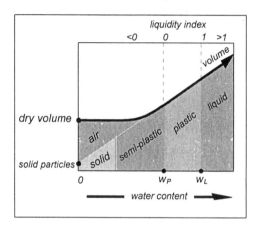

Figure 1.6: Consistency limits for fine-grained soils.

The plastic limit w_P on the other hand, can be determined from a second test using a 240 grams cone (*i.e.* a cone three times heavier than the standard one). The idea stems from Skempton's finding that the shear strength of a soil at the liquid limit is about 100 times smaller than that at the plastic limit. However, there is a strong experimental evidence showing that, for any of the two tests, the penetration under the liquid limit is about 3 times higher than that under the plastic limit. Hence the slope of the 80 g cone line in figure 1.7 :

$$\tan \alpha = \frac{w_L - w_P}{\log (20/d_o)} \approx \frac{w_L - w_P}{\log 3} \qquad (1.25a)$$

Equally, results measured from 10 different fine grained soils indicate that under identical moisture content, the ratio of penetration of two cones with masses $m_2 = 240\,g$ and $m_1 = 80\,g$ is proportional to the square root of the ratio m_2/m_1. Therefore the slope of the two parallel lines in figure 1.7 is:

$$\tan \alpha = \frac{\Delta w}{\log (20/d_1)} \approx \frac{\Delta w}{\log \sqrt{m_2/m_1}} = \frac{\Delta w}{\log \sqrt{3}} \qquad (1.25b)$$

Equating equations 1.25 (which are identical) and rearranging, it follows that:

$$w_P = w_L - \frac{\log 3}{\log \sqrt{3}} \Delta w = w_L - 2\Delta w \tag{1.26}$$

Notice that these limits are measured using a sample of soil whose fabric has been totally destroyed.

These limits are most useful when applied in conjunction with the plasticity chart (due to *Casagrande*) represented in terms of variation of the liquid limit of the soil versus its *plasticity index* defined as:

$$I_P = w_L - w_P \tag{1.27}$$

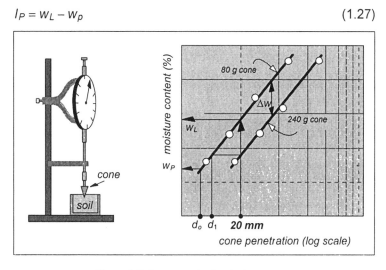

Figure 1.7: Cone penetration test.

The chart, shown in figure 1.8, provides a quick useful way of classification according to the moisture content of the soil and its plasticity index. The skewed line in the figure separates clays from silts so that, for instance, a soil with a liquid limit $w_L = 40\%$, a plastic limit $w_P = 20\%$ corresponds to a *clay of intermediate plasticity* (point B on the chart). Similarly, a soil with $w_L = 30\%$, $w_P = 4\%$ is a *silt of low plasticity* (point C on the chart). Highly plastic silts with liquid limits $w_L > 50\%$ are *organic soils* whose natural moisture content at a saturated state can be as high as 1000% (bog peat for instance) corresponding therefore to void ratios in excess of 10.

Another useful relationship between the natural *in situ* moisture content w of a soil and its plasticity index I_P is given by the *liquidity index* I_L:

$$I_L = \frac{w - w_P}{I_P} = \frac{w - w_P}{w_L - w_P} \tag{1.28}$$

Equation 1.28, as well as figure 1.6 clearly imply that:

$I_L < 0$ $\Rightarrow$ soil is in a non-plastic state,
$0 \leq I_L \leq 1$ $\Rightarrow$ soil is in a plastic state,
$I_L > 1$ $\Rightarrow$ soil is in a liquid state.

Finally, the *activity* of a soil, defined as:

$$A = \frac{I_P}{\% \, clay \, particles \, (< 2 \, \mu m)} \tag{1.29}$$

reflects the *degree of plasticity* of the soil. Fine clay mineral particles with dimensions $< 2 \, \mu m$ carry a negative surface charge, which makes them interact with polar water molecules. As a result, clays are characterised by very slow seepage rates. Also, because the liquid limit is proportional to the surface area, it follows that the greater the liquid limit, the higher the clay content, and the more compressible the soil. Typical A values for the three main clay minerals are as follows:

- kaolinite $A = 0.5$
- illite $0.5 \leq A \leq 1$
- montmorillonite $A > 1.25$.

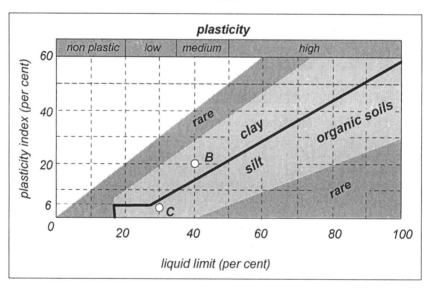

Figure 1.8: Empirical plasticity charts for soils.

From a mechanical point of view, undisturbed clays with low plasticity are characterised by small deformations when subjected to external loading. Once disturbed, a clay can potentially exhibit a marked decrease in its resistance or *shear strength,* depending on its structure. Microscopic studies of such soils, though not conclusive, tend to link the structure of natural clays to the way in which they were formed; thus a glacial till does not have the same structure as a lacustrine clay. Accordingly, once disturbed or *remoulded*, through excavation for instance, part of the natural structure will be destroyed. The effect that this structural dislocation has on the resistance of the clay can be measured by the *sensitivity*, defined as:

$$Sensitivity = \frac{strength\ of\ undisturbed\ soil}{strength\ of\ remoulded\ soil}$$

Hence, clays with a sensitivity larger than 16 are referred to as *quick clays*, and extra-sensitive clays are known to have a sensitivity in excess of 100. The structure in this case is liable to total collapse, leading to a transformation of the clay from a plastic material to a viscous liquid almost instantaneously. Quick clays can be activated by any type of shock such as vibration or earthquake activities, and are spread especially throughout Scandinavia and Canada. Bjerrum's (1954) empirical scale, illustrated in figure 1.9*a* can be used as a guide to clay sensitivity:

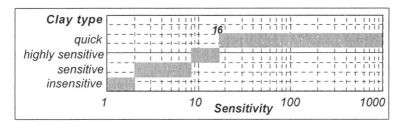

Figure 1.9a: Bjerrum's sensitivity scale

Bjerrum suggested that the sensitivity of the post-glacial Scandinavian clays (*i.e.* 10,000 to 15,000 years old clays) is related to the salt content of their pores. This suggestion is supported by the graph in figure 1.9*b* showing a dramatic increase in sensitivity when the salt content becomes smaller than 10 *g/l*. One has to bear in mind, however, that Bjerrum's suggestion is not universal; in fact Sangrey (1972)

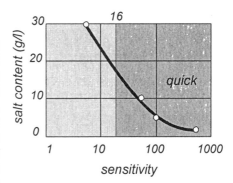

Figure 1.9b: Relationship between salt content and sensitivity for Norwegian post-glacial clays (Bjerrum, 1954, by permission of the ICE London)

reported that some of the highly sensitive post-glacial Canadian clays were deposited in fresh water.

1.5 Soil compaction

The process of compaction applies to *remoulded unsaturated soils*, and consists of increasing mechanically the *density* by reducing the volume of air contained within the soil matrix, without any significant change in the moisture content. This process is generally used in conjunction with fill materials behind retaining structures or during the construction of roads, embankments and earth dams. The increase in density, generated by a reduction in the void ratio, results in a substantial increase in *shear strength* of the soil and a marked decrease in its *compressibility* as well as *permeability*. The compaction is usually measured in terms of dry density ρ_d , whose value depends on the level of compacting energy, the soil type and its natural moisture content. Accordingly, the maximum dry density ρ_{dmax} that can be achieved for a given soil increases with increasing level of compacting energy. The maximum dry density is measured in the laboratory using compaction tests. The *standard* test is undertaken on a completely remoulded soil sample with a moisture content well below its natural value (often the sample is dried prior to testing). The test itself is conducted in stages, the first of which consists of mixing the dry soil sample with a small amount of water so that it becomes damp. An extended mould is then filled with moist soil in three equal layers, each one being compacted using 27 evenly distributed blows from a rammer weighing 2.5 *kg* and falling freely from a height of 305 *mm*. Once compaction is completed, the mould extension is then removed and the soil at the top of the mould is levelled off so that the remaining volume of compacted soil is precisely 1000 cm^3 (1 *litre*). The bulk density ρ of the soil is then calculated by weighing the known volume of the sample. A small quantity of soil is then taken randomly from within the mould and placed in an oven for drying so that the moisture content w can be calculated. Knowing ρ and w, the corresponding dry density ρ_d is thence determined from equation 1.14:

$$\rho_d = \rho/(1 + w)$$

The sample is next removed from the mould, mixed with the remainder of the original soil to which an increment of water is added to increase its moisture content. The compaction procedure is then repeated in precisely the same way as described previously. Usually five to six points are enough to yield a compaction graph such as the ones depicted in figure 1.10, corresponding to a clay with a specific gravity $G_s = 2.7$. The figure represents the variation of moisture content with the dry density at different energy levels:

- graph *EFG* corresponds to a standard compaction energy,
- graph *BCD* represents a higher compaction energy.

In both cases, the *maximum dry density* ρ_{dmax} is achieved at a water content known as the *optimum moisture content* w_{op}, and in the case of figure 1.10, it can be seen that:

- along *EFG* : $\rho_{dmax} \approx 1.72\,Mg/m^3$, $w_{op} \approx 15.7\,\%$,
- along *BCD* : $\rho_{dmax} \approx 1.845\,Mg/m^3$, $w_{op} \approx 13\,\%$,
  where $\rho_w = 1\,Mg/m^3$.

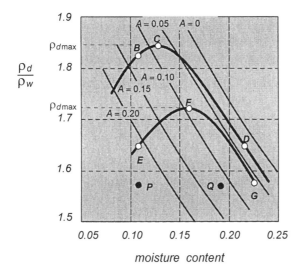

Figure 1.10: Effects of the energy of compaction on the relative dry density of a soil.

Both graphs, which are similar in shape, indicate that initially the test yields a comparatively small dry density, because at a low moisture level the relatively dry soil tends to form in lumps that have to be crushed before any significant reduction in void ratio takes place. As the moisture content increases, so does the soil workability and energy efficiency, leading thus to a gradual decrease in void ratio and a steady increase in dry density until ρ_{dmax} is reached at the optimum moisture content w_{op}. Beyond the value w_{op}, the build-up of porewater pressure within the soil matrix starts in earnest, increasing in the process the void ratio, thus decreasing the dry density of the soil.   On the other hand, the maximum dry density equation can be expressed as follows:

$$\rho_{dmax} = \rho/(1 + w_{op}) \tag{1.30}$$

and so figure 1.10 together with equation 1.30 show clearly that the higher the compaction energy, the higher the maximum dry density, and the lower the optimum moisture content.

Example 1.6

The graphs in figure 1.10, corresponding to laboratory measurements, contain valuable information for a site engineer in charge of building an embankment, for instance, using the same material. Under such circumstances, the engineer has to make a decision as to what maximum dry density (and hence what compaction energy level) is required to minimise post-construction problems related to settlement and shear strength. If, for example, the material used corresponds to point P on the figure with a natural moisture content $w = 11\%$, the choice consists of either increasing the moisture content of the soil by about 5% and using a standard compaction energy to achieve a maximum dry density similar to that of the graph EFG, or increasing the moisture content by 3% and using a high compaction energy leading to a maximum dry density comparable to that of the curve BCD. If, on the other hand, the material used has a natural moisture content $w = 19\%$ (point Q on the figure), the decision is more straightforward since either level of compaction energy used on site would lead to similar values of ρ_{dmax}, the difference being marginal. The graphs corresponding to different air contents in the figure are calculated from equation 1.16:

$$\rho_d = \frac{G_s(1-A)}{1+wG_s}\rho_w$$

On the basis of these graphs, the air content relating to both points C and F where both optimum moisture contents occur can be estimated, then the corresponding degrees of saturation can be determined from equation 1.10:

$$S = \frac{1-A}{1+A/wG_s}$$

According to figure 1.10, point C with an optimum moisture content $w_{op} = 13\%$ corresponds to an air content $A \approx 8\%$. Similarly in the case of curve EFG, the air content corresponding to point F with an optimum moisture content $w = 15.7\%$ is $A \approx 9\%$. Therefore the degrees of saturation at C and at F are respectively:

$$S_C = \frac{1-A}{1+A/w_{op}G_s} = \frac{1-0.08}{1+\frac{0.08}{0.13\times2.7}} = 75\%$$

$$S_F = \frac{1-0.09}{1+\frac{0.09}{0.157\times2.7}} = 75\%$$

These simple calculations indicate that the optimum moisture content corresponds approximately to a constant degree of saturation, usually between 75% and 80%, regardless of the level of energy used for compaction.

1.6 Practical aspects of soil compaction

Because of the random shape of solid particles, it is not physically possible to remove all the air from within a volume of an *unsaturated soil*. In other words, it is not possible to achieve full saturation through compaction. Accordingly, the graph in figure 1.10 corresponding to $A = 0$ is just a theoretical limit. Moreover, experience shows that the *maximum dry density* achieved in ideal laboratory conditions is difficult to reproduce under field conditions and so, in practice, one rather aims at achieving a *minimum* dry density *in situ* through the use of the *relative compaction* defined as follows:

$$RC = \frac{\rho_{d(field)}}{\rho_{d\,max}} \times 100\% \qquad\qquad (1.31)$$

where a value $RC = 95\%$ or thereabouts is deemed acceptable. (*Note that $RC = 95\%$ does not imply an air content $A = 5\%$*). Now consider what effect the notion of relative compaction has on the *in situ* compaction of soils. If the compacted fill were cohesive, then specifying a relative compaction of, say, 98% as is the case in figure 1.11 does not constitute the only criterion for compaction. The reason is depicted in the figure, in that an $RC = 98\%$ can be achieved at two different values of moisture content ($w_1 \approx 12\%$, $w_2 \approx 18.5\%$) on each side of the optimum value $w_{op} = 15.7\%$.

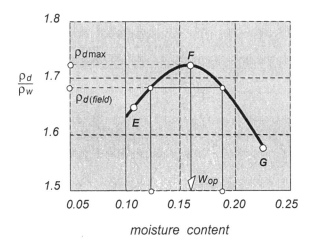

Figure 1.11: Effects of moisture content on the in situ dry density.

Consequently, the moisture content becomes a criterion for compaction and has to be specified together with the relative compaction. This effect is illustrated in figure 1.12*b* corresponding to the compaction of a layer of clay, whose natural moisture content is higher than its optimum moisture content. However, in the case of granular soils, ample experimental evidence indicates that the moisture content is not as important a criterion, and that the choice of the compaction equipment has more impact on the dry density to be achieved. On the practical side, the fill material is usually compacted in the field in layers about 0.2 *m* thick, using as many passes as needed to achieve the required density which must be checked randomly through *in situ* tests. Figure 1.12*a* shows that the compaction energy required to achieve a maximum dry density for a soil under the same moisture content increases proportionally to the increase of the thickness of the compacted layer. The type of equipment used for compaction depends on the nature of fill and the energy level required to achieve a given relative compaction. Considering that an average family car exerts an average pressure through its tyres of around $200 \, kN/m^2$, it should come as no surprise that all compaction equipment used for road building generates pressures well in excess of this value. Thus, for example, a *smooth wheel roller* produces a contact pressure of $400 \, kN/m^2$ and can be used in conjunction with all types of soils with the exception of boulder clays. When used on sands, the wheels may be vibrated to create the conditions whereby the solid particles are rearranged in an optimal way that minimises the voids, much in the way that fresh concrete is vibrated to increase its density. A *pneumatic roller* that has two or more rows of narrow tyres, whose position is alternated between consecutive rows, can generate pressures of up to $700 \, kN/m^2$ and can be used to compact sand or clay fills. S*heepsfoot rollers* on the other hand are only used for clays and can produce pressures ranging from $1.5 \, MN/m^2$ to $7 \, MN/m^2$.

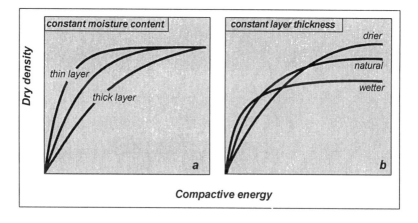

Figure 1.12 : Practical aspects of field compaction

Example 1.7

A road embankment is constructed of clay fill compacted to a bulk density $\rho = 2\,Mg/m^3$ at a water content $w = 20\%$. With an assumed specific gravity of the solid particles $G_s = 2.7$, the following quantities can be calculated:

- *the clay porosity:* it is seen that the use of equation 1.8 necessitates the knowledge of the void ratio, which, in turn, can be evaluated from equation 1.11:

$$e = G_s(1 + w)\frac{\rho_w}{\rho} - 1 = \frac{2.7 \times 1.2}{2} - 1 = 0.62$$

Therefore:

$$n = \frac{e}{1 + e} = \frac{0.62}{1.62} = 0.38$$

- *the degree of saturation:* using equation 1.7:

$$S = \frac{wG_s}{e} = \frac{0.2 \times 2.7}{0.62} = 87\%$$

- *the air content:* clearly, a combination of equations 1.7 and 1.9*b* yields:

$$A = n(1 - S) = 0.38 \times (1 - 0.87) = 4.9\%$$

- *the fill dry density:* either equations 1.12 or 1.14 yield $\rho_d = 1.67\,Mg/m^3$.

Example 1.8

A laboratory compaction test undertaken on a clay soil resulted in a maximum dry density $\rho_{dmax} = 1.65\,Mg/m^3$. The same soil, which is characterised by a specific gravity $G_s = 2.7$, was then used *in situ* to build a 7 *m* high embankment for a highway, where it was subjected to a relative compaction of $RC = 95\%$. Assuming that the (*in situ*) compacted clay has a bulk density $\rho_f = 1.8\,Mg/m^3$, then its optimum moisture content w_{op} can be estimated from equation 1.14:

$$\rho_f = \rho_{df}(1 + w_{op})$$

where the field dry density is calculated as follows:

$$\rho_{df} = 0.95\rho_{dmax} = 1.57\,Mg/m^3$$

Hence: $w_{op} = \dfrac{1.8 - 1.57}{1.57} = 14.6\%$

The air content of the embankment soil can be determined from equation 1.16:

$$\rho_{df} = \frac{G_s(1 - A)}{1 + w_{op}G_s}\rho_w \quad \Rightarrow \quad A = \frac{2.7 - 1.57 \times (1 + 0.146 \times 2.7)}{2.7} = 18.9\%$$

Now the void ratio and degree of saturation are found from equations 1.9*b* and 1.10 respectively:

$$e = \frac{A + w_{op}G_s}{1 - A} = \frac{0.189 + 0.146 \times 2.7}{1 - 0.189} \approx 0.72$$

$$S = \frac{1 - A}{1 + A/w_{op}G_s} = \frac{1 - 0.189}{1 + \frac{0.189}{0.146 \times 2.7}} = 55\%$$

1.7 Collapsible soils

Collapsible soils are naturally occurring materials, consisting predominantly of $20\mu m$ to $60\mu m$ silt and fine sand particles, loosely deposited through wind transport. In a dry state, such soils are characterised by a relatively high apparent strength, a low density, and a high porosity due to the large amount of voids between solid particles. Upon wetting however, the soil structure can potentially undergo a collapse mechanism known as *hydro-collapse*, inducing large deformations. The extent of collapse is linked to the degree of wetting, the depth of loose deposit, and the magnitude of overburden pressure. Collapsible soils deposits are widely spread across the world.

Loess, also known as yellow soil, is a typical example found in some parts of Asia, such as north-eastern Thailand, where top soils consist often of loose deposits of sandstone and siltstone fine sediments, exhibiting the characteristics of collapsible soils. Typically, loess is predominantly made of quartz, with some feldspar, bonded in a metastable open structure by clay and carbonate particles. In a dry state, loess is characterised by a low dry density, while exhibiting high shear strength. Once saturated, the bonding between solid particles degenerates, causing the open structure to collapse. The hydro-collapse as it is known, results in a denser rearrangement of solid particles, at the expense of large, sudden, and potentially dangerous settlement deformation as illustrated typically in figure 1.13. The sudden increase in moisture content (*i.e.* wetting) of such soils can be typically engendered by water retention structures such as reservoirs, or poor surface drainage. Although the hydro-collapse mechanism is complex in nature, it is somewhat similar to the structural collapse of frozen soils upon *adfreeze* disintegration. Adfreeze represents the strong ice bonds between solid particles generated by the freezing of the porewater within a soil matrix. A warming up of the soil from say $-2°C$ to $-1°C$ can potentially halve the soil shear strength and upon complete thaw, the soil structure can undergo large settlements, similar to the behaviour exhibited by loess once wetting occurs. The collapse potential refers to the magnitude of deformation ε_1 generated upon wetting of the soil as indicated in figure 1.13. This potential is typically summarised in the following table 1.4:

Table 1.4: Hydro-collapse potential magnitude

collapse potential (%)	1 - 3	3 - 5	> 5
Severity	low	moderate	high

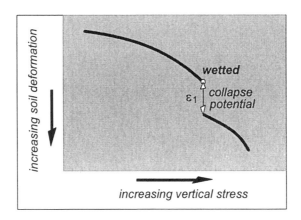

increasing vertical stress

Figure 1.13: Hydro-collapse potential

The behaviour of a collapsible soil is difficult to analyse, let alone predict. The main problems arise from the disturbance affecting the soil matrix during sampling, the degree of wetting, and the magnitude of loading. None the less, the collapse process leads to a marked increase in the soil dry density as illustrated ideally in figure 1.14a. The sharp increase is due to the rearrangement of solid particles, which has an effect of natural compaction as it were. Figure 1.14b on the other hand illustrates a typical delimitation of the area within which a soil structure is liable to collapse.

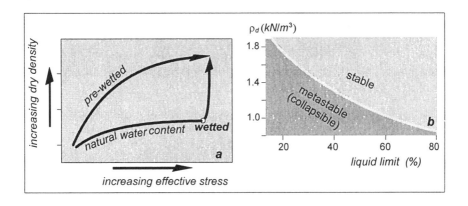

Figure 1.14: Typical relationships between dry density, stress level and liquid limit.

The effects of soil collapse can be prevented or limited using various engineering solutions, depending on *in situ* conditions. These solutions include causing the soil to collapse, so as to increase its density, prior to founding any structure. Alternatively, collapsible soils can be compacted *in situ* using a wide range of techniques presented in the following section.

1.8 Methods of deep compaction

The use of surface rollers for field compaction is essentially suitable for fill material placed in layers of controlled thickness. However, the effect of this type of equipment on an existing layer of soil is usually confined to a few metres below the surface, at best. Thus, in order to densify natural deep deposits of granular soils or soft clays, other techniques are used. These techniques rely on more sophisticated equipment, and are therefore more versatile, in that they can be used on sites of varied complexities, and can increase soil compaction at a deeper level. They include:

- *Dynamic compaction*

The method consists basically of dropping repeatedly a heavy weight of several tonnes from varying heights onto the soil. This results in compacting the soil throughout the impact area as well as in its vicinity. Experimental evidence indicates that such a technique can improve the compaction of loose granular materials up to a depth of 10 *m* below the ground surface.

- *Vibro-floatation*

The technique uses a *vibrofloat* (a large probe) made of a cylindrical tube with water jets, housing eccentrically rotating weights to produce horizontal vibratory motion. The probe is (usually) 400 *mm* in diameter, 2 *m* in length, weighing about 2 tonnes. The vibrofloat is allowed to penetrate the soil under its own weight, and on reaching the desired depth, water flow is reduced, and the vibrofloat is withdrawn in small lifts while feeding sand or gravel into the hole formed at the surface. The compacted zone around the probe can extend to a radius of up to 3*m*, and this technique is particularly effective in loose sands or granular fills.

- *Vibro-placement*

Corresponds to the same technique and procedure of vibro-floatation without water. This technique is used exclusively in conjunction with soft clays and inorganic fills. Charges of well graded gravel of granular size between 100 *mm* and 80 *mm* are added while withdrawing the probe, creating *stone columns*. The vibrofloat is repeatedly withdrawn and reinserted to ensure a uniform density. With each charge of gravel, the vibrofloat displaces the backfill horizontally into the existing soil, while at the same time compacting underneath its bottom edge. Repetition of the procedure produces an irregular cylindrical gravel column, with a diameter ranging from 0.6 m to 1 m, depending on the strength of the existing soil. Stone columns are usually installed in a square or a triangular grid pattern, with a centre-to-centre spacing of between 1 m and 3 m.

- ### *Grouting techniques*

Though all grouting techniques are based on the same principle of injecting a grout into the native soil, so as to improve its physical properties (such as strength and permeability), there are several variations on this theme. Thus, *chemical grouting* is a technique used essentially to control seepage, and hence increase the soil strength. This technique consists of injecting a chemical solution (usually sodium or acrylic solutions) into the pre-existing fine fissures within the soil mass through a *tube à manchettes* by inducing a hydrofracture (also known as *claquage*). The cost effectiveness and efficiency of the *tube à manchettes* tube system makes it one of the most widely used grouting techniques for foundations and underground excavations. The method consists of a PVC or a steel pipe with small holes perforated around the circumference at regular intervals along its length. Each set of holes is covered by a rubber sleeve or a *manchette* as illustrated in figure 1.15, so that when a grout is injected under pressure, the manchette expands allowing the grout to flow out of the pipe.

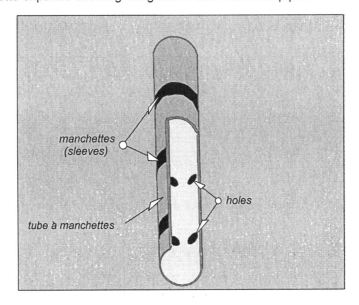

Figure 1.15: Tube à manchettes.

Once grout injection is complete, the *manchette* collapses onto the pipe, thus preventing any flow into the pipe, making the holes act as one way valves in the process. The grouting process *per se* consists of the following three steps:

- insertion of the *tube à manchettes* into a pre-drilled borehole of a larger diameter,
- use of a light sleeve grout so as to seal the *tube à manchettes* into the borehole, thus preventing any high pressure grout from flowing up the tube/borehole interface,
- proceeding from the bottom of the borehole up, each set of holes is isolated by two inflatable packers which are operated from within the *tube à manchettes* pipe and inflated so that they straddle the set of holes. The *manchette* around the isolated holes is then expanded by pumping water under pressure through the holes, causing thus a *claquage* (hydrofracture) in the soil around the sleeve. Grout is then injected under the maximum design pressure (or volume) to fill the fissures created within the soil matrix in the vicinity of the manchette.

The process is repeated by moving the packers upward and isolating the next set of holes.

Compaction grouting on the other hand is based on the same principle, in that a low viscosity silicate-based grout (circa 20% bentonite/cement grout) is injected into the native soil under controlled pressure (just above the overburden pressure) using the same technique. The grout consistency is such that it causes the native soil to compress, thus increasing its density. This technique is particularly effective when used on loose granular soils or soft clays. When this technique is used with the specific aim to, either counteract the effects of active settlements, or to compensate for the deformation of the native soil due to past settlements, it becomes known as *compensation grouting*. Finally, *jet grouting* is one of the most successful techniques, developed in Italy in the 1970s, particularly effective for seepage control, underpinning, and in situ foundation construction. This technique consists of mixing *in situ* native soil with a cement grout jetted radially under high pressure (between 30 *MPa* and 60 *MPa*; that is 300 to 600 bars). The jet may consist of a single fluid (cement grout), a double fluid (cement grout and air), or a triple fluid (cement grout, air and water). The air pressure used in conjunction with double and triple jets is usually between 700 *kPa* and 1.2 *MPa*. The high pressure enables the grout to mix with the destroyed native soil fabric, resulting in the formation of a homogeneous structural element as illustrated in figure 1.16. The size, shape and composition of the formed column depends on the rotation and lifting rates of the jet rod. Jet grouting can be applied to different soil types ranging from poorly graded granular soils to plastic clays.

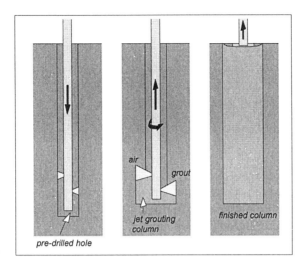

Figure 1.16: Double fluid jet grouting technique

• *soil mixing*

In some special cases of sites with restricted access, a simple technique of soil mixing can be very effective. This technique is suitable for soils with very poor engineering properties, and consists of stabilising the soil by using a double auger to break up the soil before adding a special binder (such as dry lime) and re-compacting to form a column. This is particularly effective for the stabilisation of slopes and embankments.

Problems

1.1 A thick layer of clay has an average void ratio $e = 0.75$ and a specific gravity $G_s = 2.7$, the water level being 2 m below the ground surface.

(a) Calculate the water content of the (saturated) clay below the water level.
(b) If the clay above the water table has an air content $A = 0.04$, determine its water content and degree of saturation.
(c) Calculate both bulk and saturated unit weights of the clay.

Ans: (a) $w = 28\%$,   (b) $w = 25.2\%$, $S = 90.6\%$, (c) $\gamma = 18.9\,kN/m^3$,
(d) $\gamma_{sat} = 19.3\,kN/m^3$.

1.2 Calculate the ratio γ_{sat}/γ between saturated and bulk unit weights of a clay having a void ratio $e = 1.0$, a water content $w = 25\%$, and a specific gravity $G_s = 2.7$.

Ans: $\gamma_{sat}/\gamma = 1.1$.

1.3   A cylindrical soil sample with a diameter of 100 mm and a height
of 100 mm was extracted from within a thick layer of a stiff clay.
The sample has a weight of 1320 g, and after being thoroughly
dried, its weight has reduced to 1075 g.
Assuming the clay has a specific gravity $G_s = 2.7$, determine its:
(a) water content,
(b) void ratio,
(c) degree of saturation,
(d) air content,
(e) bulk and dry densities.

Ans: (a) $w = 22.8\%$,   (b) $e = 0.97$,   (c) $S = 63.3\%$,   (d) $A = 18\%$,
(e) $\rho = 1.68\,Mg/m^3$, $\rho_d = 1.37\,Mg/m^3$.

1.4   A soil with 23% of clay content has an activity $A = 0.72$ and a
plastic limit $w_p = 16\%$.
(a) Calculate its liquid limit, then use the plasticity chart in
section 2.5 to classify the soil.
(b) In its natural state, the soil is characterised by a liquidity index
$I_L = 0.75$. Determine its natural moisture content.

Ans: (a) $w_L = 32.5\%$, $I_p = 16.6\%$, $\Rightarrow$ clay of low plasticity.
(b) $w = 28.4\%$.

1.5   A compaction test undertaken on a sample of clay with a specific
gravity $G_s = 2.7$ yielded an air content $A = 3\%$ and a maximum
dry density $\rho_{dmax} = 1.65\,Mg/m^3$. Calculate the corresponding
optimum moisture content.

Ans: $w_{op} \approx 22\%$.

1.6   A laboratory compaction test undertaken on clay yielded the
following results:

Moisture content (%)	11	13	16	21
Bulk density (Mg/m^3)	17.75	18.92	19.84	19.48

(a) Plot the variation of the dry density with the moisture content,
then determine the maximum dry density and the optimum
moisture content.
The same clay was then used for the construction of an
embankment, where it was subjected to a relative compaction

$RC = 95\%$ at the optimum moisture content.
(b) Calculate the bulk density of the compacted fill.
(c) Assuming the clay fill has a specific gravity $G_s = 2.7$,
determine its air content, degree of saturation and porosity.

Ans: (a) $\rho_{dmax} = 1.71\,Mg/m^3$, $w_{op} = 16\%$. (b) $\rho = 1.88\,Mg/m^3$,
(c) $A \approx 13.8\%$, $S = 65.2\%$, $n \approx 0.40$.

References

Agrawal, Y. C. and Riley, J. B. (1984) *Optical Particle Sizing for Hydrodynamic Based on Near-forward Scattering.* Society of Photo-Optical Instrumentation Engineers (489), pp. 68–76.

Bell, F. G. (1993) *Engineering Geology.* Blackwell Science, London.

Bjerrum, L. (1954) *Geotechnical properties of Norwegian marine clays.* Géotechnique, Vol. 4 (2), pp. 49–69.

Friedman, G.M. and Saunders, J.E. (1978). *Principles of Sedimentology.* Wiley, New York

Folk, R.L. and Ward, W.C. (1957). *Brazos river bar: a study in the significance of grain size parameters.* Journal of Sedimentary Petrology. **27**pp. 3-26

Hong Kong Geotechnical Engineering Office. (1993) *Review of Granular and Geotextile Filters.*

Lamb, S. and Sington, D. (1998) *Earth story: the shaping of our world.* BBc Book, London.

MacCave, I. N. and Syvitski, J. P. M. (1991) *Principles and Methods of Particle Size Analysis.* Cambridge University Press.

Sangrey, D. A. (1972) *Naturally cemented sensitive soils.* Géotechnique, 22, pp. 139–152.

Simon, J. B. and Kenneth, P. (2001). *GRADISTAT: A grain size distribution and statistics package for the analysis of unconolidated sediments.* Earth Surface Processes and Landforms, 26. pp. 1237-1248

Somerville, S. H. (1986) *Control of Groundwater for Temporary Works.* CIRIA Report 113, Construction Industry Research and Information Association, London.

Stanley, S. M. (1999) *Earth system history.* W. H. Freeman & company, New York.

Waltham, A.C. (1994) *Foundations of Engineering Geology.* Chapman & Hall, London.

Weiner, B. B. (1979) *Particle and Spray Sizing Using Laser Diffraction.* Society of Photo-Optical Instrumentation Engineers (170), pp. 53–56.

Weiner, B. B. (1984) *Particle Sizing Using Photon Correlation Spectroscopy.* Modern Methods of Particle Size Analysis, Edited by H.G. Barth, Wiley, New York, pp. 93–116.

CHAPTER 2

Shear strength of soils & rock masses

2.1 Peak, critical and residual strengths

The *shear strength* of a soil, that is the *maximum* resistance it can offer before the occurrence of shear failure along a specific failure plane, is intricately related to the soil *type* and *state*. Thus, the response of a granular soil to an applied load depends to a large extent on its density, whereas a fine grained overconsolidated soil exhibits markedly different behaviour to that of a normally consolidated soil as depicted in figure 2.1. In all cases, the shear strength is a quintessential design parameter on which depends the safety related to problems such as slope stability, bearing capacity and lateral thrust. Figure 2.1(*a*) shows that the stress–strain behaviour of a stiff clay or a dense sand exhibits a *peak* beyond which the strength of the soil decreases towards a *critical* value as the strain increases. If the *same* soils were in a different *state*, that is if the clay were normally consolidated and the sand were loose, then their strength would show a logarithmic increase, tending towards the critical value as the soil is further strained. On the other hand, when a soil is subject to very large strains (as in the case of an old land-slip for instance), then its post-peak strength decreases gradually until a *residual* value is reached as depicted in figure 2.1(*b*).

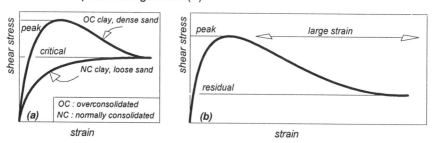

Figure 2.1: Stress–strain relationships as related to soil type and state.

From a practical perspective, the safety as well as the cost effectiveness of a design depend on how realistic are the mathematical relationships between stresses and strains. Figure 2.2 reinforces the idea that an elastic analysis can be deemed adequate provided that the effective stress level does not far exceed the *yield stress*. This applies principally to stiff overconsolidated clays whose initial behaviour is characterised by relatively large elastic strains. Normally consolidated clays on the other hand show an elastic–plastic behaviour from the onset of loading and, consequently, the assumption of elastic behaviour for such soils, even when used in conjunction with a large factor of safety, would be grossly in error and potentially unsafe. Rather, the *stiffness* of such soils, in other words the stress–strain ratio, depends on the stress level and can be estimated either as a *tangent modulus*:

$$E = \frac{\delta\sigma'}{\delta\varepsilon} \qquad (2.1)$$

or as a *secant modulus* (refer to figure 2.2):

$$E = \frac{\Delta\sigma'}{\Delta\varepsilon} \qquad (2.2)$$

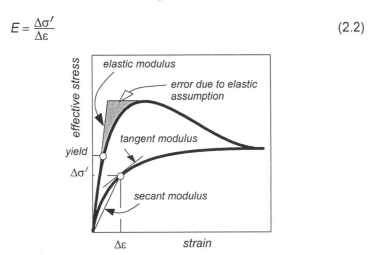

Figure 2.2: Selection of appropriate stiffness parameters.

The physical phenomena leading to soil failure under a known set of stresses are analysed in the following sections. In particular, the crucial effect of the porewater pressure on the strength of soils, with the implicit time effect, will be explored in order to dispel any confusion that may arise from the interpretation of experimental data.

2.2 Mohr's circle representation of stresses

To visualise the nature of plane stresses (*i.e.* two dimensional state of stresses), a simple method of analysis was established by Otto Mohr who suggested that the state of a sample subjected to a set of stresses can be represented graphically on a circle with a diameter corresponding to the difference between the major and minor stresses. Consider for instance the sample of cohesive soil subject to the set of principal stresses σ'_1 (major stress) and σ'_3 (minor stress) as depicted on the left-hand side of figure 2.3.

Taking compressive stresses as well as anticlockwise shear stresses as *positive*, and considering that, under fully drained conditions, failure occurs along the plane *OD* at an angle α to the horizontal within the soil mass, then the same failure plane makes an angle 2α anticlockwise with respect to the horizontal in Mohr's representation. The mathematical proof of this fundamental property of Mohr's circle can be found in any textbook on stress analysis. Most importantly however, figure 2.3 can now be used to establish the expression of the shear stress τ_f and normal stress σ'_n, acting on the failure plane.

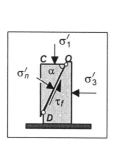 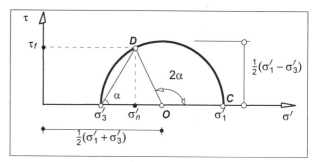

Figure 2.3: Mohr–Coulomb failure criterion for a fully drained cohesive soil.

Starting with the shear stress at failure, it is easy to see that:

$$\tau_f = OD\sin\beta = OD\sin(\pi - 2\alpha)$$
$$= \frac{1}{2}(\sigma'_1 - \sigma'_3)\sin 2\alpha \qquad (2.3)$$

As for the normal effective stress at failure σ'_n:

$$\sigma'_n = \frac{1}{2}(\sigma'_1 + \sigma'_3) - \frac{1}{2}(\sigma'_1 - \sigma'_3)\cos(\pi - 2\alpha)$$

$$= \frac{1}{2}(\sigma'_1 + \sigma'_3) + \frac{1}{2}(\sigma'_1 - \sigma'_3)\cos 2\alpha \qquad (2.4)$$

Figure 2.3 also shows that the maximum shear stress occurs at an angle $\alpha = 45°$ for which the stresses corresponding to equations 2.3 and 2.4 reduce to:

$$t = \frac{1}{2}(\sigma'_1 - \sigma'_3) \qquad (2.5a)$$

$$s' = \frac{1}{2}(\sigma'_1 + \sigma'_3) \qquad (2.5b)$$

If, in addition, the two new stress variables, namely the *deviator stress q* and the *mean effective stress p'* are defined as follows:

$$q = (\sigma'_1 - \sigma'_3) \hspace{3cm} (2.6a)$$

$$p' = \frac{1}{3}(\sigma'_1 + 2\sigma'_3) \hspace{2.5cm} (2.6b)$$

then, by virtue of the effective stress principle $\sigma = \sigma' + u$, it is straightforward to establish that:

$$t = t', \quad q = q', \quad s = s' + u, \quad p = p' + u$$

meaning that the same equations 2.5a and 2.6a apply under effective or total stresses because water has no shear resistance. Accordingly, if Mohr's circle is represented in terms of total stresses, then the circle in figure 2.3 has simply to be shifted to the right-hand side by a distance corresponding to the porewater pressure u.

2.3 Stress–strain relationships at failure

2.3.1 Effective stress analysis

The behaviour exhibited in figure 2.1 is affected by the *type* and *state* of the soil. The failure stresses measured from different laboratory tests (whose details will be presented later) on the *same* natural clay are depicted in figure 2.4 (Josseaume and Azizi, 1991). It is very tempting *prima facie* to apply a linear regression analysis, so that the entire stress range at failure can be described by a unique linear equation. However, when the *state* of the clay is taken into account, a somewhat different picture emerges as shown in figure 2.5. All failure stresses corresponding to a *normal consolidation state* can be fitted with a line having a zero intercept and a slope β'_c.

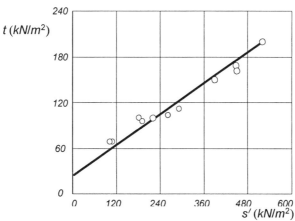

Figure 2.4: Failure stresses for a natural stiff clay.

As the clay becomes *overconsolidated* (due to the loading conditions of different tests), the relationship between stresses at failure becomes curved. For *heavily overconsolidated* samples, the behaviour at failure can be described by a linear equation with an intercept a' and a slope β_p'.

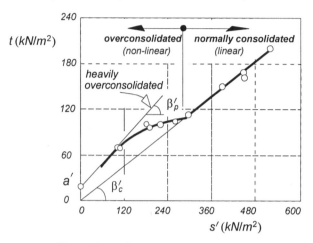

Figure 2.5: Effect of soil state on failure stresses.

Relating the behaviour depicted in figure 2.5 to that of figure 2.1, an overall picture of the shear strength associated with the state of natural soils can be drawn. Thus, for heavily overconsolidated clays, the peak shear strength can be estimated from a simple linear equation, established as early as 1776 by Charles Augustin Coulomb, who was the first to suggest that the shear strength, along a potential failure plane, of a soil subject to a normal stress σ_n' on the same plane (see figure 2.3) can be modelled with the following linear equation:

$$\tau_f = c' + \sigma_n' \tan \phi_p' \tag{2.7}$$

ϕ_p' represents the *peak angle of friction* and c', often referred to as *apparent cohesion,* was first thought to reflect the interparticle bonds otherwise known as cementation. It was not until Terzaghi established his effective stress equation some 150 years later that the nature of the intercept c' became clearer. In fact, experimental evidence suggests that, apart from some very sensitive soils, cementation in clays is insignificant (Bjerrum and Kenny, 1967). Rather, the apparent cohesion (that is the degree of shear strength exhibited by heavily overconsolidated clays under zero normal effective stress) is the result of curve fitting, and reflects the increase in effective stresses due to the negative porewater pressure and the suction that ensues within the clay mass.

The behaviour at failure of normally consolidated clays as well as granular soils does not exhibit any cohesion, and is therefore represented by the following simplified version of Coulomb equation 2.7:

$$\tau_f = \sigma'_n \tan \phi'_c \qquad (2.8)$$

ϕ'_c refers to the *critical angle of friction*. If the soil is subject to large deformations (refer to figure 2.1), then the behaviour at failure would be characterised by a *residual angle of friction* ϕ'_r as depicted in figure 2.6. Notice that in practice the angle ϕ'_r is usually used in conjunction with the design of slopes for which failure could be activated on an old land-slip where the soil has experienced large displacements in the past as in the case of slope stability problems. Moreover, ϕ'_r can be significantly smaller than ϕ'_c depending on the nature of the clay and its mineralogy (Lupini *et al.*, 1981). Figure 2.6 therefore represents the failure loci, better known as *failure envelopes,* for different types of soils at different states.

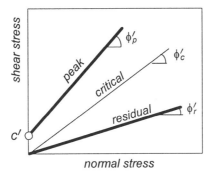

Figure 2.6: Failure envelopes.

Let us now use Mohr's circle of stresses to establish the relationships between different stresses at failure, as well as the link between the slopes β' in figure 2.5 and ϕ' in figure 2.6. Thus with reference to figure 2.7 in the case of a heavily overconsolidated clay, it is seen that:

$$\alpha = \frac{\pi}{4} + \frac{\phi'_p}{2} \qquad (2.9)$$

and therefore:

$$\sin 2\alpha = \sin\left(\frac{\pi}{2} + \phi'_p\right) = \cos \phi'_p, \qquad \cos 2\alpha = -\sin \phi'_p$$

Substituting for α in equations 2.3 and 2.4, it follows that:

$$\tau_f = \frac{1}{2}(\sigma'_1 - \sigma'_3) \cos \phi'_p \qquad (2.10)$$

$$\sigma'_n = \frac{1}{2}(\sigma'_1 + \sigma'_3) - \frac{1}{2}(\sigma'_1 - \sigma'_3)\sin\phi'_p \tag{2.11}$$

Inserting these quantities in equation 2.7 and rearranging :

$$(\sigma'_1 - \sigma'_3) = 2c'\cos\phi'_p + (\sigma'_1 + \sigma'_3)\sin\phi'_p \tag{2.12}$$

This equation can be further simplified, yielding thus the general relationship between effective minor and major stresses :

$$\sigma'_1 = \sigma'_3\tan^2\left(\frac{\pi}{4} + \frac{\phi'_p}{2}\right) + 2c'\tan\left(\frac{\pi}{4} + \frac{\phi'_p}{2}\right) \tag{2.13}$$

or

$$\sigma'_3 = \sigma'_1\tan^2\left(\frac{\pi}{4} - \frac{\phi'_p}{2}\right) - 2c'\tan\left(\frac{\pi}{4} - \frac{\phi'_p}{2}\right) \tag{2.14}$$

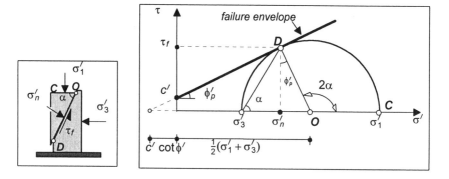

Figure 2.7: Mohr–Coulomb failure envelope for a heavily overconsolidated clay.

The relationship between the angles β'_p and ϕ'_p, as well as the intercepts a' and c' in figures 2.5 and 2.6 respectively can now be established in a straightforward way by substituting for the quantities t and s' from equations 2.5 into equation 2.12. Whence:

$$t = c'\cos\phi'_p + s'\sin\phi'_p \tag{2.15}$$

and therefore, according to figure 2.5, it is seen that:

$$c' = \frac{a'}{\cos\phi'_p} \tag{2.16}$$

$$\phi'_p = \sin^{-1}(\tan\beta'_p) \tag{2.17}$$

Also, using equations 2.6, it is easy to show that:

$$(\sigma_1' + \sigma_3') = \frac{2}{3}(\sigma_1' + 2\sigma_3') + \frac{1}{3}(\sigma_1' - \sigma_3') = 2p' + \frac{q}{3} \qquad (2.18)$$

Inserting this quantity into equation 2.12 then rearranging, it follows that:

$$q = \frac{6\cos\phi'}{3 - \sin\phi'}c' + \frac{6\sin\phi'}{3 - \sin\phi'}p' \qquad (2.19)$$

Equation 2.19 indicates that, when plotted in the space (p', q), the linear stress path *at failure* is characterised by a slope:

$$M = \frac{6\sin\phi'}{3 - \sin\phi'} \qquad (2.20)$$

Both equations 2.19 and 2.20 will be used to their full potential in chapter 8.

Example 2.1

The following failure stresses were measured on three samples of an overconsolidated clay:

$\sigma_1' \, (kN/m^2)$	250	400	645
$\sigma_3' \, (kN/m^2)$	110	180	305

These same results are plotted in terms of the stress variables (s', t) (refer to equations 2.5) in figure 2.8, thus yielding an intercept $a' \approx 10 \, kN/m^2$ and a slope $\tan\beta_p' = 0.7/2 = 0.35$.

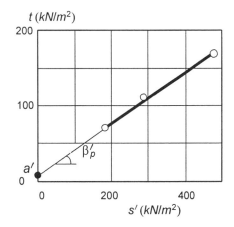

Figure 2.8: Measured results.

Making use of equations 2.16 and 2.17, it follows that:

$$\phi_p' = \sin^{-1}(0.35) = 20.5°,$$

$$c' = \frac{a'}{\cos\phi_p'} = \frac{10}{\cos 20.5} = 10.7 \, kN/m^2$$

Granular soils, as well as normally consolidated clays, do not exhibit any cohesion intercept at failure, the corresponding Mohr's circle being as depicted in figure 2.9. Accordingly, equations 2.10 to 2.14 apply provided that all terms related to cohesion are dropped and that the critical angle of shearing resistance ϕ'_c is substituted for ϕ'_p.

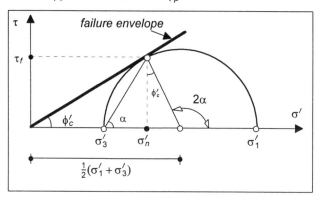

Figure 2.9: Mohr–Coulomb failure envelope for normally consolidated clays and granular soils.

2.3.2 Total stress analysis

Consider the time effect on the behaviour of a *saturated soil* subject at its surface to a *total stress increment* of magnitude $\Delta\sigma$. As soon as $\Delta\sigma$ is applied, one would expect the volume of soil to change (though it *is* possible for the stress increment to be such that it does not generate any volume change). For that to happen, water must be either expelled from within or absorbed by the soil matrix depending on the magnitude of $\Delta\sigma$ (a stress increase caused by a foundation loading, or a stress decrease generated by an excavation for instance); in other words, a *flow rate* must be established. If the soil in question is a *clay*, then the corresponding permeability is bound to be very small -bearing in mind that a permeability $k = 10^{-8}\,m/s$ corresponds to water seeping at 31.5 cm (roughly one foot) per year- and therefore in the *short term* (*i.e.* a few days or even a few weeks after the stress increment $\Delta\sigma$ is applied) any flow of water will be insignificant. As a result, the clay experiences virtually no volume change in the short term, meaning that the interlocking of solid particles within the clay matrix remains unchanged, and so does the effective stress. In accordance with the effective stress principle $\sigma = \sigma' + u$, it follows that in the *short term*:

$$\sigma' = \text{constant} \quad \Rightarrow \quad \Delta\sigma' = 0 \quad \Rightarrow \quad \Delta\sigma = \Delta u$$

Thus in the *short term*, any stress increase $\Delta\sigma$ applied at the surface of a *saturated* clay is transmitted to the porewater, generating an *excess porewater pressure* $\Delta u = \Delta\sigma$. It is therefore essential to realise that, in the short term, shear failure of a saturated clay occurs under a *constant volume* prior to any dissipation of the porewater pressure taking place, that is before the occurrence of any *consolidation*. As such, the behaviour of the clay is referred to as *unconsolidated undrained*. Under these circumstances, the change in effective stress is zero, and equation 2.7 reduces to the following:

$$\tau_f = c_u \tag{2.21}$$

where c_u denotes the *undrained shear strength* of the clay. Meanwhile, using the subscript u (for undrained), the shear strength of the clay can be estimated from equation 2.10:

$$c_u = \frac{1}{2}(\sigma_1' - \sigma_3') \cos\phi_u = t \cos\phi_u \tag{2.22}$$

Substituting for the stress variable t from equation 2.15 into the above equation, then rearranging:

$$c_u = c_u \cos^2\phi_u + s' \sin\phi_u \cos\phi_u \quad \Rightarrow \quad \phi_u = 0 \tag{2.23}$$

Therefore under *undrained conditions*, the *angle of shearing resistance* is reduced to zero (*i.e.* a horizontal failure envelope), and the shear resistance of the clay is provided by its undrained shear strength c_u as depicted in the Mohr's circle representation in figure 2.10. A thorough analysis of the undrained shear strength of clays follows in section 2.4.3.

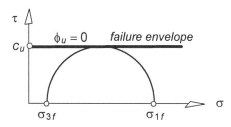

Figure 2.10: Mohr–Coulomb failure envelope for an undrained cohesive soil.

In practice, several techniques have been developed to estimate the shear strength parameters c', ϕ' and c_u, two of which are most widely used to test soils in the laboratory: the direct shear and the triaxial tests. Although both were developed to test a variety of soils, the shear box is used in the following analysis in conjunction with granular soils, whereas cohesive soils will be tested exclusively in a triaxial apparatus.

2.4 Shear strength of coarse-grained soils: direct shear test

Granular soils such as sands derive their shear strength from friction between solid particles, and the shear box test is well suited for such types of soils. The apparatus is depicted schematically in figure 2.11, and the test procedure consists basically of shearing a sand sample while subjecting it to a constant vertical pressure. The sample itself is confined in a metal box split horizontally so that the lower and upper halves can move relative to each other. Because of the relatively high permeability of granular soils, the test is undertaken at a relatively high pace so that a horizontal speed of about $1\,mm/min$ is usually used during testing. As the test progresses, the horizontal displacement Δl and the corresponding shear force S, as well as the change in sample thickness Δh (*i.e.* the vertical movement) are measured at regular time intervals.

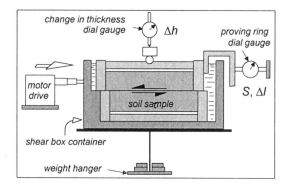

Figure 2.11: Shear box apparatus.

Knowing that the sample has a (square) cross-sectional area A, the vertical normal stress is calculated in a straightforward way:

$$\sigma = \frac{N}{A} \qquad\qquad (2.24)$$

where N is the normal force, applied through a weight hanger (refer to figure 2.11), that takes into account any lever arm effect. In calculating the shear stress, however, care must be taken to divide the measured shear force by the corresponding (decreasing) cross-sectional area:

$$\tau = \frac{S}{A^*} \qquad\qquad (2.25)$$

with : $A^* = A\left(1 - \frac{\Delta l}{\sqrt{A}}\right) \qquad\qquad (2.26)$

The behaviour of a sand during a direct shear test depends on its state, in other words on its initial density. Thus, a sample of *dense sand* has a large degree of interlocking between solid particles so that, at the onset of a shear test, the sand has to go through a looser state prior to the occurrence of shear failure as depicted schematically in figure 2.12. This behaviour, known as *dilation*, implies therefore an increase in volume and hence a decrease in density. The shear stress reaches its peak at a relatively low strain on the corresponding stress–strain curve, then a strain softening ensues, leading eventually to a *critical shear strength* τ_c as shown in figure 2.13.

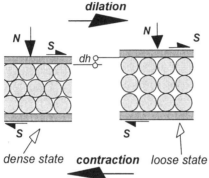

Figure 2.12: Loose and dense states for sands.

This *critical* value τ_c is linked to the rate of dilation represented by the angle υ in the figure. It is seen that, for a dense sand, dilation increases initially to reach a maximum υ_{max} under the peak shear stress τ_{max}, then decreases subsequently. For a *loose sand* on the other hand, the normal stress applied during shear causes the sand to become denser at the beginning of test, thus heralding a decrease in volume. The corresponding *negative* angle of dilation eventually reaches a maximum value $\upsilon_{max} = 0$ when the shear stress on the stress–strain curve tends towards the maximum asymptotic value τ_c depicted in figure 2.13. Because sands are deprived of cohesion, the corresponding effective angle of friction ϕ' varies in proportion to the shear stress τ. Accordingly, when the shear stress reaches the critical value τ_c, equations 2.8, 2.15 and 2.19 apply:

$$\tau_c = \sigma'_n \tan \phi'_c \tag{2.27}$$

$$t = s' \sin \phi'_c \tag{2.28}$$

$$q = M p' \tag{2.29}$$

M being the slope given by equation 2.20.

Consequently, if several shear tests were carried out on the same sand, each under a different but constant normal stress σ'_n, then the corresponding set of stresses at failure can easily be determined from graphs similar to those in figure 2.13, so that the measured values of τ_c can be plotted against the corresponding values of σ'_n; similarly, all τ_{max} values can be plotted in the same figure yielding thus a value ϕ'_{max} of the effective angle of friction as depicted in figure 2.14 from which it is seen that:

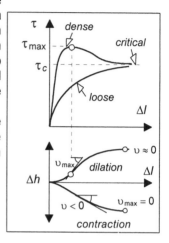

$$\phi'_{max} = \phi'_c + \upsilon_{max} \qquad (2.30)$$

Figure 2.13: Contraction and dilation of sands.

Figure 2.14 shows that, for loose sands, $\upsilon_{max} = 0$ and the maximum angle of friction ϕ'_{max} in this case corresponds to the critical angle ϕ'_c. Accordingly, the maximum shear stress of a sand can be calculated as follows:

$$\tau_{max} = \sigma'_n \tan \phi'_{max} \qquad (2.31)$$

and the relationship between the *critical* and *maximum* shear stresses can then be established by combining equations 2.27, 2.30 and 2.31. Whence:

$$\tau_c = \frac{\tau_{max} - \sigma' \tan \upsilon_{max}}{\dfrac{\tau_{max}}{\sigma'} \tan \upsilon_{max} + 1} \qquad (2.32)$$

The latter relationship indicates that for a *loose sand*, $\upsilon_{max} = 0$ and thus $\tau_c = \tau_{max}$.

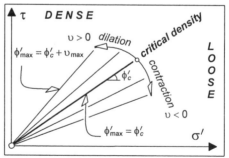

Figure 2.14: Critical density of a sand.

Typical values of the critical friction angle ϕ'_c, as well as the maximum dilation angle υ_{max} of some of the granular soils are listed below:

type of soil	$\phi'_c\,(°)$	$\upsilon_{max}\,(°)$
silt	28	3–4
silty sand	30	3–5
uniform sand	28	5–7
well graded sand	33	10–12
sandy gravel	35	12–15

2.5 Shear strength of saturated fine-grained soils: the triaxial test

2.5.1 The triaxial apparatus

The triaxial test is a sophisticated experiment that needs to be undertaken with great care if the measured results are to have any physical meaning. Contrary to what the name might imply, the test is not truly *triaxial* since only two sets of stresses can be applied to a soil sample, namely a vertical stress $\sigma_v = \sigma_1$ and a horizontal stress $\sigma_h = \sigma_3$. However, it is easy to see that, were σ_1 and σ_3 to be *principal stresses* (*i.e.* assuming that no shear stress develops at each end of the sample), then the intermediate stress σ_2 becomes irrelevant as far as the *shear strength* of the soil is concerned. The essential details of a triaxial apparatus are depicted in figure 2.15, where a cylindrical sample with a length to diameter ratio of 2, insulated by a rubber membrane, can be subjected to a chosen set of principal stresses $(\sigma_1, \sigma_2 = \sigma_3)$, under *controlled drainage conditions.* The all-round cell pressure σ_3 is applied hydraulically through a cell fluid, whereas the vertical stress σ_1 is applied mechanically through a piston. Because the contact between the piston and the top end of the sample is assumed to be reduced to a point contact, using the vertical load P applied through the piston and the known cross-sectional area of the sample A, the vertical stress σ_1 can be calculated in a straightforward way:

$$\sigma_1 = \sigma_3 + \frac{P}{A} \qquad (2.33)$$

More importantly, the deviator stress, defined in equation 2.6*a*, can now be calculated at any stage of loading from equation 2.33:

$$q = (\sigma_1 - \sigma_3) = \frac{P}{A} \qquad (2.34)$$

The quantity q can be expressed equally in terms of total or effective stresses. Also, in what follows, the stresses σ_v and σ_1 are used interchangeably, and so are σ_h and σ_3. Tests corresponding to various *stress paths* (such as the one depicted in figure 2.5) can therefore be undertaken under *undrained* or *drained* conditions, simulating both *short term* and *long term* behaviour of the tested soil. Let's first examine the difficulties related to soil sampling and sample preparation in the laboratory prior to testing. In this respect, it is useful to mention that, although it can accommodate different types of soils including sands, the triaxial apparatus will be used exclusively in what follows to test cohesive soils, mainly *saturated clays*.

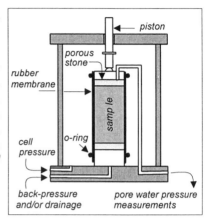

Figure 2.15: Triaxial apparatus.

2.5.2 State of a clay sample prior to testing

Consider the case of an element of a saturated clay located at a depth z as illustrated in figure 2.16. The corresponding state of *in situ* total stresses are such that:

$$\sigma_v = \sigma'_{vo} + u_o \qquad (2.35)$$

$$\sigma_h = K_o \sigma'_{vo} + u_o \qquad (2.36)$$

with : $\quad K_o = \dfrac{\sigma'_h}{\sigma'_v} \qquad (2.37)$

where σ'_{vo} represents the effective vertical stress *in situ,* u_o the porewater pressure at depth z, and K_o is known as the *coefficient of earth pressure at rest* and corresponds to the ratio of horizontal to vertical effective stresses *in situ*.

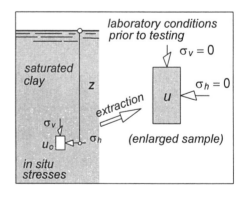

Figure 2.16: Stress release due to sampling.

As such, K_o depends on the type of soil, on its mode of deposition and especially on its stress history. Hence, for a *normally consolidated* clay, K_o can be estimated as follows (Jaky, 1944):

$$K_o = \left(1 + \frac{2}{3}\sin\phi'\right)\tan^2\left(\frac{\pi}{4} + \frac{\phi'}{2}\right) \approx 1 - \sin\phi' \qquad (2.38a)$$

For overconsolidated clays, K_o is related to the overconsolidation ratio *OCR* of the soil and can be evaluated using the following (Mayne and Kulhawy, 1982):

$$K_o = (1 - \sin\phi')\,OCR^{\sin\phi'} \qquad (2.38b)$$

It is clear from equations 2.38 that K_o varies from around 0.5 to 0.6 for normally consolidated clays, to well in excess of 1 in the case of heavily overconsolidated clays as indicated in figure 2.17. The clay becomes overconsolidated during the unloading process from point *A* to point *B,* and the corresponding K_o increases gradually with increasing OCR.

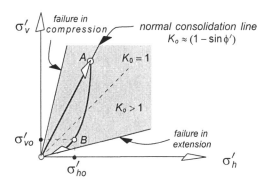

Figure 2.17: Variation of the coefficient K_o with the OCR of a soil.

Referring back to figure 2.16, it is seen that on extraction from the ground, the sample is relieved of the total stresses, so that the applied stress increments at the end of the extraction process are:

$$\Delta\sigma_v = -(\sigma'_{vo} + u_0) \qquad (2.39)$$

$$\Delta\sigma_h = -(K_o\,\sigma'_{vo} + u_0) \qquad (2.40)$$

At the end of this process of unloading, the clay sample *can* become overconsolidated, and consequently its volume can potentially increase (*i.e.* expand). However, any volume expansion can only occur physically if the clay has access to water. Failing that, the porewater pressure inside the sample becomes negative:

$$u = u_o + \Delta u < 0 \qquad\qquad (2.41)$$

The porewater pressure increment Δu generated by the unloading can be estimated from the Skempton (1954) relationship:

$$\Delta u = B[\Delta\sigma_h + A(\Delta\sigma_v - \Delta\sigma_h)] \qquad\qquad (2.42)$$

where A and B are porewater pressure parameters. In particular, B has a maximum value of one for *saturated* soils. A on the other hand, depends on the state of the clay, on the stress path, as well as on the magnitude of deformation. Figure 2.18 shows typical variations of parameter A with the axial deformation during an undrained triaxial test on a saturated sample of a lightly overconsolidated clay.

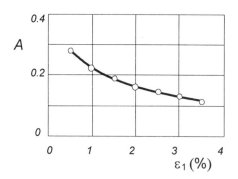

Figure 2.18: Typical variations of A with deformation.

There is ample experimental evidence to suggest that, at failure, the porewater pressure parameter A_f is related to the overconsolidation ratio of the clay. In general, $A_f \geq 0$ for normally consolidated to lightly overconsolidated clays, and $A_f < 0$ for heavily overconsolidated clays; the following limits being typical:

normally consolidated clays	$0.6 < A_f < 1.3$
lightly overconsolidated clays	$0 < A_f < 0.6$
heavily overconsolidated clays	$-0.5 < A_f < 0$

Thus, for a sample of a saturated clay (*i.e.* $B = 1$), a substitution for the quantities $\Delta\sigma_v$ and $\Delta\sigma_h$ from equations 2.39 and 2.40 into equation 2.42, then an insertion of the ensuing quantity Δu into equation 2.41 yields the expression of the (negative) porewater pressure within the clay mass after extraction from the ground:

$$u = -\sigma'_{vo}[K_o(1 - A_s) + A_s] \tag{2.43}$$

where A_s represents the porewater pressure parameter of the soil after extraction from the ground, whose value is *different* from that of A_f at failure. Equation 2.43 indicates that, while the total stresses after extraction are zero, the corresponding effective stresses are somewhat different from those applied *in situ* prior to extraction, in that the new assumed isotropic set of effective stresses generated by the unloading process is:

$$\sigma'_v = \sigma'_h = -u = \sigma'_{vo}[K_o(1 - A_s) + A_s] \tag{2.44}$$

Equally important, equation 2.43 suggests that a *suction* of water develops within the clay sample, creating in the process a gradient of moisture content from the periphery of the sample towards its centre. In some instances, this gradient can cause the moisture content in the inner part of the sample to be higher than that in the outer limits by as much as *4 percentage points* (see for instance Bjerrum (1973)), mainly because the soil is more disturbed at the periphery of the sample. This fact presents the engineer with the following dilemma: prior to any testing, the clay sample should ideally have both stress and moisture conditions similar to that *in situ*. However in practice, it is not physically possible to restore these two variables jointly to their field values since applying *in situ* stresses to the sample *will* cause the clay to have a moisture content different from the one in the field and *vice versa*. Nonetheless, given that the soil behaviour is very sensitive to the stress history, it is advisable in this case to restore the *in situ* stress conditions at the expense of having an initial moisture content slightly different from that in the field.

2.5.3 Undrained shear strength of saturated clays

If a clay layer is subjected to a total stress increase $\Delta\sigma$ at its surface, then, because of the low permeability of such type of soils, the immediate (short term) effect is manifested as a rise in porewater pressure of a magnitude $\Delta u = \Delta\sigma$; the effective stresses remaining unaltered. Under these circumstances, the clay resistance to the applied pressure is entirely provided by the *undrained shear strength* c_u. Accordingly, a simulation of the short term behaviour of a clay in a triaxial apparatus consists of preventing any drainage from taking place during testing, the corresponding triaxial test being known as *unconsolidated, undrained test*. The behaviour thus exhibited by a clay sample in the laboratory is representative of that of a saturated clay layer subject to a stress change lasting for a short period of time. For instance, the time needed to undertake an excavation or to build a foundation in a clay is relatively short, of the order of few weeks perhaps, during which the behaviour of the clay is virtually *undrained,* since the corresponding low permeability prevents any excess porewater pressure dissipation from occurring within this short time span. The unconsolidated, undrained triaxial test consists of applying a confining pressure σ_3 around the clay sample, which is then sheared immediately under constant volume conditions; in other words, without allowing any drainage to take place. The state of stresses throughout the test can be summarised as follows.

• **Phase 1** - the sample is placed in the triaxial apparatus: both vertical and horizontal total stresses are nil, the values of the negative porewater pressure, as well as the (isotropic) effective stresses being given by equations 2.43 and 2.44 respectively:

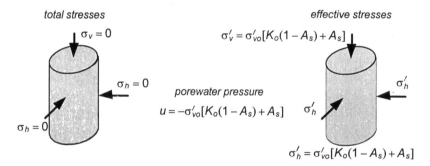

• **Phase 2** - a confining pressure of a magnitude σ_3 is applied around the sample, no drainage is allowed: the effective stresses therefore remain constant and the confining pressure is transferred entirely to the porewater pressure. Hence the ensuing stresses:

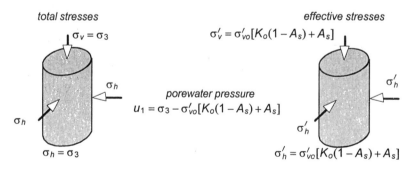

• **Phase 3** - the sample is immediately sheared under constant volume (*i.e.* no drainage allowed) until the occurrence of failure. The corresponding stresses *at failure* are σ_{vf}, σ_{hf} and u_f.

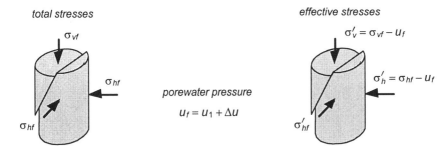

The porewater pressure increment Δu is calculated from equation 2.42 in which $B = 1$ (saturated clay) and $\Delta\sigma_3 = 0$ since the confining pressure σ_3 is maintained constant throughout the test. Accordingly, equation 2.42 reduces to the following:

$$\Delta u = A_f \, \Delta\sigma_1 \qquad (2.45)$$

But the quantity $\Delta\sigma_1$ represents the difference between the final (*i.e.* at failure) and initial (*i.e.* at the onset of shear) values of vertical stress:

$$\Delta\sigma_1 = \sigma_{vf} - \sigma_h \qquad (2.46)$$

Since the confining pressure is constant (*i.e.* $\sigma_3 = \sigma_h = \sigma_{hf}$), equation 2.45 can therefore be expressed as follows:

$$\Delta u = A_f(\sigma_v - \sigma_h)_f \qquad (2.47)$$

Hence the corresponding porewater pressure *at failure*:

$$u = u_1 + \Delta u$$

$$= \sigma_{hf} - \sigma'_{vo}[K_o(1 - A_f) + A_f] + A_f(\sigma_v - \sigma_h)_f \qquad (2.48)$$

The effective stresses *at failure* can now be established:

$$\sigma'_{vf} = \sigma_{vf} - u_f$$

$$= (\sigma_v - \sigma_h)_f + \sigma'_{vo}[K_o(1 - A_f) + A_f] - A_f(\sigma_v - \sigma_h)_f \qquad (2.49)$$

$$\sigma'_{hf} = \sigma_{hf} - u_f$$

$$= \sigma'_{vo}[K_o(1 - A_f) + A_f] + A_f(\sigma_v - \sigma_h)_f \qquad (2.50)$$

Moreover, the deviator stress *at failure* has already been established *via* equation 2.12:

$$(\sigma_{vf} - \sigma_{hf}) = (\sigma'_v + \sigma'_h) \sin\phi' + 2c' \cos\phi' \qquad (2.51)$$

Thus, a combination of equations 2.49, 2.50 and 2.51 yields:

$$(\sigma_v - \sigma_h)_f = \frac{2\sigma'_{vo}[K_o(1 - A_f) + A_f] \sin\phi' + 2c' \cos\phi'}{1 + (2A_f - 1) \sin\phi'} \qquad (2.52)$$

At the onset of shear, the effective vertical stress, given by equation 2.44, is the *same* for all samples, regardless of the magnitude of the confining pressure applied to each one of them. Consequently, all samples tested under different confining pressures possess the *same* overconsolidation ratio, and therefore have identical A_f values, so that the right-hand side of equation 2.52 corresponds to a *constant.* This, in turn, indicates that the deviator stress at failure has a *constant* value, *irrespective* of the magnitude of the confining pressure. Figure 2.19 shows that the deviator stress at failure corresponds in fact to the diameter of Mohr's circle and, accordingly, the constancy of the deviator stress during *unconsolidated undrained* triaxial tests implies that all corresponding Mohr's circles at failure have the same diameter. Under such conditions, the angle of shearing resistance of the soil is reduced to $\phi_u = 0$, and equation 2.52 then becomes:

$$(\sigma_v - \sigma_h)_f = 2c_u \qquad (2.53)$$

c_u is the undrained shear strength of the clay as shown in figure 2.19, where the quantities σ_v and σ_1 (as well as σ_h and σ_3) are used interchangeably.

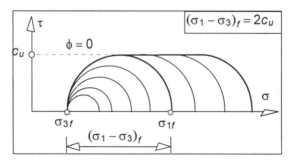

Figure 2.19: Undrained shear strength of clays.

The undrained shear strength c_u is a fundamental soil design parameter, in that it governs the clay behaviour in the short term. It can readily be shown that, for a *saturated normally consolidated clay* especially, the relationship between c_u and the moisture content w is similar to that depicted on the left-hand side of figure 2.20 where it is seen that a slight decrease in moisture content can lead to a significant increase in c_u. Accordingly, the undrained shear strength of a normally consolidated clay increases linearly with depth from a theoretical value of zero at the ground surface. However, in practice, any desiccation caused by whatever means (plant roots for instance) causes c_u to increase according to the graph shown on the right hand side of figure 2.20. Also, experimental evidence indicates that, for an *overconsolidated clay,* the variation of moisture content with depth is not as significant, and so the undrained shear strength in that case does not vary appreciably with depth.

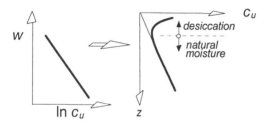

Figure 2.20: Variation of c_u with depth for a normally consolidated clay.

It should be borne in mind, however, that the undrained shear strength of a (stiff) clay, measured in the laboratory on a sample of a small size (usually 76 mm long with a diameter of 38 mm), often represents an overestimate of the actual value in the field; the reason being that a small size sample is unlikely to contain slip planes or fissures that characterise a thick stiff clay layer in situ (see Simpson et al., 1979). Skempton (1957) established the following empirical relationship between the ratio c_u/σ'_v of the undrained shear strength to the effective overburden pressure, and the plasticity index I_p, applicable exclusively to *normally consolidated clays:*

$$\frac{c_u}{\sigma'_v} \approx 0.11 + 3.7 \times 10^{-3} I_p \qquad (2.54)$$

The *consistency* of a clay is related to its undrained shear strength c_u, and the following table can be used as a guide.

clay consistency	$c_u\,(kN/m^2)$
very soft	< 20
soft	20–40
firm to medium	40–75
stiff	75–150
very stiff	> 150

2.5.4 Drained shear strength parameters of saturated clays

The *unconsolidated undrained test* analysed previously can only yield the undrained shear strength of the clay because of the constancy of the deviator stress at failure, regardless of the magnitude of the confining pressure. Therefore a different type of test will have to be undertaken if the effective parameters (*i.e. c' and ϕ'*) corresponding to the long term behaviour of the soil were to be measured. The *consolidated undrained test,* throughout which the variation of porewater pressure is measured, simulates the conditions of works extending over a period of time, long enough to assume that the excess porewater pressure induced by the loading has entirely dissipated, leading thus to a full consolidation of the clay. If, at that stage the soil is loaded rapidly, then its behaviour will be undrained, and provided that the porewater pressure is known at any stage of the undrained loading, then the effective stresses can easily be calculated, yielding in the process the drained shear strength parameters of the clay. The *consolidated undrained triaxial test with porewater pressure measurement* consists therefore of *consolidating* the clay sample under a confining pressure σ_3 (read σ_h), then shearing it under *undrained conditions* while measuring the porewater pressure until the occurrence of failure. It is important at this stage to mention that for the measurement of porewater pressure to be of any significance, the sample must be sheared at *low speed* so that the excess porewater pressure generated continuously during this phase has time to *equalise* throughout the sample (see for instance Bishop and Henkel (1962)). In this respect, a shear speed lower than 0.001 *mm/min* (just under 1.5 *mm per day*) might be needed to fulfil this requirement in the case of a stiff clay. Compared with the previous test, the state of stresses throughout a *consolidated undrained test* consists of the following phases.

- *Phase 1 is identical to that of the previous unconsolidated undrained test.*

- *Phase 2* - A confining pressure σ_3 is applied around the sample, which is then allowed to consolidate fully. Once all excess porewater pressure has dissipated, the corresponding stresses are:

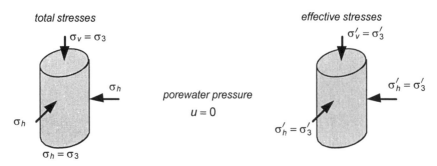

- **Phase 3** - The sample is sheared without allowing any drainage to take place (*i.e.* the volume of the sample remains constant throughout shear). The stresses at failure are therefore:

total stresses   *effective stresses*

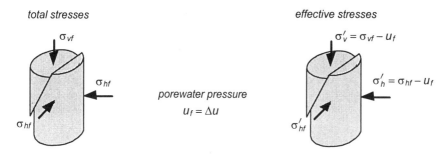

porewater pressure

$u_f = \Delta u$

The porewater pressure at failure is identical to that given by equation 2.47:

$$u_f = \Delta u = A_f(\sigma_v - \sigma_h)_f \tag{2.55}$$

Hence the effective stresses at failure:

$$\sigma'_{vf} = \sigma_{vf} - A_f(\sigma_v - \sigma_h)_f \tag{2.56a}$$

$$\sigma'_{hf} = \sigma_{hf} - A_f(\sigma_v - \sigma_h)_f \tag{2.56b}$$

Finally, a combination of equations 2.51 and 2.56 yields the deviator stress at failure:

$$(\sigma_v - \sigma_h)_f = \frac{2\sigma_3 \sin\phi' + 2c'\cos\phi'}{1 + (2A_f - 1)\sin\phi'} \tag{2.57}$$

Significantly, equation 2.57 indicates that the deviator stress at failure (*i.e.* the diameter of Mohr's circle) depends on the magnitude of the confining pressure σ_3. This is illustrated in figure 2.21 where two samples of the same saturated clay have been consolidated under different pressures such that, at the end of consolidation, the volume of the sample subject to the lowest confining pressure has increased in a way that the clay has become *heavily overconsolidated*. The second sample, on the other hand, is in a *normally consolidated* state. At the onset of undrained shear, the porewater pressure increases gradually within both samples and, eventually, at failure, a *positive* porewater pressure is measured in connection with the normally consolidated clay sample, whilst the heavily overconsolidated one exhibits a *negative* porewater pressure. The question of how the *effective shear strength* parameters ϕ' and c' can be determined then arises once the corresponding Mohr's circles are drawn. Evidently, the *total stress* circles are of little, if any, importance since ϕ' and c' are related to effective stresses. Yet, it is still unclear how figure 2.21 can possibly be of any use to measure these two parameters. More confusing perhaps is the fact that the behaviour depicted in this figure characterises the *same* saturated clay which, when subject to a confining pressure smaller than its preconsolidation pressure σ'_p (*i.e.* the maximum effective vertical stress ever applied to the soil) becomes overconsolidated. On the other hand, the state of clay becomes normally consolidated under consolidation pressures greater than σ'_p.

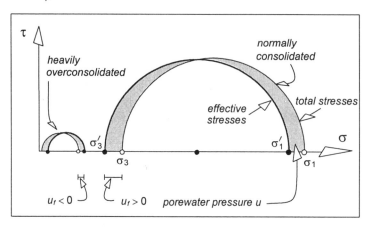

Figure 2.21: Effect of the state of a clay on its strength.

To clarify this somewhat confusing situation, let us concentrate for a moment on the *stress paths* during the undrained shear phase. In this respect, figure 2.22 depicts a typical behaviour where the variation of porewater pressure u clearly reflects the state of the soil: for a normally consolidated clay (*i.e.* $OCR = 1$), u increases continuously until the occurrence of failure, while in the case of an overconsolidated clay, the porewater pressure increases initially, only to decrease after having reached a peak, even becoming negative for heavily overconsolidated clays as the soil dilates on shearing.

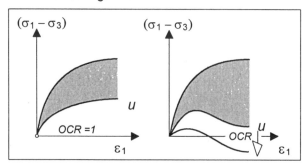

Figure 2.22: Effects of the state of a clay on the porewater pressure at failure.

These effects are better illustrated in figure 2.23 using the stress variables *(q, p')* defined by equations 2.9 and 2.10. Furthermore, the *total stress path* in the space *(q, p')* is linear with a slope of 3 as shown in the figure (see also Azizi, 2007). The measurement of porewater pressure at the onset of shear allows *the effective stress path* to be found, and the figure further illustrates the effect of the state of clay on the shape of the effective stress path. Thus, the normally consolidated clay (consolidated under σ'_{31}) has a *positive* porewater pressure at failure. However, as the overconsolidation ratio increases, the porewater pressure at failure decreases (clay sample consolidated under σ'_{32}), only to become *negative* when the clay becomes heavily overconsolidated (sample consolidated under σ'_{33}).

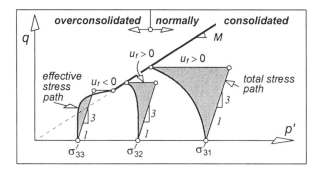

Figure 2.23: Effective and total stress paths for different states of a clay.

A clearer picture is now starting to emerge in relation to the *drained behaviour* of clays, such a picture being dominated by the *state* of the clay. Thus for a *soft normally consolidated clay*, the behaviour is characterised by an *ultimate* or a *critical* angle of shearing resistance ϕ'_c and no apparent cohesion ($c' = 0$) as shown in figure 2.24.

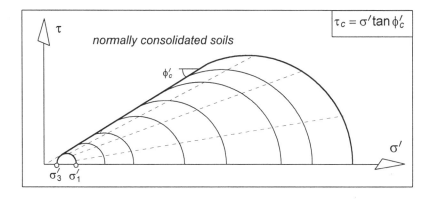

Figure 2.24: Behaviour of a normally consolidated clay.

In the absence of cohesion, equation 2.52 yields the following deviator stress at failure:

$$(\sigma_1' - \sigma_3')_f = \frac{2\sigma_3 \sin\phi_c'}{1 + (2A_f - 1)\sin\phi_c'} \qquad (2.58)$$

where σ_3' represents the (effective) consolidation pressure and A_f is the porewater pressure parameter at failure. On the other hand, the behaviour of a *stiff overconsolidated clay* is more typical of that depicted in figure 2.25. The *critical* (or ultimate) angle of shearing resistance ϕ_c' of the clay is easily measured from the linear portion of the failure envelope where the clay is normally consolidated. As soon as the clay becomes overconsolidated, that is, when the confining pressure becomes smaller than the preconsolidation pressure, the failure envelope becomes markedly non-linear, and once more the question to be answered is what values should be assigned to both the effective cohesion c' and the angle of shearing resistance ϕ' so that the entire behaviour of the clay can be represented by a unique mathematical equation:

$$\tau_f = c' + \sigma' \tan\phi' \qquad (2.59)$$

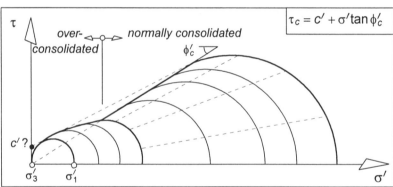

Figure 2.25: Typical behaviour of an overconsolidated clay.

The answer depends in part on the stress level to be applied in the field: if the magnitude of effective stresses is expected to cause the clay to become normally consolidated, then the ultimate critical conditions of $\phi' = \phi_c'$ and $c' = 0$ must be applied. If, however, after being loaded, the clay is still overconsolidated, then a (subjective!) engineering judgement must be made. In this respect, figure 2.25 makes it clear that neglecting the apparent cohesion might affect the shear strength of the soil, especially if the clay in question is heavily overconsolidated. Alternatively, assigning a high value to c' such as the one corresponding to the intercept of the tangent to the non-linear portion of the failure envelope (refer to figure

2.25) can be potentially dangerous, as this might increase dramatically (and artificially) the shear strength of the soil, knowing that such intercepts can be as high as $100\,kN/m^2$ in some instances. Figure 2.26 depicts results measured from consolidated undrained triaxial tests with porewater pressure measurements undertaken on a natural stiff clay (Josseaume and Azizi, 1991). The slope M of the linear portion, calculated from equation 2.20, yields an *effective critical* angle of shearing resistance $\phi'_c = 22°$. Now, there is a need to consider carefully what value might be assigned to c', if the shear strength of the clay is to be modelled by an expression similar to equation 2.19.

$$q = \frac{6\cos\phi'}{3 - \sin\phi'}\,c' + \frac{6\sin\phi'}{3 - \sin\phi'}\,p'$$

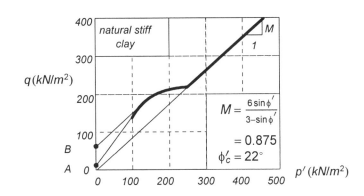

Figure 2.26: Behaviour of a natural stiff clay.

Manifestly, the somewhat contentious parameter c' is difficult to determine with sufficient accuracy because of its intricate link to the soil density and therefore to the void ratio, whose value varies with depth (*i.e.* with the effective overburden pressure) as illustrated in figure 2.27. Referring back to figure 2.26, it is seen that, were the non-linear part of the failure envelope to be prolonged as illustrated, the intersection with the q-axis at point A then yields a deviator stress $q_A \approx 10\,kN/m^2$. Alternatively, if the tangent to the curved portion is used, the ensuing deviator stress at point B will be $q_B \approx 60\,kN/m^2$. In both cases, c' is calculated from equation 2.19 in which p' is zero:

$$c' = q_{A,B}\left(\frac{3 - \sin\phi'_c}{6\cos\phi'_c}\right) \tag{2.60}$$

Hence: $c'_A = 4.7\,kN/m^2$, $c'_B = 28.3\,kN/m^2$

This simple example epitomises the practical difficulties that an engineer would face in selecting an appropriate value (if at all !) for c' and, in this particular instance, it is prudent to opt for the smaller of the two values.

Generally, it is advisable to limit c' to a maximum of $15\,kN/m^2$ for stiff heavily overconsolidated clays and to extend the value $c' = 0$ from normally consolidated to lightly overconsolidated clays.

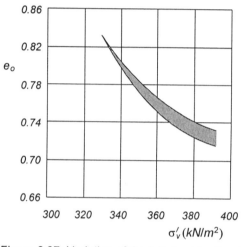

Figure 2.27: Variation of the initial void ratio with depth.

The drained shear strength parameters can also be determined from *consolidated drained triaxial tests* which consist of consolidating soil samples of the same clay under different confining pressures, then shearing them under *drained* conditions, thus allowing their volume to change. It is important to mention however that, as implied by its name, this type of test requires the sample to be sheared under drained conditions. In other words, the shear speed must be such that no build up of excess water pressure can occur during shear. To fulfil this requirement, shear speeds of as low as $5 \times 10^{-4}\,mm/min$ may be needed, implying an axial deformation of less than 1% *per day* in the case of a 76 *mm* long clay sample. Taking into account the time needed for test preparation and consolidation, it is obvious that a carefully undertaken consolidated drained test necessitates weeks rather than days to be achieved. This can deter an engineer from opting for this type of test, especially when a consolidated *undrained* triaxial test with porewater pressure measurement can be achieved comparatively quickly, and can yield similar information about the *effective* shear strength parameters as detailed previously. However, there is a need to undertake this type of *consolidated drained triaxial test* to simulate some specific stress paths. The procedure of such tests is similar in nature to that applicable to a consolidated *undrained* test, with the exception of the shear phase which must be undertaken under drained conditions. Accordingly, *at failure*, the state of stresses is as shown below. Evidently, the behaviour of the clay depends on the magnitude of the confining pressure, and therefore on the corresponding overconsolidation ratio.

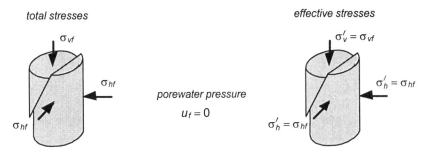

Figure 2.28 shows that a normally consolidated clay ($OCR = 1$) exhibits a behaviour characterised by a strain hardening, due to the (positive) compressive volumetric strains ε_v (*i.e. contraction* of volume). On the other hand, an overconsolidated clay initially displays a compressive volumetric strain, followed by a volume expansion that reaches a maximum when the deviator stress is at its peak.

The rate of expansion then starts to decrease, and the deviator stress tends towards its ultimate critical value q_c under which the expansion ceases. Figure 2.28 clearly indicates the link between an increasing expansion and an increasing *OCR*. In fact, it is well established that, as the *OCR* and the plasticity index increase, so does the difference between the peak shear stress q_{max} and the critical shear stress q_c. Moreover, the angle of shearing resistance associated with the critical shear stress of an overconsolidated clay is usually appreciably smaller than that corresponding to the peak shear strength.

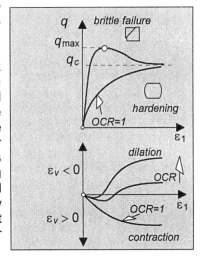

Figure 2.28: Effect of the OCR on the peak strength of a clay.

On the practical side, the *critical effective angle of friction* is an important parameter for the analysis of the stability of slopes. Although this topic is tackled in details elsewhere, it is important to mention in this respect that the use of peak shear parameters measured in the laboratory, on samples of small sizes, often leads to an overestimation of the factor of safety against shear failure (error on the unsafe side!). Several instances of slope failures reported in the literature are due precisely to this mechanical extrapolation of shear parameters measured in the laboratory to field conditions (see for example Skempton (1964), Skempton and La Rochelle (1965), Henkel (1957) and Palladino and Peck (1972)).

2.6 Quality assurance related to triaxial testing

The quality of the results measured during a triaxial test is inevitably linked to the testing procedure, especially that relating to sample preparation prior to testing. It has already been shown that sampling causes the porewater pressure in the clay to become negative, generating in the process a migration of moisture from the periphery of the sample where the soil fabric has been disturbed towards its centre. Ideally, prior to any testing taking place, each soil sample must be consolidated under stress field conditions ($\sigma'_v = \sigma'_{vo}$, $\sigma'_h = K_o \sigma'_{vo}$), where σ'_{vo} represents the effective overburden pressure and K_o is the coefficient of earth pressure at rest given by equation 2.38. In practice, however, the impediment to restoring these anisotropic stresses results from the fact that consolidation under these circumstances *must* occur under zero radial strain ($\varepsilon_r = 0$), known as K_o -condition, and refers to the fact that soils *in situ* are semi-infinite media, and as such, they do not deform radially when subjected to any type of loading. Though feasible, the stringent condition of zero lateral strain during consolidation is very difficult to maintain in the laboratory since there is a need to adjust the stress ratio, that is the coefficient K_o, almost continuously while consolidation progresses under $\varepsilon_r = 0$.

An alternative to the above procedure consists of assuming a uniform distribution of the negative porewater pressure throughout the sample, then consolidating the clay, prior to any testing, under an *isotropic* effective stress field, the magnitude of which is given by equation 2.43:

$$\sigma'_v = \sigma'_h = -u \qquad\qquad (2.61)$$

Under these conditions, applying an isotropic effective stress to the clay sample amounts to measuring its isotropic swelling pressure. This can easily and accurately be achieved using the set-up depicted in figure 2.29, whereby a *nil indicator* is connected through a valve to the drainage circuit on one side and to a container filled with de-aerated water on the other side. Prior to opening the valve, an isotropic fluid pressure, with a magnitude *estimated* from equation 2.43 is applied around the sample, both ends of the drainage circuit of the nil indicator being at atmospheric pressure, hence there is an initial horizontal level of mercury.

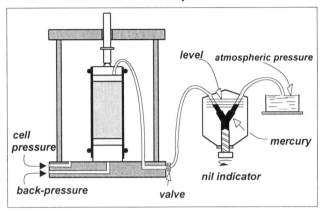

Figure 2.29: Use of a nil indicator to prevent any volume change of the sample prior to testing.

Once the valve is opened, one of three possibilities occurs:

- **(a)** The applied pressure σ_h is such that it cancels out the negative porewater pressure, in which case the level of mercury in the nil indicator remains equalized.

- **(b)** The porewater pressure is still negative, and consequently water is sucked into the sample making the mercury move upward in the left-hand side of the nil indicator. In this case, the pressure σ_h must be increased gradually until the mercury level is again equalized.

- **(c)** The porewater pressure within the sample becomes positive causing water to be expelled through the drainage lead and mercury to move upward on the right-hand side of the nil indicator. Consequently, σ_h needs to be adjusted downward until a balanced mercury level is re-established.

Clearly, the first possibility above, though not impossible, is highly unlikely to occur, and the pressure σ_h almost inevitably will need to be adjusted until an equilibrium in the form of a horizontal mercury level (indicating zero porewater pressure inside the sample) is achieved. Because of the low permeability of clays, the adjustment can be a slow process, and can take several hours in the case of a stiff clay. The fluid pressure applied around the sample, under which an equilibrium is achieved is known as the *isotropic swelling pressure* σ_s of the clay. It corresponds to the limit confining (effective) pressure for which the porewater pressure within the clay is zero. Accordingly, any confining pressure smaller than σ_s will cause the porewater pressure to become negative, generating in the process a suction of water and causing the volume of the sample to expand. The task of restoring the stress conditions to as near as practically possible to those applied *in situ* can become futile if the sample is subjected to substantial disturbances during the extraction process and the subsequent transportation, storage and preparation before testing. Assuming that an appropriate sampling technique is used to extract high quality samples, which are then adequately stored in the laboratory under controlled temperature and humidity conditions so that the moisture content of the clay remains virtually unchanged, the careful preparation of every sample should then become the focus of the experimenter in order to minimise the remoulding of the clay which can affect, in a major way, the quality of the measured results during testing. Of course, every step in sample preparation can potentially lead to the clay being markedly remoulded. These steps include cutting and trimming of the sample, applying a filter paper, then a rubber membrane around the clay, and saturating then connecting the drainage circuit.

Clearly, an accumulation of differing degrees of disturbance related to these steps can be detrimental to the quality of the subsequent measured results. For instance, cutting a 38 *mm* diameter, 76 *mm* long sample of a soft clay is a highly delicate operation which, if not handled carefully, can easily cause the sample to have an initial deformation before being loaded, thus altering the behaviour of the clay. Also, placing a *saturated* filter paper around the sample, then connecting a *saturated* drainage circuit (including saturated porous stones on each side of the sample) will cause a stiff clay to suck water through its periphery in order to balance the negative porewater pressure existing within the soil matrix, leading to an increase in volume prior to any stresses being applied or to any measurements being made. Similarly, applying a high back pressure in a single step to a sample of a stiff clay may cause the water to flow between the membrane and the periphery of the sample, leaving the clay unsaturated. To minimise these 'side effects', the procedure detailed below, which has the advantage of not altering the volume of the sample prior to the application of a confining pressure, can be applied. Although it is more suited to stiff clays, the procedure can be used in conjunction with any type of soil, and consists of the following steps.

> •(*a*) Once cut to the required dimensions, a *dry* filter paper, shaped in the manner depicted in figure 2.30, is carefully placed around the sample. In so doing, care must be taken to ensure that only a very small amount of water is sprayed on two points to make the

paper stick to the sample, which is then put on the pedestal of the triaxial cell on top of a *dry* porous stone overlain by a *dry* circular filter paper.

•(*b*) A rubber membrane is placed around the sample on top of which a *dry* circular filter paper and a *dry* porous stone are then laid.

•(*c*) The *empty* drainage circuit is then connected to the sample, and the triaxial cell filled with fluid under a pressure estimated from equation 2.43 (*i.e.* a cell pressure equivalent in magnitude to $-u$, where u represents the *negative* porewater pressure developed within the sample after extraction from the ground.

•(*d*) The drainage circuit is closed at one end, then the air contained within it is pumped out at the other end. This step takes about two minutes to complete.

•(*e*) The pump is carefully disconnected so as not to allow any air to re-enter the circuit, which is then immediately immersed in a bucket of de-aerated water. Because of the negative pressure inside the circuit created by pumping, water is automatically sucked in, saturating in the process the entire drainage circuit including the porous stones and filter papers. This step takes no longer than two to three minutes.

•(*f*) Once saturated, the drainage circuit is thereafter connected to a nil indicator as depicted in figure 2.29, and the adjustment of the cell pressure is undertaken in accordance with the procedure described earlier.

Once equilibrium is reached (*i.e.* a confining pressure under which the porewater pressure inside the sample is reduced to zero), a back pressure is applied to the soil *in steps* in order to ensure a very high degree of uniformity of the back pressure throughout the sample. In this respect, it is strongly advisable to apply the same pressure *simultaneously* inside and outside the sample, so that the state of effective stresses is not altered. Accordingly, a back pressure Δu, which is *per se* used to saturate the soil, is applied inside the sample through the drainage circuit, while the cell pressure σ_3 is increased at the same time by the same increment Δu. In the absence of the possibility of increasing concurrently both the back pressure and the cell pressure by the same amount, it is preferable to increase the cell pressure first, then apply the back pressure, thus eliminating the possibility, albeit remote, of the back pressure causing the water to flow between the periphery of the sample and the rubber membrane. Experimental evidence shows that in the case of stiff clays, back pressures as high as $1500\,kN/m^2$ are needed to achieve a high degree of saturation of 98% (Berre, 1981). However, these levels of back pressure can only be applied using specially adapted triaxial equipment. In fact, a standard piece of equipment (*i.e.* a Bishop triaxial cell) is designed to withstand a maximum cell pressure of $1200\,kN/m^2$ and, adopting the procedure described previously by which both back pressure and cell pressure are increased at the same time, it is clear that there is a limit to the maximum back pressure that can realistically be applied to the soil. For instance, if a stiff clay needs to be tested under an effective confining pressures as high as $800\,kN/m^2$ using standard equipment, then the maximum back pressure to which the clay can be subjected will be limited to $400\,kN/m^2$.

On the practical side, applying a back pressure of, say, $400\,kN/m^2$ to a $38\,mm$ diameter clay sample of low permeability (10^{-10} m/s for example) in one increment, may create preferential drainage paths, thus resulting in a differential consolidation of the soil. To alleviate this problem, the back pressure must be applied in gradually increasing increments, at time intervals long enough to allow the pressure throughout the sample to be as uniform as possible. An example related to the application of $400\,kN/m^2$ back pressure to a stiff clay with a permeability $k = 10^{-11}$ m/s is given in the following table. Notice the time related to each increment decreases as the back pressure increases, thus reflecting the gradual increase in saturation of the soil.

back pressure increment (kN/m^2)	application time (days)
50	3
50	2
100	1
200	1

The degree of saturation must be checked at the end of the last increment of back pressure. The corresponding procedure consists simply of closing the drainage circuit, then increasing the (isotropic) cell pressure by an increment $\Delta\sigma_3$ and measuring the increment of porewater pressure Δu thus generated through a pressure transducer connected to the drainage circuit. Skempton equation 2.42 can then be used to calculate the coefficient B of saturation and, because the increment of deviatoric stress is zero ($\Delta\sigma_3 = \Delta\sigma_1$), the equation takes the simpler form:

$$\Delta u = B\Delta\sigma_3 \qquad\qquad (2.62)$$

Hence, the clay is fully saturated if $B = 1$, in other words when $\Delta u = \Delta\sigma_3$. In practice, one aims at achieving a degree of saturation corresponding to a minimum of $B = 0.98$. The use of a lateral filter paper around the sample as depicted in figure 2.30 has the advantage of markedly reducing the time needed for the excess porewater pressure inside the sample either to dissipate (during a drained loading), or to become uniform (as in undrained shear, for example).

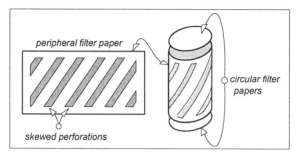

Figure 2.30: Use of peripheral filter paper during testing.

Gibson and Henkel (1954) established a relationship that yields the time t needed to achieve an average degree of consolidation U:

$$U = 1 - \frac{h^2}{\eta c_v t} \qquad (2.63)$$

where h represents the length of the drainage path (half the sample length if the soil is drained on both ends), c_v corresponds to the coefficient of vertical consolidation (see Azizi, 2007 for instance), and η is a coefficient that depends on drainage conditions, whose values are summarised in the following table.

Table 2.1: Coefficient η (from Bishop and Henkel, 1962)

drainage conditions	η
sample drained at one end	0.75
sample drained at both ends	3.0
sample drained radially	32.0
sample drained at both ends as well as radially	40.4

Equation 2.63 can be rearranged in the following way:

$$t = \frac{h^2}{(1 - U)\eta c_v} \qquad (2.64)$$

The latter equation indicates that a sample of clay for which drainage occurs radially through a lateral filter paper, as well as vertically at both ends ($\eta = 40.4$) consolidates 13.5 times faster than when the sample is drained at the ends only ($\eta = 3$). Also, equation 2.64 can be used to check the adequacy of the shear speed used during undrained shear, in the knowledge that any ensuing excess porewater pressure Δu cannot be representative of the undrained behaviour unless it is distributed uniformly throughout the sample.

Example 2.2

Consider the undrained shear of a 38 mm diameter, 76 mm long sample of a stiff clay, with a coefficient $c_v = 2 \times 10^{-8}\,m^2/s$ and with drainage conditions represented by a coefficient $\eta = 40.4$ in table 2.1. Considering that, in practice, a degree of uniformity of the excess porewater pressure $U = 95\%$ is deemed satisfactory, let us, first, use equation 2.64 to calculate the corresponding time t_{95}:

$$t_{95} = \frac{38^2 \times 10^{-6}}{(1 - 0.95) \times 40.4 \times 1.2 \times 10^{-6}} = 596\ min$$

Accordingly, the sample must be sheared undrained for about 10 *hours* before the excess porewater pressure reaches a degree of uniformity of 95%, which in turn indicates that any measurement of porewater pressure taken within 10 *hours* of the onset of shear is *not* representative of the clay behaviour. Thus, it is necessary to select a shear speed that yields a minimum axial deformation, say $\varepsilon_1 = 0.005$, in 10 *hours*, leading hence to a shear speed:

$$v = \varepsilon_1 \frac{l}{t_{95}} = \frac{0.005 \times 76}{600} = 6.3 \times 10^{-4}\ mm/min$$

Adopting this speed for the entire undrained shear phase, one can then easily calculate the degree of uniformity U of the excess porewater pressure throughout the test since, for any selected time t, U can be calculated from equation 2.63, while the axial strain is determined in a straightforward way:

$$\varepsilon_1 = \frac{t v}{l}$$

with $v = 6.3 \times 10^{-4}\ mm/min$ and $l = 76\ mm$ (the sample length). The ensuing results, plotted in figure 2.31, show the extent to which the degree of uniformity U of the excess porewater pressure is below the required minimum value of 0.95. Clearly, any measurement of excess porewater pressure Δu for which U falls outside the shaded area in the figure are erroneous. In particular, Δu is not representative of the clay behaviour up to an axial deformation of 0.5% when the sample is drained radially as well as vertically (refer to the graph in bold in the figure).

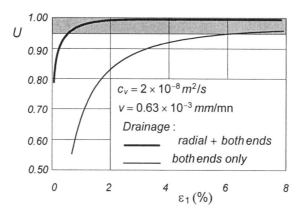

Figure 2.31: Effect of the shear speed on the degree of uniformity of excess porewater pressure.

However, were the sample to be drained only at the ends, the excess porewater pressure measured during shear will *not* be typical of the clay behaviour until the axial deformation reaches the significant value of 6.6%, which is most probably beyond failure considering the (stiff) nature of the clay in this case. It is clear therefore that a good deal of care in sample handling, preparation, saturation and consolidation is not enough to ensure results of high quality with respect to (drained or undrained) shear. In fact it would be very unfortunate if, after going through all the trouble of meticulous preparations, the experimenter overlooked the details related to the selection of an adequate shear speed during an undrained triaxial test for example. In conclusion, it is vitally important for the operator to be aware of the many pitfalls related to laboratory triaxial testing. A clear procedure that includes the means of checking the quality of measurements is therefore a necessity, without which the risk of making the wrong interpretations increases dramatically. Figure 2.32 (Azizi and Josseaume, 1988) shows results measured at the end of consolidation (*i.e.* prior to shear) for some undrained triaxial tests, carefully undertaken according to the procedure detailed previously that includes the use of a nil indicator. These results, together with those of figure 2.26 indicate that the stiff clay in question has a swelling pressure of around $250\,kN/m^2$.

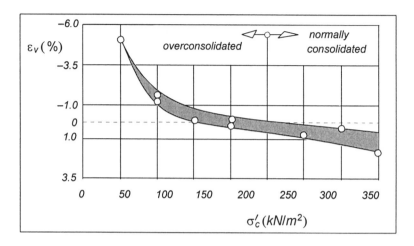

Figure 2.32: Natural stiff clay: volume change vs consolidation pressures.
(Reproduced by permission of the Laboratoire Central des Ponts et Chaussées.)

2.7 The shear vane test

However careful an operator is, soils tested in the laboratory are almost inevitably remoulded to a certain extent. To minimise the disturbance, *in situ* tests, when properly carried out, can yield high quality results which complement those obtained under laboratory conditions. The *shear vane test* is a theory-based reliable *in situ* test, specifically developed for saturated clays with undrained shear strengths of up to $100 \, kN/m^2$. The equipment, depicted schematically in figure 2.33, consists of four thin stainless rectangular blades, welded to a steel rod. The length L of the vane and its width D are typically $100 \, mm$ and $50 \, mm$ respectively, though vanes with $L = 150 \, mm$ are often used for clays with undrained shear strengths larger than $50 \, kN/m^2$. Once pushed gently into the ground to the required depth, the vane is then rotated at a rate of about $6°$ *per minute* until the occurrence of failure where a maximum torque T (*i.e.* moment of resistance) is recorded. Since the test is carried out quickly, the corresponding behaviour of the clay is therefore undrained. If the clay is *anisotropic,* then its *vertical* undrained shear strength c_{uv} developed throughout the length of the vane, is distinct from its *horizontal* component c_{uh} occurring on the horizontal top and bottom sides of the vane as shown in figure 2.33. Accordingly, the maximum torque is the sum of a vertical and a horizontal components:

$$T = T_v + T_h \qquad\qquad (2.65)$$

Referring to figure 2.33, the undrained shear strength c_{uv} is assumed to be fully mobilised throughout the length of the vane. Hence the corresponding torque is:

$$T_v = c_{uv}\pi DL\frac{D}{2} \quad = c_{uv}\pi D^2\frac{L}{2} \tag{2.66}$$

On the other hand, experimental evidence (refer to Wroth (1984)) strongly suggests that the distribution of c_{uh} on the top and bottom sides of the vane is rather similar to that shown in figure 2.33. Under these circumstances, c_{uh} depends on the ratio r/R, where r represents the radial distance from the vane centre and R is the vane radius; so that in accordance with figure 2.34, the torque T_h is evaluated as follows:

$$T_h = 2\int_0^R c_{uh}\, 2\pi r^2\, (r/R)^n\, dr \tag{2.67}$$

where the value of the exponent n can be as high as 5.

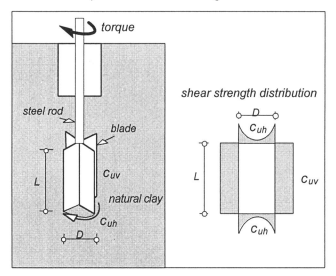

Figure 2.33: Vane shear apparatus.

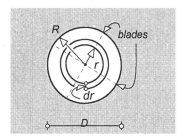

Figure 2.34: Boundary conditions

A straightforward integration of equation 2.67 then yields:

$$T_h = c_{uh} \pi \frac{D^3}{2(n+3)}$$ (2.68)

Consequently, the total moment resistance $(T_h + T_v)$ is:

$$T = \pi D^2 \left[c_{uv} \frac{L}{2} + c_{uh} \frac{D}{2(n+3)} \right]$$ (2.69)

Equation 2.69 is the general expression relating the undrained shear strength of an *anisotropic* clay to the maximum torque recorded during an *in situ* shear vane test. If the conditions of isotropy can be assumed to prevail, then $c_{uv} = c_{uh} = c_u$. Moreover, if the vane is characterised by a ratio $L/D = 2$, then equation 2.69 yields an *apparent undrained shear strength* c_u:

$$c_u = \frac{T}{\pi D^3} \frac{(n+3)}{(n+3.5)}$$ (2.70)

This equation is plotted in figure 2.35 as the variation of the dimensionless quantity $\pi D^3 c_u / T$ *versus* the coefficient n. The graph shows clearly the limited effect of n on the undrained shear strength of the clay and, for all intents and purposes, a value $n = 2$ can be used in conjunction with equations 2.69 and 2.70.

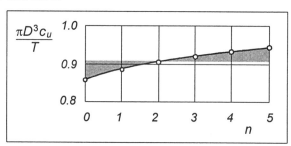

Figure 2.35: Effect of the exponent n on the undrained shear strength of a clay.

Defining the *strength ratio* as being:

$$\xi = \frac{c_{uh}}{c_{uv}}$$ (2.71)

then using $n = 2$, the quantity c_{uv} in equation 2.69 can be calculated as follows:

$$c_{uv} = \frac{10T}{\pi D^2(5L + \xi D)} \qquad (2.72)$$

Obviously, when $L = 2D$, the above equation reduces to:

$$c_{uv} = \frac{10T}{\pi D^3(\xi + 10)} \qquad (2.73)$$

so that when the clay is *isotropic*, $\xi = 1$ and equation 2.73 further reduces to the following:

$$c_u = \frac{10T}{11\pi D^3} \qquad (2.74)$$

One should bear in mind that both equations 2.73 (for anisotropic clays) and 2.74 (for isotropic clays) were derived using $n = 2$ and $L = 2D$, the quantity T being the total torque measured during the test.

Example 2.3

Consider the case of two shear vane tests, carried out on a clay. The first, made using a vane with a length $L = 150\,mm$ and a diameter $D = 50\,mm$, yielded, at failure, a torque $T_1 = 57\,Nm$, while the second, undertaken at the same depth, using this time a vane characterised by the dimensions $L = D = 50\,mm$, registered at failure a torque $T_2 = 23.9\,Nm$. Let us, in the first instance, explore the clay anisotropy by calculating the strength ratio ξ using equation 2.72 for both tests. Thus:

• from test 1:

$$c_{uv} = \frac{10 \times 57 \times 10^{-3}}{\pi \times 5^2 \times 10^{-4} \times (5 \times 0.15 + 0.05\xi)} = \frac{5700}{58.9 + 3.93\xi}\ kN/m^2$$

• a similar analysis of test 2 yields:

$$c_{uv} = \frac{2390}{19.63 + 3.93\xi}\ kN/m^2$$

Whence a strength ratio $\xi = 2.22$, leading to the following components of shear strength:

$$c_{uv} = 84.3\,kN/m^2, \qquad c_{uh} = 187.1\,kN/m^2$$

The shear vane test can also be used to determine the sensitivity of a clay. Consider for example the case of a third test carried out on a clay that can be described as isotropic, using a vane with a diameter $D = 50\,mm$ and a length $L = 100\,mm$. At failure, a torque $T = 37\,Nm$ was measured, following which, the vane was rotated rapidly several times to remould the clay, yielding in the process a maximum torque $T = 9\,N.m$. In order to estimate the sensitivity of the clay, both undrained shear strengths corresponding to undisturbed and remoulded clays must be determined using equation 2.74. Hence, for the undisturbed clay:

$$c_u = \frac{10 \times 37 \times 10^{-3}}{11 \times \pi \times 5^3 \times 10^{-6}} = 85.6\,kN/m^2$$

Similarly for the remoulded soil:

$$c_u = \frac{85.6 \times 9}{37} = 20.8\,kN/m^2$$

Whence a sensitivity:

$$S = \frac{85.6}{20.8} = 4.1$$

This value indicates that tested clay can be described as sensitive.

2-8 Shear strength of rocks

The physical behaviour of a rock mass depends on its nature and state. (Refer to Azizi (2007) for detailed analysis of the process of rock formation, including the mineral constitution). The engineering behaviour of rock masses is essentially defined by their shear strength, which is affected by several factors, in particular:

- *Rock type:* intact crystalline rocks such as granite are much stronger than intact clastic rocks such as sandstone,
- *Rock mineralogy:* within the same type of rock, the shear strength is affected by the mineral composition of the rock structure. For example, in their intact state, the calcite-rich limestone is much more resistant than the weak, friable chalk; both being sedimentary rocks,
- *Weathering:* a chemical process that alters the structure of the rock, and can ultimately lead to its decomposition. Thus rocks such as granite, disintegrated under the effect of millions of years of weathering, become too soft and friable to the point that it can be mined for china clay using a jet of water.
- *Size and density of discontinuities:* rock masses usually contain fractures, which are classified according to their density (or spacing). These fracture vary from microfissures with an average spacing of between 1 mm and 1 cm, to joints characterised by an

average spacing of between 1 cm and 1m. Fractures with an average spacing exceeding 1 m are defined as faults,
- *sample size:* as in the case of clays, only small in situ cored rock samples are tested in the laboratory. These samples are unlikely to contain enough discontinuities so as to be truly representative of the rock mass in situ. Consequently, test results almost invariably yield an overestimate of the actual shear strength in situ.

Moreover, the shear strength of a rock mass (which must not be confused with the rock hardness) can be affected by the cleavage planes. In fact, cleavage may in some instances have a major effect on the capacity of a rock mass to withstand a pressure of whichever type (compressive or shear). Such an effect is typically illustrated in figure 2.36, where the same rock characterised by one main cleavage plane is used. It is seen that the rock is least resistant when subjected to an external pressure applied at a 45° angle with respect to the cleavage plane. Unsurprisingly perhaps, the maximum resistance of the rock is developed when the applied pressure is normal to the cleavage plane. The intermediate resistance corresponding to the case where the line of action of the load is parallel to the cleavage plane reflects the mode of failure engendered by splitting (see figure 2.37). The informative nature of the figure emphasises the importance of accurately knowing the main cleavage planes of a rock mass prior to cutting building blocks from a quarry for instance. Some of the building repair works to which the palace of Westminster in London (famous for its Big Ben tower) is often subjected relate to the fact that some limestone blocks were cut at the wrong angle with respect to the bedding plane, and are thus being replaced due to their steady disintegration.

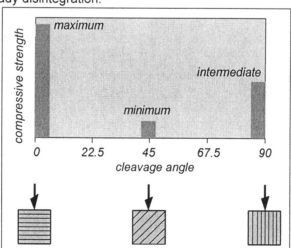

Figure 2.36: Effect of cleavage and bedding planes on the shear resistance of an intact rock

The shear strength of a rock mass also depends on its saturation moisture content and the level of confining pressure. The reader should recall that the moisture content of a saturated material w_s can be expressed in terms of its void ratio e or its porosity n and specific gravity G_s in the following way (refer to equations 1.7 & 1.8, section 1.1):

$$w_s = \frac{e}{G_s} \qquad \text{or} \qquad w_s = \frac{n}{G_s(1-n)} \qquad (2.75)$$

Accordingly, intact igneous and metamorphic rocks, characterised by very low saturation moisture contents due to their low porosity, do exhibit large shear strength characteristics. Typical examples include intact granite and marble, with $w_s \approx 0.5\%$. Some sedimentary rocks on the other hand do have very high saturation moisture contents, and are thus characterised by very low shear strength. Chalk, for instance, with a typical saturation moisture content $w_s \approx 19\%$, has very poor shear resistance (refer to table 2.3). Figure 2.37 illustrates the effects of confinement and saturation on the shear strength of a rock. The maximum shear stress that can be applied to a rock structure is achieved under dry confined stress conditions. The shear resistance decreases significantly when the rock in question is subjected to a uniaxial stress field (see figure 2.38) under dry conditions, reaching a minimum value when the unconfined rock becomes saturated.

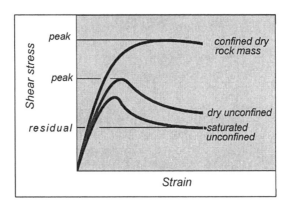

Figure 2.37: Effect of confinement pressure on the shear strength of a rock

Figure 2.37 also indicates that under confined stress conditions, rocks are ductile, in that they can withstand large elasto-plastic deformation without fracturing (refer to Azizi (2007) for the degree of rock folding). Under unconfined stress conditions, rocks usually exhibit a brittle behaviour characterised by a significant drop in shear strength beyond a peak value. Furthermore, the graphs in figure 2.37 show an initial (non-linear) elastic behaviour in all cases, regardless of the level of confinement. The elastic characteristics of rocks are best represented by the elasticity modulus E

(also defined as Young's modulus): the smaller E, the more elastic is the material.

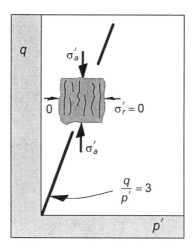

Figure 2.38: Splitting failure related to unconfined stress conditions in rocks

The following useful table 2.2 contains typical values of E for different materials, including rubber for comparison purposes. Note that E is expressed in GN/m^2 ($1\ GN/m^2 = 10^6\ kN/m^2$).

Table 2.2: Elasticity modulii of a selected number of materials

Material	$E(GN/m^2)$
Diamond (D)	1000
Nickel (Ni)	214
Iron (Fe)	196
Copper (Cu)	124
Aluminium (Al)	69
Unweathered granite	75
Unweathered marble	60
Hard limestone	30
Slate	30
Chalk	6
Dense sand	0.035 to, 0.055
Loose sand	0.01 to 0.024
Stiff clay	0.01 to 0.025
Soft clay	0.002 to 0.005
Rubber	0.01 to 0.1

Although rocks are less elastic than sands or clays, they do exhibit similar behaviour in terms of stress-strain relationship as depicted in figure 2.39. Such behaviour can be (approximately) modelled using a Mohr-Coulomb type equation:

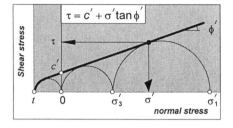

$$\tau = c' + \sigma' \tan \phi' \qquad (2.76)$$

Figure 2.39: Tensile strength of rocks

However, unlike clays or sands, rocks *do* have a tensile strength *t* depending on their degree of weathering and fracture density. Typical shear strength characteristics corresponding to different unweathered rock types are indicated in the useful figure 2.40.

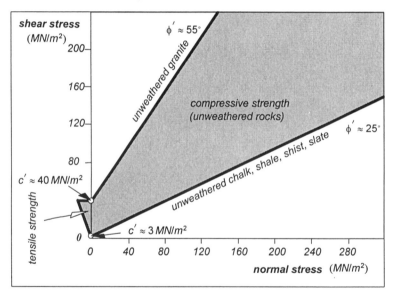

Figure 2.40: Shear strength of unweathered rocks

Notwithstanding its informative nature, the figure shows that under zero normal stress conditions, rocks exhibit shear strength ranging from a very respectable $3,000 \, kN/m^2$ for unweathered chalk or slate, to a very substantial $40,000 \, kN/m^2$ for unweathered granite. These values can fully be appreciated when contrasted to the drained shear strength of a stiff clay under similar zero normal stress conditions, which is usually limited to $15 \, kN/m^2$. *Typical average* values of the shear strength parameters c' and ϕ' for different soils and rocks are summarised in table 2.3. Notice that in the case of clay and mud, the cohesion figures correspond to undrained loading conditions. The table, which also includes dry and saturated unit weights (γ_d and γ_{sat}) of the materials in question, is compiled using *average values* and should not be used as a substitute for measured parameters.

Table 2.3: Typical average shear strength parameters of soils and rocks

Soil type			cohesion kN/m²	$\gamma_d - \gamma_{sat}$ kN/m³	ϕ' (°)
Cohesionless / Loose sand		Uniform grain size		14 - 19	28-34
		mixed grain size		17 - 21	32-40
Dense sand		Uniform grain size		16 - 20	34-40
		mixed grain size		18 - 21	38-46
Gravel		Uniform grain size		17 - 19	34-37
		mixed grain size		20 - 22	38-45
Blasted-broken rocks	Basalt			17 - 22	40-50
	Chalk			10 - 13	30-40
	Granite			17 - 20	45-50
	Limestone			16 - 19	35-40
	Sandstone			13 - 17	35-45
	Shale		undrained	16 - 20	30-35
Cohesive / Mud - clay	Soft bentonite		10 - 20	6 - 13	7-13
	Very soft organic clay		10 -30	6 - 14	12-16
	Soft slightly organic clay		20 -50	10 - 16	17-22
	Soft glacial clay		30 - 70	12 - 17	22-28
	Stiff glacial clay		70 - 150	17 - 20	20-25
	Glacial till of mixed grain size		150-250	20 - 23	27-32
Unweathered rock	Hard igneous: Granite, Basalt, Porphyry		35000 - 55000	25 - 30	35-45
	Metamorphic: Quartzite, Gneiss, Slate		20000 - 40000	25 - 28	30-40
	Sedimentary (hard): Limestone, Dolomite, Sandstone		10000 - 30000	23 - 28	35-45
	Sedimentary (soft): Sandstone, Chalk, Shale, Coal		1000 - 20000	17 - 23	25-35

2-9 Engineering properties of soils and rocks

The engineering properties of rocks are best defined by the following parameters:

- *Poison's ratio:* an elastic parameter corresponding to the ratio of lateral strain to axial strain in the direction of a given uniaxial stress change (see figure opposite):

$$v = -\frac{\varepsilon_r}{\varepsilon_1} \qquad (2.77)$$

(compressive strains are positive). Poisson ratio can be negative for foam material (a compressive uniaxial stress can cause a reduction in volume),

- *Elasticity modulus E* as defined earlier (see table 2.2),

- *Bulk modulus:* a parameter linking the elasticity modulus to Poisson's ratio as follows:

$$K = \frac{E}{3(1-2v)}, \qquad (2.78)$$

- *Shear modulus* reflecting the effect of shear stress and expressed as follows:

$$G = \frac{E}{2(1+v)}. \qquad (2.79)$$

Average values of different engineering parameters of *intact rocks* are summarised in table 2.4. These values should be used cautiously so as to take into account, when applicable, any regional variations due to a loss of structural integrity of the rock mass.

The different parameters and corresponding units used in the table are as follows:

G_s : specific gravity,
w_s (%) : saturation moisture content,
ϕ' (°) : angle of shearing resistance,
c' (MN/m^2) : cohesion under zero normal stress $(1\ MN/m^2 = 10^3 kN/m^2)$,
$t(MN/m^2)$: tensile strength as per figure 2.40,
$E(GN/m^2)$: elasticity (or Young's) modulus $(1\ GN/m^2 = 10^6 KN/m^2)$,
$K(GN/m^2)$: bulk modulus,
$G(GN/m^2)$: shear modulus,
v : Poisson's ratio.

Table 2.4: Average value of engineering properties of some rocks

		G_s	w_s	ϕ'	c'	t	E	K	G	ν
Igneous	granite	2.7	0.5	55	35	15	75	50	30	0.25
	basalt	2.9	1	50	40	15	90	80	34.5	0.31
Sedimentary	hard limeston	2.7	1.5	35	30	10	60	40	24	
	hard sanstone	2.8	5	45	15	5	30	20	12	0.23
	soft limestone	2.4	8	35	5	2	15	10	6	
	soft sandstone	2.5	14	40	4	1	4	2.7	1.6	to
	chalk	2.3	19	25	3	0.3	6	4	2.4	
	mudstone	2.3	5	30	N/A	N/A	10	6.7	4	0.26
	hard shale	2.3	8	25	N/A	N/A	2	1.3	0.8	
Metamorphic	shist	2.8	1.5	25	10	3	20	17.5	7.6	0.30
	gneiss	2.8	0.5	30	30	10	45	39.5	17.2	
	marble	2.6	0.5	35	32	10	60	52.6	22.9	to
	slate	2.7	0.5	25	25	10	30	26.3	11.5	0.32

Similarly, *average values* of different engineering parameters corresponding to different types of soils are presented in table 2.5

Table 2.5: Average value of some engineering properties of soils

	$w_s(\%)$	G_s	$\phi'(°)$	$E(MN/m^2)$	ν
dense sand	15	2.6	38 to 45	35 to 55	0.3 to 0.45
medium dense	to	to	35 to 40	17 to 28	0.25 to 0.4
loose sand	30	2.7	28 to 35	10 to 24	0.2 to 0.4
silty sand	10 to 20	2.65	23 to 28	10 to 17	0.2 to 0.4
stiff clay	20	2.65	19 to 24	10 to 25	0.2
firm clay	to	to	20 to 25	5 to 10	to
soft clay	30	2.75	22 to 28	2 to 5	0.5
organic silts	40 to 80				
organic clays	50 to 100	*very poor engineering properties*			
peat	500 to 1000				

Problems

2.1   A series of *drained* triaxial tests were undertaken on samples of a
normally consolidated clay. At failure, the following results were
measured in terms of radial and deviator stresses :

$\sigma_3 (kN/m^2)$	50	100	150	200
$q (kN/m^2)$	64	129	193	257

Plot these results as the variation of deviator stress *versus* the
mean effective stress at failure, then estimate the effective angle of
shearing resistance of the clay.

Ans : $\phi' \approx 23°$

2.2   Four shear box tests were performed on a clean dense sand, under
four different values of effective vertical stresses. The
corresponding peak shear stresses are as follows.

$\sigma_1' (kN/m^2)$	30	60	90	120
$\tau_{max} (kN/m^2)$	28	63	96	120

Estimate the effective angle of friction at the critical density,
knowing that, on average, the sand has a maximum dilation angle
$\upsilon_{max} = 10°$.

Ans : $\phi_c' \approx 35°$

2.3   A drained triaxial test is to be performed on a *76 mm* long, *38 mm*
diameter sample of firm clay with a coefficient of vertical
consolidation $c_v = 2.7\, m^2/y$.

(a) Knowing that the minimum shear speed that can be generated
by the testing equipment is $v_{min} = 6 \times 10^{-4}\, mm/min$, assume the
sample will only be drained at both ends then check if the
requirement of a minimum excess porewater pressure dissipation
$U = 97\%$ beyond an initial axial deformation $\varepsilon_1 = 0.003$ can be
fulfilled.
(b) Will the shear speed be adequate to fulfil the same
requirements were the sample to be drained radially as well as
vertically ?
(c) Plot the corresponding graphs of porewater pressure dissipation
versus axial strain.

Ans :   (a) $v = 7.3 \times 10^{-5}\, mm/min < 6 \times 10^{-4}\, mm/min$ (inadequate)
(b) $v = 9.83 \times 10^{-4}\, mm/min$ (adequate)

2.4   Two samples of a normally consolidated clay were consolidated in triaxial cells under different cell pressures σ_3, then sheared under undrained conditions by gradually increasing the deviator stress q while keeping σ_3 constant. The values at failure of the measured deviator stress q_f and the porewater pressure u_f were as follows.

$\sigma_3 \, (kN/m^2)$	$q_f (kN/m^2)$	$u_f (kN/m^2)$
200	120	96
300	203	123

(a) Determine the shear strength parameters of the clay c' and ϕ'.
(b) Calculate the shear and effective normal stresses at failure for both tests.

Ans: (a) $c' = 0$, $\phi' = 21.4°$

(b) $\sigma_3 \, (kN/m^2)$	$\tau_f (kN/m^2)$	$\sigma'_f (kN/m^2)$
200	55.9	142.5
300	94.5	241.1

2.5   Two undrained triaxial tests were carefully undertaken on two clay samples A and B, which were consolidated then sheared under the respective (constant) cell pressures $\sigma_{3A} = 80 \, kN/m^2$ and $\sigma_{3B} = 250 \, kN/m^2$. The results were measured in terms of deviator stress and porewater pressure as follows.
sample A:

$q (kN/m^2)$	0	80	112	138	145
$u (kN/m^2)$	0	16	18	5	-12

sample B:

$q (kN/m^2)$	0	100	150	180	190	195
$u (kN/m^2)$	0	30	55	88	100	105

(a) Plot the effective and total stress paths in (q,p') and (q,p) spaces.

(b) Calculate the porewater pressure parameter at failure A_f and comment on the state of the clay.

Ans: (a) Sample A: $A_f = -0.08$
(b) Sample B: $A_f = 0.54$

References

Azizi, F. and Josseaume, H. (1988) *Loi de comportement des sols raides: détermination de la courbe d'état limite de l'argile verte de Romainville.* Rapport des Laboratoires des Ponts et Chaussées, Série Géotechnique, GT-33.

Berre, T. (1981) *Triaxial Testing at the Norwegian Geotechnical Institute.* N.G.I. Publication 134, Oslo.

Bishop, A. W. and Henkel, D. J. (1962) *The Measurement of Soil Properties in the Triaxial Test, 2nd edn.* Arnold, London. In Soils and Rocks. ICE, London, pp. 251–264.

Bjerrum, L. (1973) *Problems of soil mechanics and construction on soft clays and structurally unstable soils (collapsible, expansive and others).* Proceedings of the 8th I.C.S.M.F.E, Moscow, pp. 111–160.

Bjerrum, L. and Kenny, T. C. (1967) *Effect of structure on the shear behaviour of normally consolidated quick clays.* Proceedings of the Oslo Conference on Geotechnics, Vol. 2, pp. 19–27.

Gibson, R. E. and Henkel, D. J. (1954) *Influence of duration of tests at constant rate of strain on measured drained strength.* Géotechnique (4), pp. 6–15.

Henkel, D. J. (1957) *Investigation of two long term failures in London clay slopes at Wood Green and Northolt.* Proceedings of the 4th I.C.S.M.F.E, London, pp. 315–320.

Jaky, J. (1944) *The coefficient of earth pressure at rest.* Journal of the Society of Hungarian Architects and Engineers, 78 (22), pp. 355–358.

Josseaume, H. and Azizi, F. (1991) *Détermination expérimentale de la courbe d'état limite d'une argile raide très plastique: l'argile verte du Sannoisien.* Revue Française de Géotechnique, 54, pp. 13–25.

Lupini, J. F., Skinner, A. E. and Vaughan, P. R. (1981) *The drained residual strength of cohesive soils.* Géotechnique, 31 (2), pp. 181–213.

Mayne, P. W. and Kulhawy, F. H. (1982) *Relationships in soil.* ASCE Journal, 108, GT6, pp. 851–872.

Palladino, D. J. and Peck, R. B. (1972) *Slope failures in an overconsolidated clay in Seattle, Washington.* Géotechnique, 22 (4), pp. 563–595.

Simpson, B., Calabresi, G., Sommer, H. and Wallays, M. (1979) *Design parameters for stiff clays. General report.* Proceedings of the 7th European Conference on Soil Mechanics and Foundation Engineering, Brighton, Vol. 5, pp. 91–125.

Skempton, A. W. (1954) *The pore pressure coefficients A and B.* Géotechnique, 4 (4), pp. 143–147.

Skempton, A. W. (1957) *Discussion on the Planning and Design of the New Hong Kong Airport.* Proceedings of the I.C.E, Vol. 7, pp. 305–307.

Skempton, A. W. (1964) *Long term stability of clay slopes.* Géotechnique, 14 (2), pp. 77–102.

Skempton, A. W. and Bjerrum, L. (1957) *A contribution to the settlement analysis of foundations on clay.* Géotechnique, 7 (4), pp. 168–178.

Skempton, A. W., and La Rochelle, P. (1965). *The Bradwell slip: a short term failure in London clay.* Géotechnique, 15 (3), pp. 221–242.

Wroth, C. P. (1984) *The interpretation of in situ tests.* 24th Rankine Lecture. Géotechnique, 34 (4), pp. 449–489.

CHAPTER 3

The stability of slopes

3.1 Slope instability

Instability of natural slopes (generally the product of erosion), or artificial slopes (created by cuttings, excavations or the building of embankments for instance) results in most cases of a combination of gravitational forces and water pressures. Accordingly, when it occurs, failure involves a mass of soil within which the forces due to gravity (*i.e.* the weight of soil mass) are out of balance. The presence of water, if anything, increases the imbalance since it plays the role of a lubricant at the surface along which the soil mass is moving, gradually increasing its velocity and leading ultimately to total failure. The mechanisms by which failure occurs differ depending on the nature and state of soil. Figure 3.1 depicts a translational slip whereby the failure surface is for all intents and purposes parallel to the slope, and the movement of the failing soil mass consists mainly of a translation.

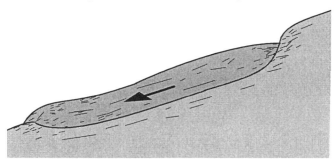

Figure 3.1: Translational slope failure.

On the other hand, figure 3.2 illustrates an almost circular slip surface where failure occurs mainly through rotation of the volume of the failing soil. As will be seen shortly, the position of the centre of rotation plays an important role in the stability analysis of such slopes. In both cases, failure occurs (theoretically) once the driving shear forces due to the weight of the moving soil mass become equal to, if not larger than, the resisting intrinsic shear forces that the soil possesses. In stress terms, if the shear stress *mobilised* by the failing soil mass at its base is τ_{mob}, and if the shear *strength* of soil is referred to as τ_f, then the *factor of safety* against shear failure is simply defined as:

$$F = \frac{\tau_f}{\tau_{mob}} \qquad (3.1)$$

Accordingly, failure occurs (in theory) when $F \le 1$. In practice though, failure is related more to the velocity with which the failing block of soil is moving; in this respect, experimental evidence shows that failures *do* occur for slopes with factors of safety of up to 1.25 as indicated in figure 3.3 (Pouget *et al.* (1985)).

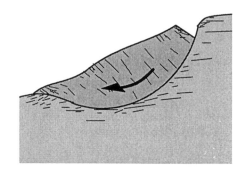

Figure 3.2: Rotational slope failure.

Notwithstanding the purely informative nature of the graph, it is tempting to assume that slopes with a factor of safety $F \ge 1.25$ are stable. However, such an assumption is *only realistic* as long as parameters *representative* of soil behaviour are used in the calculation. Several instances of slope failure occurring with a factor of safety of 1.5 or more were reported in the literature (see for instance Skempton (1964), Skempton and La Rochelle (1965), Palladino and Peck (1972)). In all cases, wrong shear strength values (usually overestimates) were used in the calculations. Potential problems related to the determination of soil parameters based on laboratory measurements were highlighted in section 2.6 (chapter 2). In particular, one has to remember that the undrained shear strength c_u of a (stiff) clay, measured in the laboratory on a small size sample often represents an overestimate of the actual c_u value *in situ*, because it is unlikely that a small sample would contain fissures that characterise a thick stiff clay layer in the field.

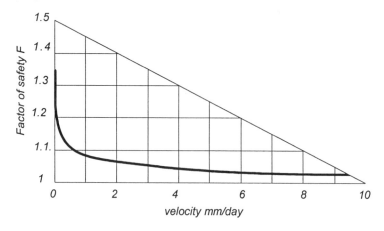

Figure 3.3 : Relationship between slope velocity and factor of safety.
(Reproduced by permission of the Laboratoire Central des Ponts et Chaussées.)

It is therefore essential to bear in mind that the outcome of any design method depends entirely on the soil parameters used. This, in turn, indicates that not only the designer must master design techniques, but equally important, he (she) must be careful when selecting reliable values of relevant soil parameters. Accordingly, the selection of appropriate and reliable soil strength parameters is not an option, but rather a precondition to a 'safe' design. This selection depends on the *state* of the soil (*i.e.* overconsolidated or normally consolidated, dense or loose), on drainage conditions, and on failure criteria. Thus, if failure is predicted to occur under drained conditions along an old slip surface, then the residual angle of shearing resistance will be most appropriate for the design, and the soil shear strength is calculated as follows:

$$\tau_f = \sigma'_n \tan \phi'_r \qquad\qquad (3.2)$$

If, on the other hand, failure would occur within a soil mass that has never experienced failure in the past then, *à priori,* it would be appropriate to select the peak angle of shearing resistance in conjunction with overconsolidated or dense soils, or the critical angle if the soil is normally consolidated or loose (see figures 2.1 and 2.6) . However, in practice, it is advisable to use the critical angle, so that for normally consolidated or lightly overconsolidated clays, as well as for (dense and loose) sands, the drained shear strength is estimated from equation 2.8:

$$\tau_f = \sigma'_n \tan \phi'_c \qquad\qquad (3.3)$$

For heavily overconsolidated clays, the drained shear strength might be affected by the apparent cohesion, so that:

$$\tau_f = c' + \sigma'_n \tan \phi'_c \qquad\qquad (3.4)$$

For slow draining soils (mainly clays), the excess porewater pressure generated at the onset of loading may create conditions whereby failure can take place in the short term (that is before the occurrence of any significant dissipation of excess porewater pressure). In which case, the undrained shear strength c_u must be used as in equation 2.21:

$$\tau_f = c_u \qquad\qquad (3.5)$$

The following slope stability analyses are based on equations 3.3 to 3.5.

3.2 Stability of infinite slopes

3.2.1 General case of flow

Slopes with a failure mechanism such as the one depicted in figure 3.1 are often assumed to be of infinite length because of the usually large ratio of slip plane length to its depth. Consequently, the soil behaviour is modelled according to figure 3.4, whereby the potential slip plane, situated at a depth z, is assumed to be parallel to the ground surface, sloping at an angle β.

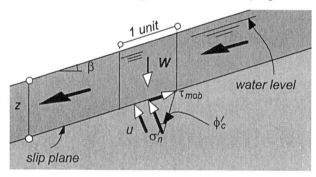

Figure 3.4: General case of an infinitely long slope and failure criteria.

Moreover, it is seen that (irrespective of the direction in which water is flowing), provided the pressure head h_p is constant along the slip plane, then the porewater pressure u can be estimated as follows:

$$u = h_p \gamma_w \tag{3.6}$$

γ_w being the unit weight of water. In the case of a purely frictional material (i.e. $c' = 0$), the shear strength at failure is related to the effective normal stress according to equation 3.3. On the other hand, for an element of soil 1-unit long, 1-unit wide and z units deep as the one depicted in figure 3.4, the equilibrium requirements are such that:

$$\sigma'_n + u = W\cos\beta \tag{3.7}$$

$$\tau_{mob} = W\sin\beta \tag{3.8}$$

where τ_{mob} is the mobilised shear stress. The total weight W of the element is calculated as follows:

$$W = 1 \times 1 \times z\gamma \, \cos\beta \tag{3.9}$$

with γ being the total unit weight of soil (*i.e.* neglecting the difference between bulk and saturated unit weights). The shear strength of equation 3.3 can now be expressed as follows:

$$\tau_f = \sigma'_n \tan\phi'_c = [(W\cos\beta) - u]\tan\phi'_c$$

Thus, substituting for W from equation 3.9 into the expression of τ_f and τ_{mob}, then rearranging, it is straightforward to show that equation 3.1 reduces to:

$$F = \frac{\tau_f}{\tau_m} = \frac{\tan\phi'_c}{\tan\beta}\left(1 - \frac{u}{z\gamma\cos^2\beta}\right) \tag{3.10}$$

now, introducing u from equation 3.6, it follows that:

$$F = \frac{\tan\phi'_c}{\tan\beta}\left(1 - \frac{\gamma_w h_p}{z\gamma\cos^2\beta}\right) \tag{3.11}$$

The factor of safety therefore depends on the slope angle β, the depth of the slip plane z and the pressure head h_p. To establish the expression of h_p, consider the general case of flow sketched in figure 3.5, whereby the sliding soil mass of thickness z, through which water is flowing at an angle α to the horizontal, is assumed to be dry at the top, up to a depth z_w. If a standpipe is inserted to the depth of the slip plane, the water would rise to the depicted height h_p. Hence from the geometry of the figure:

$$h_p = (z - z_w)\frac{\cos\beta\cos\alpha}{\cos(\alpha - \beta)} \tag{3.12}$$

Substituting for h_p into equation 3.11, the general expression of the factor of safety in the case of a slope of infinite extent in a frictional soil affected by water seepage, is then established:

$$F = \frac{\tan\phi'_c}{\tan\beta}\left[1 - \frac{\gamma_w}{\gamma}\frac{\cos\alpha}{\cos\beta\cos(\alpha - \beta)}\left(1 - \frac{z_w}{z}\right)\right] \tag{3.13}$$

Clearly, the factor of safety depends on the *direction of flow*.

3.2.2 Flow parallel to the slope

In this case the angles α and β are identical, and equation 3.13 reduces to the following:

$$F = \frac{\tan\phi'_c}{\tan\beta}\left[1 - \frac{\gamma_w}{\gamma}\left(1 - \frac{z_w}{z}\right)\right] \tag{3.14}$$

so that for a dry slope ($z_w = z$), the factor of safety is:

$$F = \frac{\tan \phi'_c}{\tan \beta}$$
(3.15)

Similarly, for a waterlogged slope ($z_w = 0$):

$$F = \frac{\tan \phi'_c}{\tan \beta}\left(1 - \frac{\gamma_w}{\gamma}\right)$$
(3.16)

On the other hand, assuming a ratio $\frac{\gamma_w}{\gamma} \approx \frac{1}{2}$, then equation 3.14 can be expressed as follows:

$$F = \frac{1}{2}\frac{\tan \phi'_c}{\tan \beta}\left(1 + \frac{z_w}{z}\right)$$
(3.17)

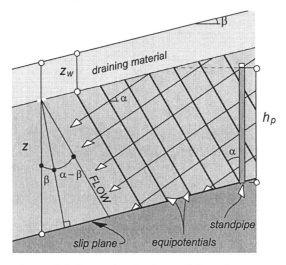

Figure 3.5: General water flow within a slope.

The latter equation shows that, when the water is flowing parallel to the slope, the factor of safety is proportional to the ratio of the depth z_w of the water table (measured from the ground surface) to the thickness z of the sliding soil layer. Under such circumstances, the value of the factor of safety can be determined using the charts in figure 3.6 which are used in a straightforward way, in that for a soil having a critical angle of shearing resistance ϕ'_c and sloping at an angle β, the value F' is read on the appropriate (interpolated if need be) curve, and the factor of safety F is thereafter calculated as follows:

$$F = F'\left(1 + \frac{z_w}{z}\right)$$
(3.18)

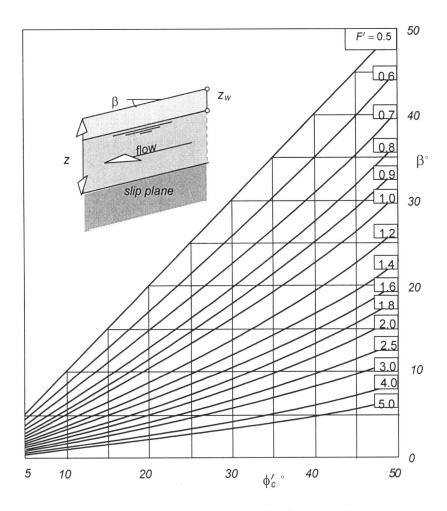

Figure 3.6: Charts for the calculation of the factor of safety for infinite slopes with water flowing parallel to the slope.

3.2.3 Horizontal flow

A horizontal flow implies an angle $\alpha = 0$ (refer to figure 3.5), in which case equation 3.13 yields:

$$F = \frac{\tan \phi_c'}{\tan \beta}\left[1 - \frac{\gamma_w}{\gamma}\frac{1}{\cos^2\beta}\left(1 - \frac{z_w}{z}\right)\right] \qquad (3.19)$$

3.2.4 Vertical (downward) flow

The slope is, in this case, waterlogged meaning that $z_w = 0$ and, since the angle $\alpha = \pi/2$, equation 3.13 is then written as follows:

$$F = \tan\phi'_c / \tan\beta \qquad (3.20)$$

Notice that equations 3.20 and 3.15 are identical, indicating that the stability of the slope is *not* affected by water seepage in the case of a vertical downward flow.

3.3 Effect of cohesion on the stability of infinite slopes

For heavily overconsolidated clays, the drained shear strength is affected by the apparent cohesion. However, the stability analysis is not altered a great deal; the reason being that, while the *mobilised* shear stress within the soil mass remains the same as defined by equation 3..8, the shear strength is now given by equation 3.4. Thus, substituting for τ_f from equation 3.4 into equation 3.10, it can readily be shown that the factor of safety is as follows:

$$F = \frac{c'}{z\gamma\sin\beta\cos\beta} + \frac{\tan\phi'_c}{\tan\beta}\left[1 - \frac{\gamma_w}{\gamma}\frac{\cos\alpha}{\cos\beta\cos(\alpha-\beta)}\left(1 - \frac{z_w}{z}\right)\right] \qquad (3.21)$$

with z and z_w as per figure 3.5.

A comparison of equations 3.21 and 3.13 shows that, for cohesive soils, the factor of safety against sliding is simply increased by an amount $2c'/z\gamma\sin 2\beta$ as opposed to a granular soil. For instance, a slope inclined at an angle $\beta = 15°$ to the horizontal, in a soil characterised by a cohesion $c' = 10\,kN/m^2$ and a total unit weight $\gamma = 20\,kN/m^3$ with a 6 m deep slip plane, will have its factor of safety against sliding increased by an appreciable value of 0.33, irrespective of the flow direction or the water level within the slope.

Example 3.1

The frictional soil of a waterlogged slope, inclined at an angle $\beta = 15°$ to the horizontal, is characterised by a critical angle of shearing resistance $\phi'_c = 32°$ ($c' = 0$). *In situ* tests, undertaken at different locations, indicated the presence of a layer of fissured hard rock at a depth $z = 5m$, running parallel to the surface. Also, piezometer readings indicated that water is flowing parallel to the slope. Required are:
- (a) the factor of safety against sliding under the stated conditions;
- (b) the depth z_w to which the water table must be lowered if a minimum factor of safety $F = 1.5$ were needed.

•(a) First, estimate the constant F' from the charts of figure 3.6: for $\phi'_c = 32°$ and $\beta = 15°$, $F' \approx 1.2$. From the supplied information, the top of the rock layer represents an obvious potential slip plane, hence $z = 5\,m$ and $z_w = 0$ (waterlogged slope). From equation 8.18, the factor of safety is:

$$F = F'\left(1 + \frac{z_w}{z}\right) = 1.2$$

This value suggests that the slope is unstable (bear in mind that a minimum factor of safety of 1.25 is needed).

•(b) This time, a factor of safety $F = 1.5$ is required. Hence, making use of equation 3.18, it follows that: $1.5 = 1.2 \times (1 + \frac{z_w}{5})$ or alternatively: $z_w = 5 \times (\frac{1.5}{1.25} - 1) = 1\,m$. Thus, the water table must be lowered by 1 m for the factor of safety to meet the stated requirement.

Example 3.2

The clayey soil of a natural slope, inclined at an angle $\beta = 12°$ to the horizontal, is characterised by a residual angle of shearing resistance $\phi'_r = 14°$ ($c' = 0$). A thorough site investigation revealed the presence of an old shallow slip plane, running roughly parallel to the slope, and situated at a depth $z = 3\,m$. The water table is at a depth $z_w = 1.5\,m$ below ground level, and the flow is assumed to be parallel to the slope. From the charts of figure 3.6, it is seen that:

$$\phi'_r = 14°, \quad \beta = 12° \quad \Rightarrow \quad F' = 0.6.$$

Equation 3.18 then yields the following factor of safety:

$$F = F'\left(1 + \frac{z_w}{z}\right) = 0.6 \times \left(1 + \frac{1.5}{3}\right) = 0.9$$

indicating that the slope is actually failing.

3.4 Undrained analysis of the stability of infinite slopes

For slopes undertaken in clays, the excess porewater pressure generated during construction, or a short time after the end of construction (that is a few days or even few weeks), may trigger failure. Given the short time during which failure occurs, the excess porewater pressure remains virtually unchanged, and the soil resistance is provided by the undrained shear strength c_u as per equation 3.5. Knowing that under undrained conditions, the angle of shearing resistance is $\phi_u = 0$, then substituting for c_u in equation 3.21 yields the following expression of the factor of safety of an infinite slope, with an angle β, under undrained conditions:

$$F = \frac{c_u}{2\gamma \cos \beta \sin \beta} = \frac{c_u}{\gamma \sin 2\beta} \qquad (3.22)$$

3.5 Stability of slopes with a circular failure surface

3.5.1 Total stress analysis

The shape of the failure surface such as the one illustrated in figure 3..2 is often assumed to be circular. The slip circle, as opposed to the sliding surface analysed earlier, involves a larger volume of soil and occurs, usually, in steeper slopes. The analysis at failure of such slopes consists mainly of finding the most unfavourable slip circle corresponding to the smallest value of the factor of safety. Moreover, because of the nature of the sliding surface, failure can occur in the short term under undrained conditions, or in the long term when any excess porewater pressure will have dissipated. Accordingly, separate analyses involving either total stresses (for the short term) or effective stresses (for the long term) must be undertaken. Consider, for instance, the short term undrained behaviour of an embankment at the end of its (rapid) construction. Based on the previous analysis, it is seen that the shear strength of a fully saturated clay is represented by equation 3.5. Moreover, figure 3.7 shows that the instability of the slope is mainly due to the total weight W of the sliding soil mass (including any surcharge when applicable).

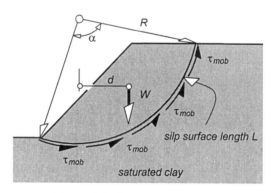

Figure 3.7: Circular slip surface.

The shear stress mobilised throughout the length L of the (circular) slip surface is related to the shear strength of the clay through equation 3.1:

$$\tau_{mob} = \frac{\tau_f}{F}$$

Now, considering the equilibrium of moments with respect to the centre of rotation in figure 3.7, it follows that:

$$Wd = \tau_{mob} LR \tag{3.23}$$

But the length of the slip surface is $L = R\alpha$. Hence, substituting for τ_{mob} and L into equation 3.23, then rearranging:

$$F = \frac{c_u R^2 \alpha}{Wd} \tag{3.24}$$

The factor of safety is related to the slip circle through the radius R and the angle α. Consequently, it is imperative to find the *smallest* value of F, locating in the meantime the likely slip surface. Although there may be cases whereby the location of the critical slip circle can roughly be guessed, the task of finding the minimum factor of safety is usually undertaken using a trial and error approach which can be tedious and might involve the use of literally dozens, sometimes in excess of a hundred, different potential slip circles (as opposed to the three depicted in figure 3.8, used to illustrate the method). Obviously, this type of analysis is generally undertaken numerically.

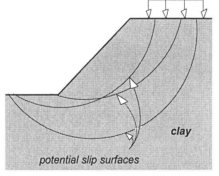

Figure 3.8: Determination of the critical slip circle.

For the specific case whereby the slope instability occurs within a layer of *homogeneous* soil, underlain by a layer of *hard* soil (such as rock), the charts produced by Taylor in 1948 and depicted in figure 3.9 can be useful. These charts were developed in terms of total stresses, and relate the *stability number N* to the *depth factor D* (refer to figure 8.9) and to the slope angle β. The *minimum* factor of safety is thereafter calculated as follows:

$$F_{min} = \frac{c_u}{N \gamma H} \tag{3.25}$$

where γ represents the bulk unit weight of soil and H is the slope height as per figure 3.9.

Consider for instance, the case of a slope with a height $H = 8\,m$, an angle $\beta = 35°$, and a depth coefficient $D = 2$, made in a clay having an undrained shear strength $c_u = 50\,kN/m^2$ and a bulk unit weight $\gamma = 20\,kN/m^3$. Figure 3.9 yields, in this case, a stability number $N \approx 0.178$. Thus, the *minimum* factor of safety for the slope is:

$$F_{min} = \frac{50}{0.178 \times 20 \times 8} = 1.75$$

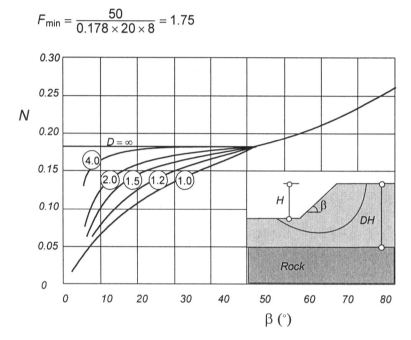

Figure 3.9: Taylor stability numbers for total stress analysis of slopes.

3.5.2 Effective stress analysis: Bishop's procedure

In considering the long term stability of a slope, the *excess* porewater pressure is presumed to have all but dissipated and, accordingly, an effective stress analysis becomes a necessity. The aim being, as in the case of total stress analysis, to determine precisely the critical *circular* slip surface and through it the minimum factor of safety that must be used for design. This implies that the porewater pressure must be evaluated at any point so that the corresponding effective stress can be calculated. Figure 3.10 depicts a slope with the water table as shown. If the water is assumed to be *static* (*i.e. no seepage*), then for any selected vertical element (or slice) within the failing soil mass, such as the one illustrated in the figure, the corresponding porewater pressure at base level can be estimated as follows:

$$u \approx z_w \gamma_w \tag{3.26}$$

where z_w represents the piezometric height of water and γ_w is the unit weight of water.

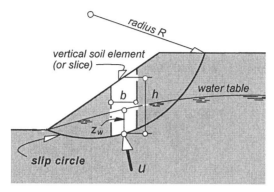

Figure 3.10: Evaluation of the porewater pressure at the base of a soil element in the case of a static water table.

The effective stress analysis can then begin in earnest, knowing that the failure criterion is represented in its general form by equation 3.4:

$$\tau_f = c' + \sigma'_n \tan \phi'_c$$

so that the mobilised shear stress is obtained by reducing τ_f by an adequate factor of safety according to equation 3.1:

$$\tau_{mob} = \frac{c'}{F} + \frac{\sigma'_n \tan \phi'}{F} \tag{3.27}$$

With reference to figure 3.11, let the entire soil mass above the slip circle be on the verge of failure, then consider in isolation, an element of a base length l, *one unit wide*, and having a total weight w. Since the element is on the verge of failure, equilibrium requires that vertical forces, as well as moments with respect to the centre of rotation O, must balance. Hence solving for moments for all elements into which the soil mass is divided, it follows that:

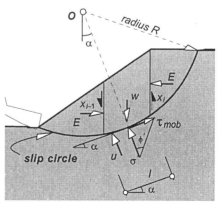

Figure 3.11: Stresses related to a slip circle failure mechanism.

$$\Sigma \tau_{mob} / R = \Sigma wR \sin \alpha \tag{3.28}$$

Moreover, the equilibrium of vertical forces requires that:

$$w + (x_{i-1} - x_i) = (\sigma' + u) l \cos \alpha + \tau_{mob} l \sin \alpha \tag{3.29}$$

The tangential forces x_i are unknown, however the equilibrium would not be affected in any significant way were the quantity $(x_{i-1} - x_i)$ to be neglected (in fact an error estimated at less than 1% would be incurred by ignoring the latter quantity (see Bishop and Morgenstern (1960), for instance). Also, according to equation 3.27, the effective normal stress is such that:

$$\sigma'_n = \frac{\tau_{mob} F - c'}{\tan \phi'_c} \tag{3.30}$$

Thus, neglecting the quantity $(x_i - x_{i-1})$, then substituting for σ'_n from equation 3.30 into equation 3.29 yields:

$$\tau_{mob} = \frac{(w - ub) + \dfrac{c'b}{\tan \phi'}}{Fl\left(\dfrac{\sin \alpha}{F} + \dfrac{\cos \alpha}{\tan \phi'} \right)} \tag{3.31}$$

with $b = l \cos \alpha$.

Inserting the quantity τ_{mob} from equation 3.31 into equation 3.28, then rearranging, it follows that:

$$F = \frac{1}{\Sigma w \sin \alpha} \Sigma \left\{ \left[c'b + w\left(1 - \frac{ub}{w} \right) \tan \phi' \right] \frac{1}{\cos \alpha + \dfrac{\tan \phi' \sin \alpha}{F}} \right\} \tag{3.32}$$

Now introducing the pore pressure ratio as defined by Bishop and Morgenstern (1960):

$$r_u = \frac{ub}{w} = \frac{u}{\gamma h} \tag{3.33}$$

where γ corresponds to the appropriate soil unit weight (*i.e.* bulk or saturated) and h is the height of the element as per figure 3.10. Equation 3.32 can then be rewritten as follows:

$$F = \frac{1}{\Sigma w \sin \alpha} \Sigma \left\{ [c'b + w(1 - r_u) \tan \phi'] \frac{1}{\cos \alpha + \dfrac{\sin \alpha \tan \phi'}{F}} \right\} \tag{3.34}$$

Equation 3.34 corresponds to the general expression of the factor of safety used in conjunction with Bishop's method of analysis of the stability of slopes (see also Bishop (1955)). The method is one of the most widely used in engineering practice because of its adaptability; and notwithstanding the fact that more sophisticated (and somewhat complex) methods have been developed (see for instance Morgenstern and Price (1965), Spencer (1967)), it remains one of the most reliable methods in use. Notice that, because the factor of safety F appears on both sides of equation 3.34, an iterative procedure is therefore required to solve it, and the details of the calculations (which are usually undertaken numerically) are presented in the following worked example.

Example 3.3

Consider the case of a slope made in a multi-layered soil consisting of a top layer of soft clay overlaying a thick layer of a moderately firm clay. Both clays have the same bulk unit weight $\gamma = 20\,kN/m^3$, and the slope geometry is as depicted in figure 3.12. Let us now apply a Bishop type effective stress analysis to assess (if only partly) the long term stability of the cut, assuming that the water table is well below the excavation base.

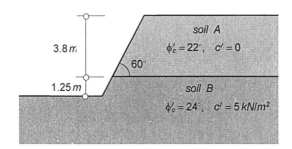

Figure 3.12: Slope geometry and soil characteristics.

In essence, the method aims at finding the most critical slip circle, and this can only be achieved through trial and error by selecting several (sometimes in excess of a hundred) different slip circles until the one yielding a minimum factor of safety is located. Two of these potential slip circles are depicted in figure 3.13 for purely illustrative purposes. Since the aim of this worked example is to present the working of the method, rather than to find the critical slip circle (which would be a tedious task to achieve using hand calculations anyway!), let us concentrate on one slip surface such as circle 1 in figure 3.13, and calculate the corresponding factor of safety.

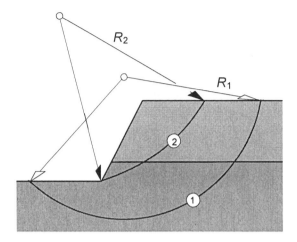

Figure 3.13: Selection of potential failure surfaces.

The procedure, as described earlier, consists of subdividing the (potentially) failing soil surface into vertical elements or slices. Because no restriction of any type is imposed on the selection of elements, and to make the hand calculations more palatable, five elements are selected as depicted in figure 3.14. Notice that the base of each element is assumed to be planar; this does not alter the accuracy of the outcome of the analysis in any way, if only because the circular shape of the slip surface 1 in figure 3.13 is roughly preserved.

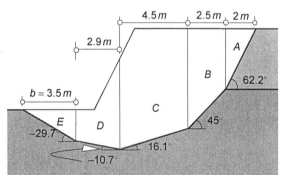

Figure 3.14: Selection of vertical slices.

Some of the most relevant dimensions are indicated in figure 3.14, so that the quantities needing to be used in conjunction with the iterative procedure related to equation 3.34 can be summarised as follows.

slice	$w(kN/m)$	$\phi'(°)$	$c'(kN/m^2)$	$b(m)$	$\alpha(°)$	$w\sin\alpha(kN/m)$
A	76	22	0	2.0	62.2	67.2
B	252.5	24	5	2.5	45.0	178.5
C	606.5	24	5	4.5	16.1	168.2
D	187.9	24	5	2.9	-10.7	-34.9
E	70	24	5	3.5	-29.7	-34.7

Whence the (constant) quantity: $\Sigma w\sin\alpha = 344.3\,kN/m$.

The iterative calculations can now be undertaken, and consist of:

- choosing an initial factor of safety (usually $F = 1$);
- calculating, for each slice, the quantity $m_\alpha = \cos\alpha + \dfrac{\tan\phi_c' \sin\alpha}{F}$;
- estimating, for each slice, the value $\xi = \dfrac{1}{m_\alpha}[c'b + w\tan\phi_c']$, knowing that the porewater pressure is, in this case, $u = 0$.

Accordingly, it is easy to show that, when an initial factor of safety $F = 1$ is selected, the calculations yield the following results.

slice	$m_\alpha = \cos\alpha + \dfrac{\tan\phi_c' \sin\alpha}{1}$	$\xi(kN/m)$
A	0.82	37
B	1.02	122
C	1.08	271
D	0.90	109
E	0.65	75

Thus:

$$\Sigma \frac{1}{m_\alpha}[c'b + w\tan\phi_c'] = \Sigma\xi = 614\,kN/m$$

leading to a new factor of safety, calculated according to equation 3.34:

$$F = \frac{614}{344.3} = 1.78$$

It is therefore seen that the calculated factor of safety differs markedly from the selected (initial) value $F = 1$. Consequently, one or more iterations are needed for convergence to occur (that is for the selected and calculated factors of safety to be almost identical).

Let the new selected value of F be the last calculated one: $F = 1.78$. Under such circumstances, the calculations, undertaken in exactly the same way as above are such that:

slice	$m_\alpha = \cos\alpha + \dfrac{\tan\phi'_c \sin\alpha}{1.78}$	$\xi\,(kN/m)$
A	0.67	46
B	0.88	142
C	1.03	284
D	0.94	104
E	0.74	66

Whence the sum: $\Sigma\xi = 642\ kN/m$

and the new factor of safety: $F = \dfrac{642}{344.3} = 1.86$

This value is larger than the initial value of 1.78, and therefore another iteration needs to be undertaken using the latest calculated value $F = 1.86$ to start the calculations:

slice	$m_\alpha = \cos\alpha + \dfrac{\tan\phi'_c \sin\alpha}{1.86}$	$\xi\,(kN/m)$
A	0.66	47
B	0.88	142
C	1.03	284
D	0.94	104
E	0.75	65

Hence the quantity: $\Sigma\xi = 642\ kN/m$

and the corresponding factor of safety: $F = \dfrac{642}{344.3} = 1.86$

Both selected and calculated values being identical, the factor of safety corresponding to the slip circle 1 in figure 3.13 is therefore $F = 1.86$. This value, however, does *not necessarily* correspond to the minimum factor of safety since the slip surface 1 is unlikely to be the most critical. The way to determine this critical surface consists of selecting several more potential circular slip surfaces and undertaking the same iterative calculations for each one of them until a minimum factor of safety is obtained. Clearly, this task would be difficult to achieve by hand calculations. Rather, the entire procedure can be programmed fairly easily.

3.5.3 Effect of porewater pressure on the long term stability of slopes

In the previous example, the water table was assumed to be well below the slip surface so that the analysis was not affected in any way by the porewater pressure. Now let the water table rise to the level depicted in figure 3.15, in a way that it can still be considered static (*i.e.* neglecting any seepage forces). Assuming that both bulk and saturated unit weights of the soil layers are identical $(\gamma = 20 kN/m^3)$, then the calculations of the factor of safety are undertaken in precisely the same way as previously except that, this time, the porewater pressure has to be evaluated for each element according to equation 3.26: $u = z_w \gamma_w$, where z_w is as per figure 3.15.

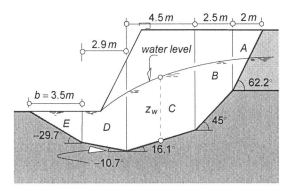

Figure 3.15: Effect of partial submersion of slopes on the overall stability.

In order to study the effect of porewater pressure on the stability, the same slip circle 1 in figure 3.13 has to be considered. Hence, with reference to figure 3.15, it follows that the total weight for each slice and the quantities $c'b$, as well as the sum $\Sigma w \sin \alpha$ have the same values as calculated previously for the dry slope. Accordingly, the quantities used in conjunction with equation 3.34 are as follows.

slice	$z_w (m)$	$u (kN/m^2)$	$ub (kN/m)$	$(w - ub) \tan \phi'_c (kN/m)$
A	0.7	7	14	25
B	2.5	25	62.5	83.6
C	3.7	37	166.5	193.5
D	2.2	22	63.8	54.6
E	1.0	10	35	15.4

The iterative calculations are identical to those corresponding to the dry case, except that the porewater pressure is now taken into account to estimate the factor of safety. Whence, starting with an initial factor of safety $F = 1$, the ensuing calculations yield the following:

slice	$m_\alpha = \cos\alpha + \dfrac{\tan\phi_c'\sin\alpha}{1}$	$\dfrac{1}{m_\alpha}[c'b + (w - ub)\tan\phi_c']\,(kN/m)$
A	0.82	30
B	1.02	94
C	1.08	200
D	0.90	77
E	0.65	51

leading to: $\displaystyle\sum \dfrac{1}{m_\alpha}[c'b + (w - ub)\tan\phi_c'] = 452\ kN/m$

Hence the corresponding calculated factor of safety:

$$F = \dfrac{452}{344.3} = 1.31$$

The calculated value of F being different from the chosen value of 1, more iterations are therefore needed to achieve convergence. Now let the chosen value be $F = 1.31$, whence:

slice	$m_\alpha = \cos\alpha + \dfrac{\tan\phi_c'\sin\alpha}{1.31}$	$\dfrac{1}{m_\alpha}[c'b + (w - ub)\tan\phi_c']\,(kN/m)$
A	0.74	34
B	0.94	102
C	1.05	205
D	0.92	75
E	0.70	47

and: $\displaystyle\sum \dfrac{1}{m_\alpha}[c'b + (w - ub)\tan\phi_c'] = 463\ kN/m$

yielding a factor of safety: $F = \dfrac{463}{344.3} = 1.34$

It can be shown that, were a new iteration to be undertaken with an initial factor of safety $F = 1.34$, then the ensuing calculated factor of safety will be $F = 1.345$. Accordingly, it is seen that, when dry, the slip surface has a factor of safety $F = 1.85$, which decreases dramatically to $F = 1.34$ if the water table were to rise to the level depicted in figure 3.15, partially submerging the slope. One therefore expects the factor of safety to decrease even further were the slope to be waterlogged. Consider the situation whereby the slope is totally submerged as illustrated in figure 3.16. Ignoring any seepage forces, and knowing that the total weight of individual slices, the quantities $c'b$, and the sum $\Sigma w \sin \alpha$ are all identical in value to the ones used in previous calculations, the basic quantities needed to start the iterative procedure related to equation 3.34 are then summarised as follows.

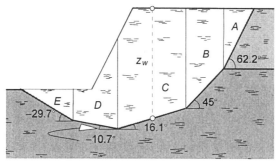

Figure 3.16: Waterlogged slope.

slice	z_w (m)	u (kN/m²)	ub (kN/m)	$(w-ub)\tan\phi'_c$ (kN/m)
A	1.9	19	38	15.3
B	5.05	50.5	126	55.5
C	6.73	67.3	303	133.5
D	3.25	32.5	94	41.2
E	1.00	10	35	15.4

Hence the following calculations using an initial factor of safety $F = 1$:

	$m_\alpha = \cos\alpha + \dfrac{\tan\phi'_c \sin\alpha}{1}$	$\dfrac{1}{m_\alpha}[c'b+(w-ub)\tan\phi'_c]$ (kN/m)
slice		
A	0.82	19
B	1.02	67
C	1.08	144
D	0.90	62
E	0.65	51

Therefore: $\Sigma \dfrac{1}{m_\alpha}[c'b+(w-ub)\tan\phi'_c] = 343\,kN/m$

yielding a factor of safety: $F = \dfrac{343}{344.2} = 0.99$

which is, for all practical purposes, identical to the initial chosen value $F = 1$, implying in the process that the slope would collapse. No wonder that slope failures are a common occurrence every time there is a prolonged period of sustained rainfall, leading to slopes being waterlogged. These simple examples, though they may appear tedious in terms of calculations, are very useful to illustrate the practical effects of managing the water level within a slope. Failing that, stability problems may get out of hand.

3.5.4 Effect of seepage forces on the stability of slopes

In the presence of seepage forces, the analysis of the slope stability is still undertaken according to equation 3.34, except that this time the porewater pressure is estimated either from a flownet or through the use of an analytical procedure such as a conformal mapping technique (Azizi, 2007). Such analyses are best illustrated by a practical example, and in this respect, let us consider the stability of the earth dam for which the flownet solution is illustrated in figure 3.17. Clearly, the stability of both upstream and downstream sides of the dam is greatly affected by the slopes, which in turn depend on the fill material. Thus, for a compacted clay characterised by a (relatively) small angle of shearing resistance (say $\phi' \leq 20°$), a slope on the downstream side as low as 4 (horizontal) to 1 (vertical) might be needed to guarantee safety *vis à vis* slope failure. In general, and purely as a guideline, the design of an earth dam must be such that the slope on the *upstream* side is between 3 to 1 (for a small sized dam), decreasing to 3.5 to 1 for a medium sized dam. On the *downstream* side, slopes varying from 2.5 to 1, decreasing to 4 to 1 as the dam size increases, are usually suitable as far as stability is concerned. Obviously, these values are of a purely informative nature, and therefore *cannot* be used as a substitute for a full analysis such as the one to be undertaken shortly. Moreover, when the *downstream* slope of an earth dam is protected by a drainage blanket, as depicted in figure 3.17, then a minimum factor of safety $F_{min} = 1.5$ is required when the dam is fully operational.

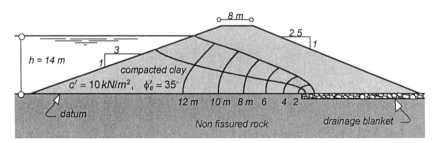

Figure 3.17: Stability of slopes subjected to seepage forces; case of an earth dam.

On the *upstream* side, however, the critical stability conditions occur when, for some reason, the water level drops very quickly. These conditions are usually referred to as *rapid drawdown*. Under such circumstances, the water pressure within the slope is hardly changed while the volume of water that used to be applied as an additional weight on top of the slope has disappeared (refer to figure 3.18). Accordingly, the stability of the *upstream* side must be analysed under this state of stresses, and a minimum factor of safety $F_{min} = 1.25$, corresponding to *rapid drawdown* conditions is required.

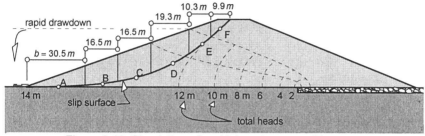

Figure 3.18: Simulation of rapid drawdown conditions.

Assuming, therefore, that rapid drawdown conditions have occurred, the analysis of the stability of the upstream slope can be undertaken in a manner similar to that used previously. Indeed, within the selected slip circle depicted in figure 3.18, six slices are chosen with the dimensions indicated in the figure. The total weight of each element can be calculated in a straightforward way assuming a saturated unit weight of clay $\gamma_{sat} = 21\,kN/m^3$. However, the porewater pressure, estimated at the middle of the base of each slice (*i.e.* at points A, B, C, D, E and F in figure 3.18), is calculated from the total head h (estimated from the flownet) and the elevation head h_e (scaled from the figure) of each point, so that for instance at D, the porewater pressure is:
$$u_D = (h - h_e)\,\gamma_w \approx (12.5 - 5.15) \times 10 = 73.5\,kN/m^2$$

Whence the following quantities are to be used in conjunction with equation 3.34 to estimate the factor of safety:

slice	$u\,(kN/m^2)$	$w\,(kN/m)$	$b\,(m)$	$\alpha\,(°)$	$w\sin\alpha\,(kN/m)$	$(w-ub)\tan\phi'\,(kN/m)$
A	140	3,200	30.5	0	0	−749
B	130	3,995	16.5	6	418	1,292
C	114	5,065	16.5	13	1,139	2,235
D	74	5,605	19.3	27	2,545	2,929
E	21	2,138	10.3	38	1,316	1,346
F	0	856	9.9	42	573	599

and the sum: $\Sigma w \sin \alpha = 5991 \, kN/m$.

The iterations, according to equation 3.34 can now be started, selecting initially a value $F = 1$ for the factor of safety; thence:

slice	$m_\alpha = \cos \alpha + \dfrac{\tan \phi'_c \sin \alpha}{1}$	$\dfrac{1}{m_\alpha}[c'b + (w - ub) \tan \phi'_c] \, (kN/m)$
A	1.00	−444
B	1.07	1,365
C	1.13	2,120
D	1.21	2,583
E	1.22	1,189
F	1.21	576

Accordingly:

$$\Sigma \frac{1}{m_\alpha}[c'b + (w - ub) \tan \phi'_c] = 7389 \, kN/m$$

and the calculated value of the factor of safety is thus: $\quad F = \dfrac{7389}{5991} = 1.23$

This value is different from the initial value of one, and therefore another iteration is needed. Using the newly calculated value $F = 1.23$ as an initial value for iteration, it follows that:

slice	$m_\alpha = \cos \alpha + \dfrac{\tan \phi'_c \sin \alpha}{1.23}$	$\dfrac{1}{m_\alpha}[c'b + (w - ub) \tan \phi'_c] \, (kN/m)$
A	1.00	−444
B	1.05	1,383
C	1.10	2,177
D	1.15	2,716
E	1.14	1,273
F	1.12	621

yielding the quantity:

$$\Sigma \frac{1}{m_\alpha}[c'b + (w - ub) \tan \phi'_c] = 7726 \, kN/m$$

and a factor of safety: $F = \dfrac{7726}{5991} = 1.29$

It is easy to show that another iteration using an initial factor of safety $F = 1.29$ yields a calculated value $F = 1.31$, which is then assumed to be the actual factor of safety under the critical conditions of rapid drawdown for the selected slip surface on the downstream side. In fact, in this particular case, it can be shown that the selected slip circle in figure 3.18 corresponds to the most critical slip surface, meaning that the value $F = 1.31$ is indeed the *minimum* factor of safety, and implying in the process that the dam is safe *vis à vis* rapid drawdown conditions. Obviously, as mentioned previously, the process of calculating the *minimum* factor of safety F_{min} can be lengthy and tedious, and is usually undertaken numerically. Bishop and Morgenstern (1960) produced very useful charts, based on equation 3.34, which can be applied to calculate F_{min} (see also Chandler and Peiris (1989)). However, these charts cannot be used *ad lib,* and it is strongly advisable to read the papers in question thoroughly to be aware of the limitations related to their use then, when applicable, to use the charts cautiously.

3.6 Location of the critical failure surface

In practice, slope stability calculations are almost exclusively undertaken numerically, so that literally hundreds of failure surfaces can be used in conjunction with Bishop's method until the one with the lowest factor of safety is located. The computational process can therefore use a random selection of slip surfaces by varying the centre of rotation or the radius of the circle, for instance. However, the process can be optimised by concentrating the calculations on a prescribed area within which the critical slip surface is likely to be located. In this respect, some purely empirical methods can be used cautiously such as the one represented graphically in figure 3.19. The method, first suggested by Fellenius (1927), applies mainly to slopes in cohesive homogeneous soils under undrained conditions (*i.e.* $\phi = 0$). The initial position of the centre of the critical slip circle is estimated from both graphs of figure 3.19, depending on the slope angle β.

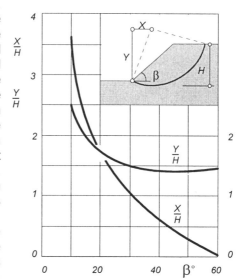

Figure 3.19: Initial location of the critical slip circle (from Whitlow (1995), reproduced by permission).

Using the initial centre of rotation, iterative calculations can then be made by varying the radius of the corresponding slip circle. Usually, a grid pattern is used whereby different centres of the slip circle estimated from figure 3.19 are tried until the critical circle yielding the minimum factor of safety is located. Bear in mind that the method related to figure 3.19 is only used to help accelerate the search for the critical slip surface and, as such, it can be cautiously extended to homogeneous soils (*i.e.* soils consisting of one layer) under drained conditions, then used in conjunction with Bishop's routine presented earlier.

3.7 Non-circular failure surface

Apart from infinite slopes, the analysis developed so far assumes that the shape of the failure surface is circular. There are many instances in practice when this assumption is no longer valid, in that the actual failure surface is between a circle and an infinite slope (which is a circle with an infinite radius). Several methods of analysis which can be applied to slope design independently of the failure surface shape are available (see Morgenstern and Price (1965), for instance). In particular, Janbu (1973) developed an analysis similar in nature to that related to Bishop's routine presented earlier, in which the expression of the factor of safety, which takes into account the resultant of the tangential forces $(x_{i-1} - x_i) = \Delta x$ applied on each slice (refer to figure 3.11), irrespective of the shape of the failure surface, is as follows:

$$F = \frac{1}{\Sigma (w + \Delta x) \sin \alpha} \Sigma \left\{ [c'b + w(1 + \Delta x - r_u) \tan \phi'] \frac{1}{\cos \alpha + \frac{\sin \alpha \tan \phi'}{F}} \right\} \quad (3.35)$$

where all symbols are as defined in equation 3.34.

Janbu suggested calculating the factor of safety F from equation 3.35 for which the quantity Δx is assumed to be zero (in which case equation 3.35 becomes identical to equation 3.34), then applying an empirically based correction factor f_o to the computed value. The correction factor f_o, estimated from figure 3.20, depends on the ratio d/L reflecting the non-circular nature of the failure surface.

Although such a method is considered reliable in engineering practice, one has to bear in mind that the graphs in figure 3.20 were developed for a non-circular failure surface with a moderate slope and, accordingly, they should be used cautiously. Also, for fairly shallow inclines (with slopes smaller than 15°, say), the analysis related to infinite slopes (refer to sections 3.2 to 3.4) may be more appropriate.

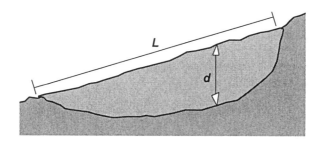

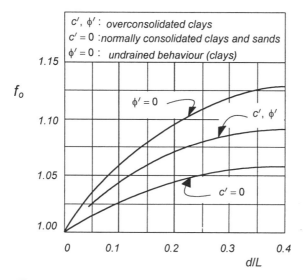

Figure 3.20: Correction factor for non-circular failure surface.

3.8 Improving the stability of unsafe slopes

3.8.1 Use of geotextile reinforcement

The use of *geotextiles* as a means of reinforcement of manmade slopes is, nowadays, a common engineering practice. Geotextiles are a by-product of petroleum, and are usually made from polyethylene or polypropylene. To date, *geogrids* consisting of a polymer mesh geotextiles such as the one depicted in figure 3.21 are extensively used. The apertures in the geogrids ensure an interlocking with the surrounding soil, thus maximising the reinforcement, in other words, the tensile forces T_i shown in figure 3.22.

These tensile forces lead to a marked improvement of the factor of safety of the slope as shall be demonstrated below.

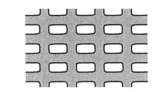

Figure 3.21: Geogrid.

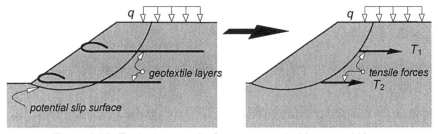

Figure 3.22: Equivalent tensile forces generated by geogrid layers.

Because of the nature of equation 3.34, a Bishop type analysis cannot easily be expanded to include the tensile forces in figure 3.22. Consequently, Fellenius' method (1927) will be applied to evaluate the effect on the overall stability of the slope of these tensile forces. Consider an isolated element at the base of which a tensile force T, generated by a geogrid layer, and inclined at an angle β as depicted in figure 3.23, is applied (*note β is positive clockwise and negative anticlockwise*) . Fellenius' method considers both the equilibrium of forces perpendicular to the base of the element and the equilibrium of moments about the centre of rotation O. Thus, referring to figure 3.23, it is seen that:

$$w \cos \alpha = l(\sigma'_n + u) - T \cos\left(\frac{\pi}{2} - (\alpha + \beta)\right) \qquad (3.36)$$

Moreover, the equilibrium of moments about O is such that:

$$\Sigma R \tau_{mob} l + R T \cos(\alpha + \beta) = \Sigma R w \sin \alpha \qquad (3.37)$$

but, according to equation 3.27:

$$l \tau_{mob} = \frac{l c'}{F} + \frac{\sigma'_n l}{F} \tan \phi'_c \qquad (3.38)$$

On the other hand, the quantity $\sigma'_n l$ can easily be found from equation 3.36:

$$\sigma'_n l = w \cos \alpha - u l + T \sin(\alpha + \beta) \qquad (3.39)$$

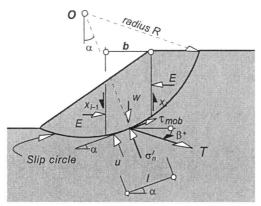

Figure 3.23: Boundary conditions related to Fellenius' method

Therefore, substituting for $\sigma'_n l$ in equation 3.38, then for the resulting quantity $l\tau_{mob}$ in equation 8.37, and knowing that $l = b/\cos\alpha$ (refer to figure 3.23), the ensuing expression of the factor of safety can readily be established:

$$F = \frac{\Sigma\left[\frac{c'b}{\cos\alpha} + \left(w\cos\alpha - \frac{ub}{\cos\alpha} + T\sin(\alpha+\beta)\right)\tan\phi'_c\right]}{\Sigma w\sin\alpha - \Sigma T\cos(\alpha+\beta)} \qquad (3.40)$$

As opposed to equation 3.34, equation 3.40 does not involve an iterative procedure for the calculation of the factor of safety.

Example 3.4

An 18.6 *m* high embankment, with a steep slope on each side as depicted in figure 3.24 is to be built using a dense silty sand characterised by a critical angle of shearing resistance $\phi'_c = 35°$ and a bulk unit weight $\gamma = 20\,kN/m^3$. Three geogrid layers, each providing a tensile force $T = 110\,kN/m$ are used to ensure the stability of both slopes. Under such circumstances, the factor of safety corresponding to the selected potential slip surface is evaluated using equation 3.40. The potentially failing soil mass is first subdivided into five elements (*a, b,...., e* in figure 3.24) with the following characteristics:

slice	$w\,(kN/m)$	$\alpha\,(°)$	$b\,(m)$	$T\,(kN/m)$
a	283	11	4	0
b	1,212	19	5.3	0
c	1,498	35	5.3	110
d	768	53	4	110
e	187	69	2.67	110

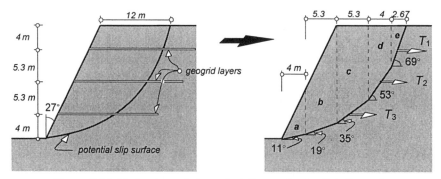

Figure 3.24: Embankment characteristics and potential slip surface.

It is easy to check that:

$$\Sigma w \sin\alpha = 2096 \, kN/m, \quad \Sigma w \cos\alpha = 3180 \, kN/m,$$

$$\Sigma T \sin(\alpha+\beta) = 310.4 \, kN/m, \quad \Sigma T \cos(\alpha+\beta) = 407.7 \, kN/m$$

(notice in this example, the angle β as per figure 3.23 is zero). Therefore, assuming zero values for both cohesion and porewater pressure, equation 3.40 yields:

$$F = \frac{(3180+310.4) \times \tan 35}{(2096-407.7)} \approx 1.45$$

In the absence of any reinforcement, the same equation would have produced a factor of safety:

$$F = \frac{3180}{2096} \tan 35 = 1.06$$

meaning that the slope will not have stood on its own.

Notice that, in practice, Fellenius' method is found to be somewhat conservative in that it yields slight underestimates of the factor of safety.

The short term total stress analysis of the same problem (i.e. a man made slope incorporating geotextile layer(s) is similar to that developed in section 3.51, with the factor of safety modified to take into account the appropriate component of the tensile force in the geotextile. Accordingly, for a slope with two geotextile layers mobilising the same tension force T per layer, each subtending an angle δ as per figure 3.25, only the components $T\sin\delta_i$ would generate a moment with respect to the centre of rotation O. The corresponding factor of safety is therefore:

$$F = \frac{c_u R^2 \alpha + R T \sum \sin \delta_i}{W.e} \tag{3.41}$$

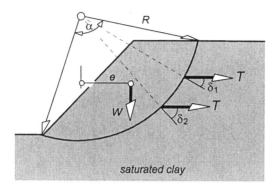

Figure 3.25: Short term analysis of a slope
incorporating geotextile layers.

Example 3.5

A highway embankment is built using a compacted clay characterised by an undrained shear strength $c_u = 40\,kN/m^2$. A preliminary undrained analysis of the slope showed the existence of a potential slip surface with the dimensions indicated in Figure 3.26.

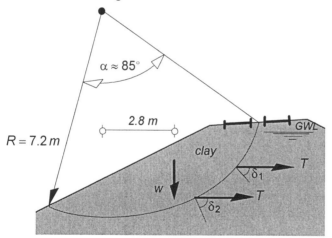

Figure 3.26: Embankment's geometry

The soil delimited by the slip surface has a weight $W \approx 1000\,kN/m$, with an eccentricity $e = 2.8\,m$. Originally, the design included the use of two geogrid layers, each providing a horizontal tension force $T = 100\,kN/m$. The angles that the radius of the circle makes with respect to the horizontal tension forces are such that $\delta_1 = \frac{2}{3}\delta_2 = 42°$. Estimate the corresponding factor of safety against failure in the short term.

Only the tension force components normal to the radius contribute to the moment equation, whence using equation 3.41:

$$F = \frac{c_u R^2 \alpha + R\,T(\sin\delta_1 + \sin\delta_2)}{W.e}$$

with

$$\beta_1 = 42°, \quad \beta_2 = \frac{2}{3}\beta_1 = 63°, \quad \alpha = 85° \approx 1.48\,rd$$

$$F = \frac{40 \times 7.2^2 \times 1.48 + 7.2 \times 100\,(\sin 42 + \sin 63)}{1000 \times 2.8} = 1.5$$

3.8.2 Use of soil nails and rock bolts

Soil nails and rock bolts consist generally of high yield steel threadbars, with nominal diameters ranging from $15\,mm$ to $63.5\,mm$. They constitute a quick, safe and economical way of stabilising slopes and cuttings in a soil or a rock mass. As opposed to ground anchors which are actively loaded, soil nails and rock bolts are passively loaded through the soil or rock mass, and as such, they provide a ground reinforcement which enhances the overall stability of a lope or a cutting.

Depending on the state and type of the ground for which they are used, rock bolts and soil nails are inserted in situ in one of two ways as illustrated in figures 3.27 & 3.28:

- an open hole is first drilled, to the required depth, then the threadbar is inserted, and the hole grouted. This technique is suitable for cohesive soils and unweathered rocks

- a self drilling hollow core bar with a continuos rolled thread is used in conjunction with cohesionless soils and highly weathered rocks. As the drilling advances, grout is applied through grouting ports.

In either case, couplers are used as appropriate to achieve the design length of the threadbars. Once the grout has set, the threadbars can then be tensioned and secured through the use of hexagonal nuts and bearing plates. In some instances, permanent nails with double corrosion protection consisting of cement grout and corrugated sheathing, complete with anti-corrosion compound inside a steel protection cap (see figure 3.27) are used.

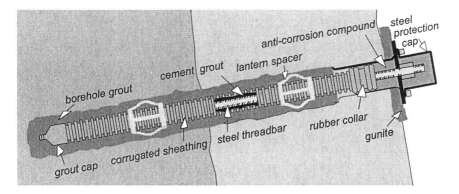

Figure 3.27: Permanent soil nail with corrosion protection

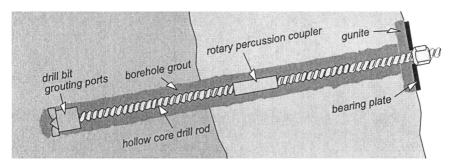

Figure 3.28: Self-drilling hollow core nail

The tension force that can be applied to rock bolts and soil nails depends on their type (threadbars or hollow core nails) and their diameters. As a guide, a 16 *mm* diameter high yield steel threadbar can be tensioned up to 76 *kN* which constitutes 62.5 % of the ultimate tension force (that is a factor of safety of 1.6). Equally, a 63.5 *mm* diameter threadbar can take 1386 *kN* in tension with the same factor of safety of 1.6 (i.e. the threadbar has an ultimate tension of 2217 *kN*). Design and manufacturing details of different types of threadbars and hollow core nails are summarised in the useful table 3.1.

Several techniques can be used in conjunction with the tensioning of rock bolts and soil nails inserted into a pre-drilled hole. Figure 3.29 illustrates three widely used methods of anchorage:

- grouted bolts used mainly for cohesive soils whereby the pre-drilled hole is grouted after the threadbar is inserted. Once the grout has set, the bar is tensioned to the required design level. This technique is the simplest, quickest and mot cost-effective for slope stabilisation

- expansion shell anchor which can equally be used as a temporary anchor without grouting. The expansion shell is designed so that the grip on the borehole sides increases as the tension force in the threadbar increases. Without grouting, this technique provides highly effective temporary anchors in unweathered rocks.

- resin grouted bolts are essentially used in conjunction with unweathered rocks; and because there is no need to grout the pre-drilled hole, the bolt is usually protected with an anti-corrosive coating.

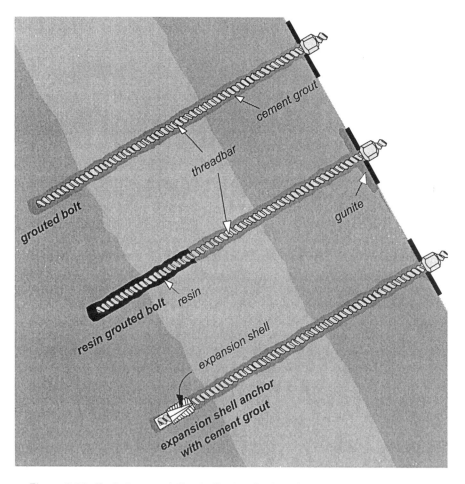

Figure 3.29: Techniques relating to the tensioning of rock bolts and soil nails

*Table 3.1: Design aspects relating to high yield steel threadbars and
self drilling hollow core nails (source: Dywidag Systems International Ltd)*

High yield steel threadbars								
nominal diameter (mm)	16	20	25	28	32	40	50	63.5
ultimate strength (kN)	121	188	295	370	482	756	1176	2217
yield strength (kN)	100	157	245	308	402	630	980	1758
weight (kg/m)	1.58	2.47	3.85	4.83	6.31	9.87	15.40	24.80

Self-drilling hollow core nails						
nominal drill rod outer diameter (mm)	19.5	23.5	25	31	34	36.5
drill bit diameter (mm)	42 51	51 76	51 76	76 90	102 115	102 115
ultimate strength (kN)	200	280	360	500	500	800
yield strength (kN)	150	230	280	400	450	630
weight (kg/m)	2.6	3.6	4.2	6.0	7.5	8.4

Example 3.6

Assume a steep cut with dimensions identical to the embankment used in
example 3.4 is made in a glacial till characterised by zero cohesion and an
angle of shearing resistance $\phi' = 28°$. If the same slip surface is also
assumed to apply, then for a clay bulk unit weight $\gamma = 20\,kN/m^3$ the
quantities tabulated in example 3.4 are valid, except from the tension
forces. In order to improve the stability of the steep cut, five $32\,mm$
diameter high yield steel threadbars are inserted deep into the ground as
per figure 3.30, then tensioned after the setting of the grout to 62.5% of the
corresponding ultimate strength in table 3.1

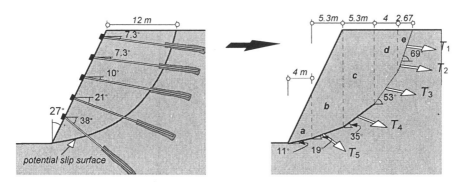

Figure 3.30: Soil nails position

Accordingly, the tension force generated in each of the five threadbars is:

$$T_1 = T_2 = \ldots = T_5 = 482 \times 0.625 = 301.25 \, kN.$$

Furthermore, the following quantities have already been calculated in example 3.4:

$$\Sigma w \sin \alpha = 2096 \, kN/m, \qquad \Sigma w \cos \alpha = 3180 \, kN/m$$

Using the inclination angles of the soil nails indicated in figure 3.30, it follows that:

$$\Sigma T \cos (\alpha + \beta) = 301.25 \times [\cos (11 + 38) + \cos (19 + 21) + \cos (35 + 10) +$$
$$\cos (53 + 7.3) + \cos (69 + 7.3)] = 862.03 \, kN/m$$

$$\Sigma T \sin(\alpha + \beta) = 301.25 \times [\sin (11 + 38) + \sin (19 + 21) + \sin (35 + 10) +$$
$$\sin (53 + 7.3) + \sin (69 + 7.3)] = 1188.37 \, kN/m$$

The factor of safety of the slope can now be calculated from equation 3.40, in which both cohesion c' and porewater pressure u are set to zero:

$$F = \frac{(3180 + 1188.37) \times \tan 28}{(2096 - 862.03)} = 1.88$$

Example 3.7

A tunnel with the dimensions indicated in figure 3.31 is excavated in a thick layer of hard sandstone. Preliminary site investigation showed that the sandstone is fissured along an $800 \, m$ long section of the tunnel, with no water ingress. A more refined site investigation indicated that blocks a & b in figure 3.31 are particularly unstable; so it was decided to stabilise both blocks using rock bolts inserted at different angles from the tunnel face as excavation progressed through the section of concern. Block a has a weight $W_a \approx 1323 \, kN/m$ and a potential slip surface of length $L \approx 16 \, m$ inclined at an angle $\alpha_a = 57°$ as indicated in figure 3.31. Block b on the other hand is characterised by a weight $W_b \approx 648 \, kN/m$ and a slip surface of length $L_b \approx 10 \, m$ dipping at an angle $\alpha_b = 66°$. Due to the cracks at the boundaries of both blocks, the sandstone properties were reduced to a cohesion $c' = 50 \, kN/m^2$ and an angle of shearing resistance $\phi' = 40°$.

Three $20 \, mm$ diameter high steel threadbars are used in conjunction with block a, each tensioned to 62.5% of the ultimate strength (see table 3.1) so that:

$$T_1 = T_2 = T_3 = 188 \times 0.625 = 117.5 \, kN \text{ per metre length of tunnel.}$$

Block b is stabilised with three $16\,mm$ diameter threadbars for every metre length of tunnel, each tensioned at 62.5% of the ultimate strength, whence:

$T_4 = T_5 = T_6 = 0.625 \times 121 = 75.6\,kN$ per metre length of tunnel.

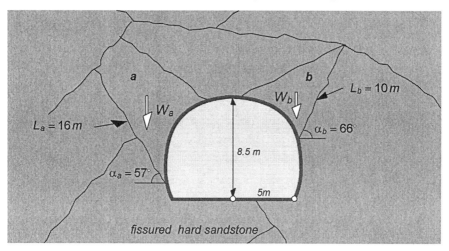

Figure 3.31: Tunnel dimensions and rock state

The angles of inclination of the rock bolts (β in equation 3.40) are as per figure 3.32 (notice the negative signs).

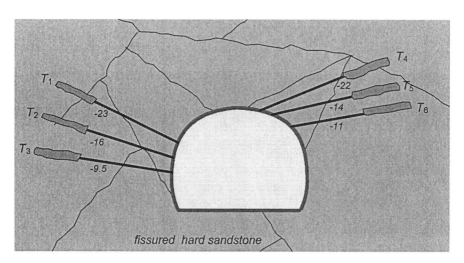

Figure 3.32: Rock bolts inclination angles

The stage is now set for the calculation of the factor of safety of each block, starting with a:

$$W_a \sin \alpha_a = 1323 \times \sin 57 = 1109,56 \, kN/m; \qquad W_a \cos \alpha_a = 720.55 \, kN/m$$

$$\Sigma T \cos (\alpha_a + \beta) = 117.5 \times [\cos (57 - 23) + \cos (57 - 16) + \cos (57 - 9.5)]$$
$$= 265.47 \, kN/m$$

$$\Sigma T \sin (\alpha_a + \beta) = 117.5 \times (\sin 34 + \sin 41 + \sin 47.5) = 229.42 \, kN/m$$

Accordingly, for zero porewater pressure, equation 3.40 yields the following factor of safety for block a:

$$F = \frac{16 \times 50 + (720.55 + 229.42) \times \tan 40}{(1109.56 - 265.47)} = 1.89$$

Block b :

$$W_b \sin \alpha_b = 648 \times \sin 66 = 520 \, kN/m; \qquad W_b \cos \alpha_b = 263.56 \, kN/m$$

$$\Sigma T \sin (\alpha_b + \beta) = 75.6 \times [\sin (66 - 22) + \sin (66 - 14) + \sin (66 - 11)]$$
$$= 174.01 \, kN/m$$

$$\Sigma T \cos (\alpha_b + \beta) = 75.6 \times [\cos 44 + \cos 52 + \cos 55] = 144.44 \, kN/m$$

Whence a factor of safety from equation 3.40:

$$F = \frac{10 \times 50 + (263.56 + 174.01) \times \tan 40}{(520 - 144.44)} = 2.3$$

3.8.3 Use of micropiles

An alternative solution to the use of geotextiles and soil nails consists of placing micropiles with diameters usually not exceeding $250 \, mm$, across the potential slip surface so that the forces resisting the slide are enhanced, and so is the factor of safety of the whole slope. Although the use of micropiles in conjunction with slopes is similar to the use of ground anchors in the case of retaining structures (see chapter 7), the fundamental behavioural difference is that anchors are essentially subject to tensile stresses whereas micropiles are usually placed either vertically or normal to the potential slip surface (refer to figure 3.33 for instance) and are, as such, subject principally to shear stresses. From a practical perspective, the designer must ensure that micropiles are designed in an effective way, thus avoiding the potentially dangerous situation whereby they become ineffectual through the development of a potential slip surface deep beneath the piles as depicted in figure 3.33.

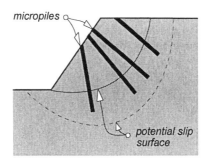

Figure 3.33: Potential problems related to the use of micropiles in conjunction with circular slip surfaces.

Figure 3.34 shows the potential pitfalls related to the inappropriate use of rigid piles to stabilise long slopes. The figure indicates the need for a comprehensive analysis of the nature of the slope to be supported and the type of pile–soil interaction likely to be generated once piles are in place.

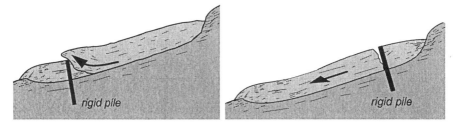

Figure 3.34: Practical aspects related to the use of rigid piles for slope stability.

However, the nature of soil–pile interaction can be very complex to analyse since, in this case, piles are subjected mainly to passive lateral loading, in other words, the piles are loaded through the potentially failing soil mass and as such, an appropriate design (in terms of pile dimensions and pile number) would require the prior knowledge of the profiles of bending moments, shear stresses and pressure distribution along the pile shaft. Moreover, piles are usually used in numbers, and therefore the design is bound to be affected by the group effect, which can be difficult to assess. Nonetheless, this type of reinforced slopes can be designed reasonably well using, for instance, a Taylor type total stress analysis, based on the assumption that the pressure at which the soil in the vicinity of the pile fails (by literally flowing around the pile shaft) is equivalent to $10\,c_u$, where c_u represents the undrained shear strength of the soil (see for instance Randolph and Houlsby (1984), Poulos and Davis (1980)).

Consider the slope in a saturated clay depicted in figure 3.35. If n identical micropiles, each with a diameter a were inserted as per the figure, and if c_u is the undrained shear strength of the clay, then clearly the shear stress mobilised throughout the length of the slip plane $(L - na)$ is:

$$\tau_{mob} = \frac{c_u}{F} \tag{3.42}$$

In addition, the shear stress mobilised by the use of n piles is:

$$\tau = \frac{1}{F}(10n\,a\,c_u) \tag{3.43}$$

F, in both equations, being the factor of safety.

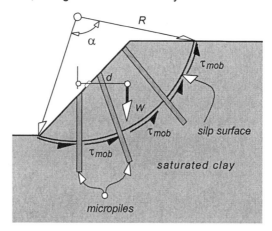

Figure 3.35: Use of micropiles in conjunction with circular slip planes.

Taking moments about the centre of rotation, it follows that:

$$Wd = \frac{1}{F}[(L-na)c_uR + 10nac_uR]$$

leading to the following expression of the factor of safety:

$$F = \frac{c_uR}{Wd}(L+9na) \tag{3.44}$$

Example 3.8

With reference to example 3.5 and figure 3.35, estimate the improvement in the factor of safety of the slope if 2 micropiles with a diameter $a = 180\,mm$ were used to stabilise the slope instead of the two geogrid layers.

First, the factor of safety prior to the installation of micropiles can be calculated from equation 3.22:

$$F_1 = \frac{40 \times 1.48 \times 7.2^2}{1000 \times 2.8} = 1.1$$

Obviously, this value indicates that the slope is unsafe; whence the use of micropiles. The new factor of safety is now estimated from equation 3.44:

$$F_2 = \frac{40 \times 7.2}{1000 \times 2.8} \times (7.2 \times 1.48 + 9 \times 2 \times 0.18) = 1.43$$

that is an increase in the factor of safety of 30%. Notice that, if the magnitude and direction of the shear forces developed in the piles along the slip plane were known, then an effective stress analysis, similar to that used in conjunction with geotextiles, can be applied, and the factor of safety of the slope can be estimated from equation 3.40.

Problems

3.1   A 6 m thick layer of boulder clay has a natural angle of slope
$\beta = 16°$, and is underlain by a layer of rock inclined at roughly the
same angle, constituting a potential slip surface. The saturated
clay is characterised by an angle $\phi' = 24°$, an apparent cohesion
$c' = 7\,kN/m^2$, and a saturated unit weight $\gamma_{sat} = 21\,kN/m^3$, the
water flow conditions being as illustrated in figure p3.1.
Preliminary calculations indicate that the natural slope should
be reduced to 12° for the requirement of a factor of safety against
failure $F = 1.3$ to be fulfilled. Alternatively, the same factor of
safety can be achieved by lowering the   water table to a depth z_w
while keeping the natural slope unaltered. Calculate z_w.

Ans: $z_w = 2.39\,m$

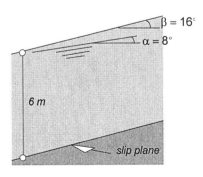

Figure p3.1

3.2   An analysis of the stability of a newly cut slope suggested that a
slip circle failure mechanism, such as the one illustrated in figure
p3.2 might develop in the short term. Knowing that the clay has an
undrained shear strength $c_u = 50\,kN/m^2$ and a saturated unit
weight $\gamma_{sat} = 20\,kN/m^3$, and assuming the failure surface is
characterised by an area $A \approx 196\,m^2$, a radius $R = 12\,m$, an angle
$\alpha \approx 90°$, and an eccentricity $d = 2.5\,m$, estimate the number of
150 mm diameter micropiles needed per metre to ensure a
minimum factor of safety against failure $F = 1.6$.

Ans: $n = 6$

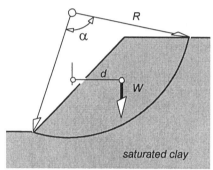

Figure p3.2

3.3   Refer to the failure surface related to the artificial slope of figure
p3.3, then consider its short term stability by estimating the factor
of safety against failure. Assume the soil has a bulk unit weight
$\gamma = 20\,kN/m^3$ and an undrained shear strength $c_u = 65\,kN/m^2$.

Ans: $F \approx 2$

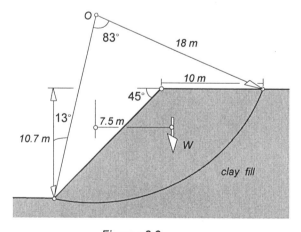

Figure p3.3

3.4 Consider the long term analysis of the stability of the slope depicted in figure $p3.3$. Assume now the long term behaviour of the clay fill is characterised by an angle $\phi' = 23°$ and an apparent cohesion $c' = 7\,kN/m^2$, then use a Bishop type analysis to estimate the factor of safety against failure.

Ans: $F \approx 1.34$

3.5 Calculate the long term factor of safety against shear failure if the slope in figure $p3.3$ were to be waterlogged.
Use $\gamma_{sat} = 21\,kN/m^3$.

Ans: $F \approx 0.7$

3.6 To improve the stability of the waterlogged slope of figure $p3.3$, layers of geogrids, each developing a horizontal tensile force of a magnitude $T = 150\,kN/m$, were placed at regular (vertical) intervals with respect to the toe of the slope. Estimate, using Fellenius' method, how many geogrid layers need be placed if a minimum factor of safety $F = 1.7$ were required when the slope becomes waterlogged.

Ans: $n = 4$

3.7 Refer to figure $p3.7$ corresponding to a general case of flow within a partially saturated medium, then define the porewater pressure ratio r_u and explain concisely its relevance to the stability of slopes. Also, show that in the case of a waterlogged slope, with seepage occurring parallel to the surface of the slope, the porewater pressure ratio is:

$$r_u \approx \tfrac{1}{2}\cos^2\beta , \quad \text{where } \beta \text{ is the slope's angle.}$$

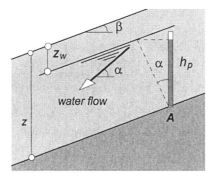

Figure p3.7

3.8   Refer to example 3.5 and consider the following scenario: two weeks in the construction, it was realised that the geogrid layers were not laid in the first 20 m section of the embankment. To rectify this mistake, the design team decided to jack 96 mm diameter micropiles in sufficient numbers for every metre width along this section. Assuming the pressure at which the soil in the vicinity of each pile fails is $10 c_u$, calculate the number of piles per metre width required to achieve a factor of safety $F \approx 1.5$.

Ans: $n = 5$

3.9   Much of the section of the Jubilee Line between Cannon Park and Queensbury is on embankments up to $8 m$ in height. A maximum speed limit of $25 km/h$ was imposed along this section due to the risk of slope failure. In order to allow the trains to run at speeds of up to $80 km/h$, London Underground decided to strengthen the embankments using boreholes filled with dry quicklime and a single central reinforcing bar. As it hydrates, the volume of lime will expand appreciably, thus increasing the friction along the pile shafts, while reducing the porewater pressure in the surrounding clay.

Assume the pressure at which the soil in the vicinity of each pile fails is $8 c_u$, then refer to the failure surface and embankment characteristics in figure p3.9, and estimate the number of 200 mm diameter, long piles required to increase the original factor of safety by about 50%.

Ans:: $n = 6$

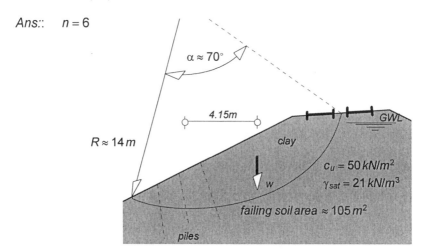

Figure p3.9

3.10 Assume the dry slope in figure p3.3 is cut in a firm clay having $c' = 0$, $\phi' = 22°$ and a unit weight $\gamma = 20\,kN/m^3$. Divide the potential slip surface into a reasonable number of elements as per example 3.4, then select an appropriate soil nail from table 3.1 in sufficient number per metre width of slope so that a factor of safety $F = 2.2$ against slope failure can be achieved. Assume each soil nail is tensioned to 62.5% of its ultimate strength (a common engineering practice).

References

Bishop, A. W. and Morgenstern, N. R. (1960) *Stability coefficients for earth slopes.* Géotechnique, 10, pp. 129–150.

Chandler, R. J. and Peiris T. A. (1989) *Further extensions to the Bishop and Morgenstern slope stability charts.* Ground Engineering, May, pp. 33–38.

Fellenius, W. (1927) *Erdstatische Berechnungen mit Reibung und Kohasion (Adhasion) und unter Annahme Kreiszylindrischer Gleitflachen.* W. Ernst, Berlin.

Janbu, N. (1973) *Slope stability computations.* In Embankment Dam Engineering, Casagrande Memorial Volume (eds R. C. Hirschfield and S. J. Poulos). John Wiley, New York.

Morgenstern, N. R. and Price, V. E. (1965) *The analysis of the stability of general slip circles.* Géotechnique, 15 (1), pp. 79–93.

Palladino, D. J. and Peck, R. B. (1972) *Slope failures in an overconsolidated clay in Seattle, Washington.* Géotechnique, 22 (4), pp. 563–595.

Poulos, H. G. and Davis, E. H. (1980) *Pile Foundation Analysis and Design.* John Wiley & Sons, New York.

Randolph, M. F. and Houlsby, G. T. (1984) *The limiting pressure on a circular pile loaded laterally in cohesive soil.* Géotechnique, 34 (4), pp. 613–623.

Skempton, A. W. (1964) *Long term stability of clay slopes.* Géotechnique, 14 (2), pp. 77–102.

Skempton, A. W. and La Rochelle, P. (1965) *The Bradwell slip: a short term failure in London clay.* Géotechnique, 15 (3), pp. 221–242.

Spencer, E. (1967) *A method of analysis of the stability of embankments using parallel interslice forces.* Géotechnique, 17 (1), pp. 11–26.

Taylor, D. W. (1948) *Fundamentals of Soil Mechanics.* John Wiley & Sons, New York.

CHAPTER 4

Limit analysis applied to the bearing capacity of shallow foundations

4.1 Introduction

The calculation of strains in the entire elastic–plastic range requires the four following criteria to be fulfilled:
- the equilibrium of stresses;
- the compatibility of strains;
- the stress–strain relationship in the elastic range through Hooke's law;
- the normality condition.

A complete solution to any boundary value problem in geotechnics can be achieved if these criteria are satisfied *simultaneously*. However, it can be argued that for most engineering problems, a complete solution covering the entire elastic–plastic range can quickly become a very time consuming luxury that, given a viable alternative, most designers *will* do without. A possible alternative consists of focusing solely on the small range of soil behaviour during which collapse occurs, and to use the powerful bounds theorem of the plastic theory to calculate an upper and a lower limits to the *actual* collapse (or ultimate) load. These limits are often so close to each other and can in some cases be identical, corresponding thus to the *true* solution. The attractiveness of this alternative is obvious when the soil strength is primarily of interest to the designer, as in the case of bearing capacity problems, lateral earth pressure or slope stability.

In essence, the *upper* and *lower bounds methods*, to be detailed shortly, represent two different approaches that Calladine (1985), in his intelligent book refers to as the *geometry* and *equilibrium* approaches respectively. Both methods are based on the assumption that the soil is characterised by a *rigid perfectly plastic* behaviour with an *associated flow rule*, so that a lower bound solution to the collapse load can be achieved by satisfying only the *equilibrium equations* and *yield conditions*, whereas an upper bound solution is arrived at by considering the balance of both internal and external energies of the *mechanism* of failure. Consequently, while being always larger than or equal to a lower bound solution, the exact collapse load is always smaller than, if not equal to, an upper bound solution. As such, the lower bound represents a *safe* estimate of the soil strength.

4.2 The upper and lower bounds theorems

• Upper bound theorem

Any chosen mechanism of deformation of a body, within which the rate of dissipation of energy is equated to the rate at which external forces do work, must give an estimate of the plastic collapse load that is higher than, if not equal to, the true collapse load.

• Lower bound theorem

If there is a set of external forces for which the stress distribution is everywhere in internal equilibrium and nowhere exceeds the yield criteria, then those forces will be carried safely by the structure, and they therefore represent a lower bound to the true collapse load.

Leaving aside the mathematical proof of these theorems which is out of the scope of this book, and can be found in Calladine (1985), for instance, these two statements imply that an upper bound solution is achieved by choosing a *kinematically admissible* collapse mechanism that consists basically of rigid blocks sliding with respect to one another, then equating the energy dissipated through shear along the slip planes to the external work done by the set of applied loads. Similarly, a lower bound solution is obtained by selecting a *statically admissible* stress field, satisfying in the process the equilibrium equations as well as the yield criteria. However, the yield criteria of a soil depends on drainage conditions, in other words on whether or not the pore water pressure is allowed to build up or to dissipate. Let us therefore consider the bounds theorems separately in conjunction with both short term *undrained* and long term *drained* behaviours of cohesive soils, and determine the collapse load q_u in the case of a *surface* footing having a width B, and transmitting a stress q to a uniformly loaded soil as depicted in figure 4.1.

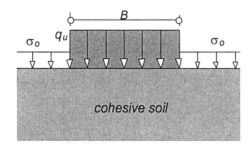

Figure 4.1: Loading conditions.

4.3 Kinematically admissible collapse mechanisms: undrained behaviour

• (a) Slip circle mechanism

This mechanism, shown in figure 4.2, assumes that failure of the volume of soil beneath the foundation occurs through rotation with respect to point O. If the angle of rotation is $d\theta$, then the downward displacement of the external edge of foundation is $B\,d\theta$, and the work done by the external loads is then:

$$\delta E = \tfrac{1}{2}\, B\, d\theta (q_u - \sigma_0) B \tag{4.1}$$

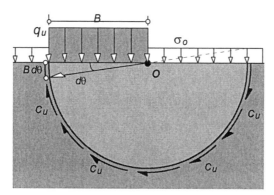

Figure 4.2: Slip circle collapse mechanism.

Similarly, the energy dissipated through shear along the slip circle is:

$$\delta W = \pi B c_u\, B\, d\theta \tag{4.2}$$

Equating both equations then rearranging, it follows that the upper bound solution of the collapse load for this mechanism is:

$$q_u = \sigma_0 + 2\pi c_u \tag{4.3}$$

• (b) Sliding rigid blocks

The corresponding collapse mechanism is shown in figure 4.3, where the rigid block beneath the foundation is pushed into the ground with a velocity V, while the middle block is pushed sideways, so making the last block move upward. All movements are resisted through friction on different slip planes with different velocities, which can easily be determined using the geometry of the blocks. Whence:

$$V_1 = V_3 = V\sqrt{2}\,, \qquad \text{and} \qquad V_2 = 2V$$

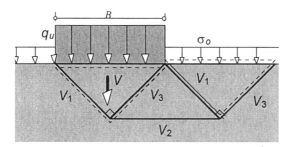

Figure 4.3: Rigid blocks collapse mechanism.

Accordingly, the work done by external forces is:

$$\delta E = (q_u - \sigma_o)\, B\, V \tag{4.4}$$

and the energy dissipated along all five slip planes is:

$$\delta W = 4\frac{B}{\sqrt{2}}c_u V\sqrt{2} + 2VBc_u = 6BVc_u \tag{4.5}$$

Thus, the upper bound solution related to this mechanism, obtained by equating the latter two equations:

$$q_u = \sigma_o + 6c_u \tag{4.6}$$

which represents an improvement on the value calculated from equation 4.3.

- **(c) Slip circle with a rotation centre above surface level**

The corresponding collapse mechanism is depicted in figure 4.4, and as in the previous case, the work done by the external loads is calculated in the knowledge that the foundation width is $B = R\sin\alpha$. Whence:

$$\delta E = \tfrac{1}{2}R\,d\theta \sin\alpha \ (q_u - \sigma_o)R\sin\alpha \tag{4.7}$$

and the energy dissipated through shear is:

$$\delta W = 2\alpha R c_u R\, d\theta \tag{4.8}$$

Equating these two quantities then yields:

$$(q_u - \sigma_o) = \frac{4\alpha}{\sin^2\alpha}\, c_u \tag{4.9}$$

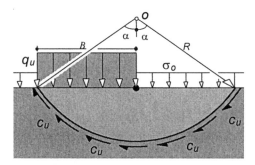

Figure 4.4: Collapse mechanism with a centre of rotation above surface level.

The ultimate collapse load is thereafter found by optimising the angle α. From equation 4.9, it is easy to establish that:

$$\frac{\partial q_u}{\partial \alpha} = \frac{4c_u}{\sin^2\alpha}\left(1 - \frac{2\alpha}{\tan\alpha}\right) \tag{4.10}$$

The optimum q_u value is found by writing $\partial q_u/\partial\alpha = 0$ in equation 4.10, yielding the transcendental equation $\tan\alpha = 2\alpha$ which is satisfied when $\alpha = 0.37\,rad$ (or $67°$). Inserting this value into equation 4.9, then rearranging:

$$q_u = \sigma_o + 5.53c_u \tag{4.11}$$

which is a marked improvement on the previous upper bound load of equation 4.6.

- **(d) Sliding rigid blocks related by a shear fan**

The mechanism depicted in figure 4.5 consists of two blocks sandwiching a shear fan constituted of an infinite number of sliding wedges. As the block beneath the foundation sinks, it pushes the first wedge of the fan which then rotates with respect to the centre O (refer to the figure) by a small angle $d\theta$ transmitting in the process the movement to the adjacent wedge. It is clear from the geometry of the figure that all slip planes, including the wedges inside the fan, have the same length $B/\sqrt{2}$. Also, the velocities along ac, cO, Od and de are identical with a magnitude of $V\sqrt{2}$. Consequently, the energy balance must be zero, and so the work due to external forces is:

$$\delta E = (q_u - \sigma_o)BV \tag{4.12}$$

the energy dissipated along the planes ac, cd and de is as follows:

$$\delta W_1 = \frac{B}{\sqrt{2}}c_u V\sqrt{2} + \frac{B}{\sqrt{2}}\frac{\pi}{2}c_u V\sqrt{2} + \frac{B}{\sqrt{2}}c_u V\sqrt{2} \qquad (4.13a)$$

$$= B V c_u\left(2 + \frac{\pi}{2}\right) \qquad (4.13b)$$

The energy dissipated through the shear fan is easily integrated in the following manner:

$$\delta W_2 = \int_0^{\pi/2} c_u \frac{B}{\sqrt{2}} V\sqrt{2}\, d\theta = c_u B V\frac{\pi}{2} \qquad (4.14)$$

Hence a total energy dissipated:

$$\delta W = c_u B V(2 + \pi) \qquad (4.15)$$

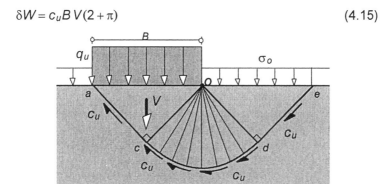

Figure 4.5: Sliding blocks related by a shear fan.

The upper bound solution corresponding to the mechanism is then found by equating equation 4.12 and 4.15; whence:

$$q_u = \sigma_0 + (2 + \pi)c_u \qquad (4.16)$$

which is the *lowest* upper bound solution (often referred to as *Prandtl* solution) that can possibly be obtained.

4.4 Statically admissible stress fields: undrained behaviour

• (a) Stress field with a single discontinuity

Consider the stress field depicted in figure 4.6 with a vertical discontinuity going through one edge of the foundation. In the absence of shear stresses, both vertical and horizontal stresses generated by the stress field are major stresses and, according to the corresponding Mohr's circles, the major vertical stress at point A with a magnitude $\sigma_A = \sigma_o$ rotates through an angle

π (double that in figure 4.6) to reach point B, becoming in the process a major horizontal stress whose ultimate magnitude at failure is $\sigma_B = 2c_u + \sigma_o$. When rotated a further 180°, σ_B then becomes a major vertical stress with an *ultimate lower bound value*:

$$q_u = 4c_u + \sigma_o \tag{4.17}$$

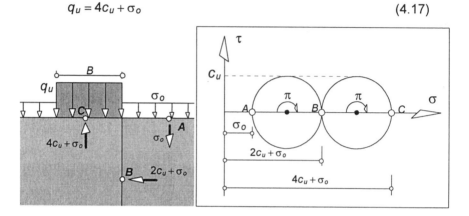

Figure 4.6: Stress field with a single discontinuity
and its corresponding Mohr's circles.

• (b) Stress field with three discontinuities

Figure 4.7 illustrates a stress field containing three discontinuities going, arbitrarily, through the right edge of the foundation. Assessing the stresses with the help of the corresponding Mohr's circles depicted in figure 4.8, it is seen that the vertical stress at point A rotates by an angle $\pi - 2\theta$ (double that in figure 4.7) to reach point B, where its magnitude increases to:

$$\sigma_B = \sigma_o + c_u + c_u \cos \beta \tag{4.18}$$

with $\quad \beta = \dfrac{\pi}{2} - \theta$ $\hspace{4cm}$ (4.19)

Therefore, the stress at B for an angle $\theta = \pi/6$ (refer to figure 4.7):

$$\sigma_B = \sigma_o + 1.5c_u \tag{4.20}$$

Moreover, it is clear from figure 8.8 that the mean stresses p_1 and p_2 corresponding to any two consecutive circles are such that:

$$p_2 - p_1 = 2c_u \cos \beta \tag{4.21}$$

or

$$\Delta p = 2c_u \sin \theta \tag{4.22}$$

so that the ultimate lower bound stress at E is:

$$q_u = \sigma_0 + 5c_u \qquad\qquad (4.23)$$

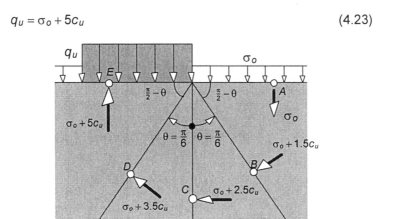

Figure 4.7: Stress field with three discontinuities.

This lower bound represents a marked improvement on the one obtained previously *via* equation 4.17.

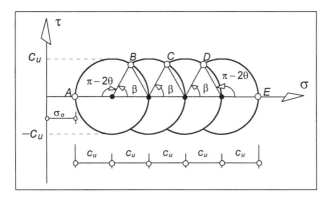

Figure 4.8: Mohr's circles corresponding to figure 4.7.

• (c) Stress field containing a stress fan

The stress field depicted in figure 4.9 has a stress fan subtending an angle $\theta = \pi/2$ and consisting of a large number of discontinuities each subtending an angle $d\theta$. Referring to the corresponding Mohr's circles of figure 4.10, it is seen that the (normal) stress at point A rotates through 90° to reach point B where its magnitude will have increased to $\sigma_0 + c_u$. Throughout the stress fan, the general relationship represented by equation 4.22 applies and, accordingly, when an elementary rotation $d\theta$ occurs within the fan, the change in the mean effective stress p is expressed as follows:

$$dp = 2c_u \sin d\theta \approx 2c_u \, d\theta \qquad (4.24)$$

Therefore, the change in the mean effective stress throughout the fan is:

$$\Delta p = \int_0^{\pi/2} 2c_u \, d\theta = \pi c_u \qquad (4.25)$$

Hence the ultimate lower bound stress at point D:

$$q_u = \sigma_0 + (2 + \pi) c_u \qquad (4.26)$$

which is the *highest* lower bound solution that can possibly be obtained.

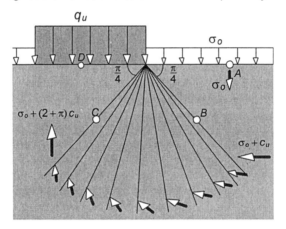

Figure 4.9: Stress field containing a stress fan.

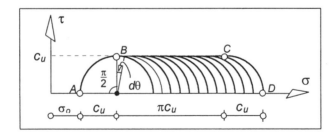

Figure 4.10: Mohr's circles corresponding to figure 4.9.

Because the highest lower bound of equation 4.26 is identical to the lowest upper bound of equation 9.16, an exact plastic solution to the ultimate bearing capacity of a surface footing is therefore achieved.

• (d) Stress field containing a stress fan: case of an inclined load

Let us derive the ultimate lower bound solution to the bearing capacity of a surface footing transmitting a load q inclined to the ground as illustrated in figure 4.11. Manifestly, the inclination of the load q will generate a shear stress τ, thus causing the major principal stress to rotate by an angle α such that:

$$\alpha = \tan^{-1}\left(\frac{\tau}{q}\right) \tag{4.27}$$

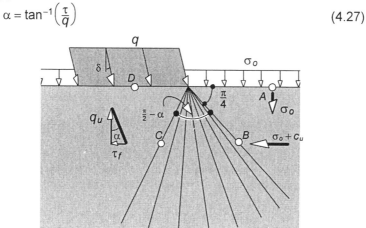

Figure 4.11: Case of inclined loading.

Moreover, any elementary rotation $d\theta$ occurring within the stress fan causes an increase in the mean stress dp according to equation 4.24, and consequently, the total change in the mean stress through the fan subtending an angle $(\frac{\pi}{2} - \alpha)$ is calculated as follows:

$$\Delta p = \int_0^{\frac{\pi}{2}-\alpha} 2c_u\, d\theta = c_u(\pi - 2\alpha) \tag{4.28}$$

Referring to the corresponding Mohr circles in figure 4.12, the lower bound solution to the normal stress is written as:

$$q_u = \sigma_0 + c_u(1 + \pi - 2\alpha + \cos 2\alpha) \tag{4.29}$$

the corresponding shear stress being:

$$\tau = c_u \sin 2\alpha \tag{4.30}$$

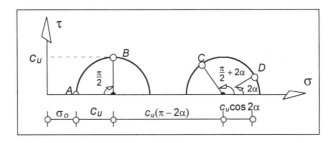

Figure 4.12: Mohr's circles corresponding to figure 4.11.

At the limit (*i.e.* at failure), the shear stress reaches its maximum value c_u when $\alpha = \pi/4$, yielding in the process the following ultimate bearing capacity:

$$q_u = \sigma_o + c_u\left(1 + \frac{\pi}{2}\right) \tag{4.31}$$

Let both equations 4.29 and 4.30 be rearranged respectively in the following way:

$$\frac{q_u - \sigma_o}{c_u} = 1 + \pi - 2\alpha + \cos 2\alpha \tag{4.32}$$

$$\frac{\tau}{c_u} = \sin 2\alpha \tag{4.33}$$

The graphs corresponding to these two equations, depicted in figure 4.13, indicate clearly that the ultimate bearing capacity corresponding to a surface footing subject to a load inclined at an angle $\alpha = \pi/4$, with a maximum shear stress, is precisely half that of a surface foundation transmitting a normal load with zero shear stress.

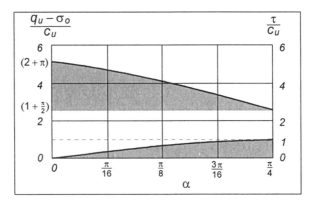

Figure 4.13: Effect of load inclination on the bearing capacity of a soil.

Also, figure 4.14, representing the variation of the normalised quantities τ/c_u and $(q_u - \sigma_0)/c_u$, shows that once it has reached its maximum value c_u, the shear stress at failure remains constant however small the corresponding normal stress may be.

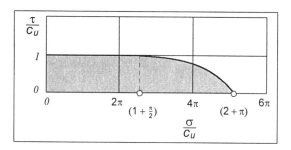

Figure 4.14: Relationship between normal and shear stresses at failure.

4.5 Kinematically admissible collapse mechanisms: drained behaviour

The following effective stress analysis of collapse mechanisms is based on the assumption that plastic deformations occur under an *associated flow rule*, meaning that the criterion of normality is fulfilled. Also, the soil is assumed to be *weightless*. Accordingly, the displacement within any chosen mechanism is characterised by a vector making an angle ϕ' (the effective angle of shearing resistance of the soil) with respect to any slip plane, thus reducing the internal work to zero, since any internal work done on a normal stress cancels out the work done on the corresponding shear stress. This therefore implies that an upper bound solution can be found by calculating the work done by the external loads, then equating it to zero. Consider the collapse mechanism of figure 4.15 where the shape of the failing block is characterised by a logarithmic spiral with the following equation:

$$\frac{r_2}{r_1} = \exp(\theta \tan \phi') \tag{4.34}$$

ϕ' being the angle of shearing resistance of the soil. When the block rotates anticlockwise by an angle $d\theta$, the average displacement of foundation is $B/2d\theta$; also according to equation 4.34:

$$OA = B\exp(\pi \tan \phi')$$

The same rotation $d\theta$ therefore causes the surface OA to have an upward displacement amounting to:

$$\frac{B}{2} d\theta \exp(\pi \tan \phi')$$

The total external work can now be determined:

$$\delta E = q_u \frac{B^2}{2} d\theta - q_o B \exp(\pi \tan \phi') \frac{B}{2} d\theta \exp(\pi \tan \phi')$$

and the upper bound solution to the bearing capacity of foundation is found by equating E to zero, hence:

$$q_u = q_o \exp(2\pi \tan \phi') \tag{4.35}$$

The latter equation yields a value $q_u = 18.7 q_o$ for an angle $\phi' = 25°$.

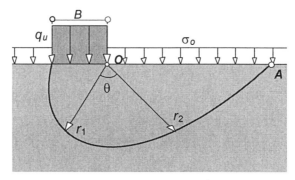

Figure 4.15: Logarithmic spiral collapse mechanism.

The next mechanism to consider is depicted in figure 4.16 and consists of a shear fan, sandwiched between two rigid blocks, subtending an angle $\theta = \pi/2$. As indicated in the figure, the velocity V makes an angle ϕ' with respect to the slip planes, and within the slip fan bounded by a logarithmic spiral, the velocity increases in proportion to the radii ratio, thus:

$$V_e = V \frac{r_2}{r_1} = V \exp\left(\frac{\pi}{2} \tan \phi'\right) \tag{4.36}$$

In addition, it easy to show that the distance OA is such that:

$$OA = B \tan\left(\frac{\pi}{4} + \frac{\phi'}{2}\right) \exp\left(\frac{\pi}{2} \tan \phi'\right) \tag{4.37}$$

Since only the vertical components of velocity are of interest (the soil is assumed to be weightless and the internal work within the slip fan is zero), it follows that:

- the (downward) vertical displacement of the block beneath the foundation is $V_1 = V \cos\left(\frac{\pi}{4} + \frac{\phi'}{2}\right)$

- the (upward) vertical displacement of the block to the right of the slip fan is $V_2 = V_e \cos\left(\dfrac{\pi}{4} - \dfrac{\phi'}{2}\right)$, or, substituting for V_e from equation 4.36:

$$V_2 = V\exp\left(\dfrac{\pi}{2}\tan\phi'\right)\sin\left(\dfrac{\pi}{4} + \dfrac{\phi'}{2}\right)$$

The external work can now be evaluated:

$$\delta E = q_u B V\cos\left(\dfrac{\pi}{4} + \dfrac{\phi'}{2}\right) - \sigma_o B\tan\left(\dfrac{\pi}{4} + \dfrac{\phi'}{2}\right)\exp\left(\dfrac{\pi}{2}\tan\phi'\right)$$

$$\times V\exp\left(\dfrac{\pi}{2}\tan\phi'\right)\sin\left(\dfrac{\pi}{4} + \dfrac{\phi'}{2}\right)$$

Finally, equating δE to zero, and rearranging yields the upper bound solution:

$$q_u = \sigma_o\tan^2\left(\dfrac{\pi}{4} + \dfrac{\phi'}{2}\right)\exp\left(\pi\tan\phi'\right) \qquad (4.38)$$

which is the *lowest* obtainable upper bound. For an angle $\phi' = 25°$, equation 4.38 yields a value $q_u = 10.7\sigma_o$, in marked contrast to the overestimate $q_u = 18.7\sigma_o$ resulting from the previous mechanism of figure 4.15.

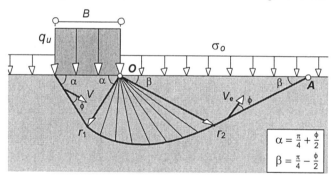

Figure 4.16: Rigid blocks related by a shear fan.

4.6 Statically admissible stress fields: drained behaviour

Prior to analysing a stress field, let us determine the effect that a rotation of a major stress has on the mean effective stress, that is the centre of the Mohr circle. Consider the case of a *frictional soil* (*i.e.* $c' = 0$) for which the failure criterion is written as follows:

$$\sigma_1' = \sigma_3'\tan^2\left(\dfrac{\pi}{4} + \dfrac{\phi'}{2}\right) \qquad (4.39)$$

Let the normal major stress rotate by a tiny angle $d\theta$, so that the corresponding Mohr circle centre moves by an amount dp' resulting in an angle $2d\theta$ as depicted in figure 4.17. Because $d\theta$ is very small, then $DA \approx DB$; also, it is clear from the figure that $\alpha = \frac{\pi}{2} - \phi' - d\theta$, and accordingly $\sin\alpha \approx \cos\phi'$.

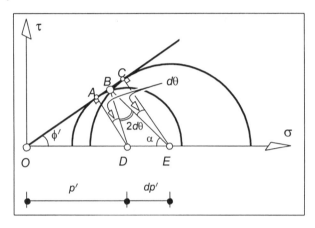

Figure 4.17: Effects of major stress rotation on p'.

On the other hand, the sine rule yields:

$$\frac{dp'}{\sin 2d\theta} = \frac{DB}{\sin\alpha} \qquad (4.40)$$

Knowing that $DB \approx DA = p'\sin\phi'$ and $\sin 2d\theta \approx 2d\theta$, then substituting for both quantities DB and $\sin\alpha$ into equation 4.40 and rearranging, it follows that:

$$\frac{dp'}{p'} = 2\tan\phi'\, d\theta \qquad (4.41)$$

Let us now consider the statically admissible stress field with one discontinuity, illustrated in figure 4.18. The corresponding Mohr circles of figure 4.19 show that the normal vertical stress σ_o at point A rotates through an angle of 180° to reach point B. Since the corresponding circle touches the failure envelope, the failure criterion of equation 4.39 is therefore applicable so that the stress at B is:

$$\sigma_B = \sigma_o \tan^2\left(\frac{\pi}{4} + \frac{\phi'}{2}\right) \qquad (4.42)$$

As one moves from B to C, the stress rotates a further 180°; whence, applying the failure criterion as in the previous case, it follows that the ultimate lower bound to the bearing capacity at C is:

$$q_u = \sigma_o \tan^4\left(\frac{\pi}{4} + \frac{\phi'}{2}\right) \tag{4.43}$$

For $\phi' = 25°$, equation 4.43 yields a value $q_u = 6.1\sigma_o$.

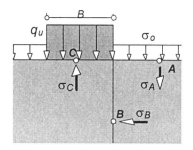

Figure 4.18: One discontinuity stress field.

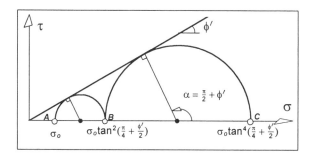

Figure 4.19: Mohr's circles corresponding to figure 9.18.

To improve on the value of the lower bound of equation 4.43, a stress field containing a stress fan can be considered. Referring to figure 4.20, the corresponding stress fan subtends an angle $\theta = \pi/2$ implying that the stress rotates by an angle π between points B and C on Mohr circles of figure 4.21. In addition, as has already been established, an elementary stress rotation $d\theta$ causes the mean effective stress p' (*i.e.* the centre of the Mohr circle) to move according to equation 4.41. Consequently, for an angle $\pi/2$ subtended by the fan, the displacement of the mean effective stress is easily integrated as follows:

$$\int_{p_1'}^{p_2'} \frac{dp'}{p'} = \int_0^{\pi/2} 2\tan\phi' \, d\theta$$

Hence: $p_2' = p_1' \exp(\pi \tan\phi')$ \hfill (4.44)

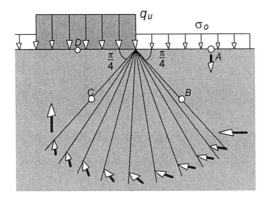

Figure 4.20: Stress field containing a stress fan.

Moreover, it is easy to show from the trigonometry of figure 4.21 that:

$$p'_1 = \frac{\sigma_o}{1 - \sin\phi'} \qquad \text{and} \qquad p'_2 = q_u\left(\frac{1}{1 + \sin\phi'}\right)$$

Substituting for both p'_1 and p'_2 in equation 4.44, then rearranging:

$$q_u = \sigma_o\tan^2\left(\frac{\pi}{4} + \frac{\phi'}{2}\right)\exp\left(\pi\tan\phi'\right) \qquad (4.45)$$

The latter equation thus yields the *highest lower bound* of the ultimate bearing capacity, which happens to be identical to the *lowest upper bound* established earlier *via* equation 4.38, whence the exact solution to the plastic collapse of a *drained weightless soil*, subject to a normal load transmitted by a surface footing.

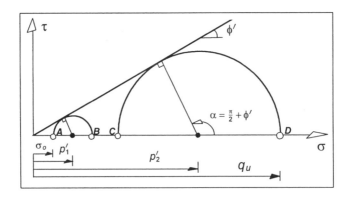

Figure 4.21: Mohr's circles corresponding to figure 8.20.

The previous analysis undertaken can easily be expanded to include the general case of a surface footing subject to an inclined load depicted in figure 4.22. Clearly, equation 4.41 must be integrated within the limits of the angle subtended by the stress fan. Hence:

$$p_2' = p_1' \exp[(\pi - 2\alpha)\tan\phi']$$

but $\qquad p_1' = \dfrac{\sigma_o}{1 - \sin\phi'}$

whence: $\qquad p_2' = \dfrac{\sigma_o}{1 - \sin\phi'} \exp[(\pi - 2\alpha)\tan\phi'] \qquad\qquad (4.46)$

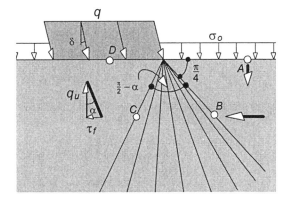

Figure 4.22: General case of an inclined loading.

Referring to figure 4.23, it is seen that both ultimate normal and shear stresses at point D are respectively:

$$q_u = p_2' + ED\cos 2\alpha \qquad\qquad (4.47a)$$

$$\tau_f = ED\sin 2\alpha \qquad\qquad (4.47b)$$

Making use of the trigonometry of the figure, it follows that:

$$\frac{p_2'}{\sin(2\alpha - \delta)} = \frac{ED}{\sin\delta} = \frac{p_2'\sin\phi'}{\sin\delta}$$

therefore:

$$\frac{\sin\delta}{\sin(2\alpha - \delta)} = \sin\phi' \quad\text{and}\quad ED = p_2'\sin\phi'$$

Substituting for ED and p_2' in equation 4.47 and rearranging yields:

$$q_u = \frac{\sigma_o}{1 - \sin\phi'}(1 + \sin\phi'\cos 2\alpha)\exp\left[(\pi - 2\alpha)\tan\phi'\right] \qquad (4.48a)$$

$$\tau_f = \frac{\sigma_o}{1 - \sin\phi'}\sin\phi'\sin 2\alpha \,\exp\left[(\pi - 2\alpha)\tan\phi'\right] \qquad (4.48b)$$

with

$$\alpha = \frac{1}{2}\left[\delta + \sin^{-1}\left(\frac{\sin\delta}{\sin\phi'}\right)\right]$$

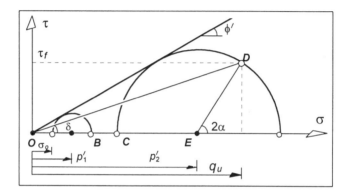

Figure 4.23: Mohr's circles corresponding to figure 4.22.

To illustrate the effects of a load inclination on the bearing capacity, the quantities q_u/σ_o and τ_f/σ_o are plotted in figure 4.24 for different angles δ in the case of a typical soil with an angle of shearing resistance $\phi' = 25°$. It is seen that the ratio q_u/σ_o decreases from its maximum value for $\delta = 0$ to a value almost 4.5 times smaller for $\delta = \phi'$.

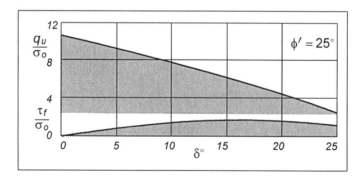

Figure 4.24: Effect of load inclination on the bearing capacity.

In fact, as suggested by Bolton (1991), there is a case to limit the load inclination to $\delta = 15°$, regardless of the type of soil, in which case the bearing capacity is roughly half that corresponding to a normal load as illustrated in the figure.

4.7 Effects of soil weight and cohesion

The analysis undertaken so far was based on the assumption that the soil on which the foundation is built is weightless and, when drained, cohesionless. Let us, first, assess the contribution of the weight of soil to the ultimate bearing capacity q_u. In this respect, a quick glance at figure 4.25, for instance, makes you realise that neglecting the self weight of the block OAB can potentially lead to a markedly underestimated ultimate load (*i.e.* too safe!).

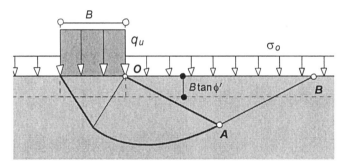

Figure 4.25: Effect of soil weight on its bearing capacity.

Several authors have suggested the use of different ways in which the weight of soil is included in the bearing capacity equation. However, a simple yet effective method based on the suggestion by Bolton can be used to the same effect. It consists of assuming that the foundation is built at a depth $B \tan\phi'$, then considering the pressure due to this extra soil weight as a load applied at foundation level. The net effect will be to increase all normal effective stresses by an amount $\sigma' = \gamma' B \tan\phi'$, with γ' referring to the effective unit weight of soil. Thus, for a normal load, equation 4.45 is altered as follows:

$$q_u + \gamma'B\tan\phi' = (\sigma_o + \gamma'B\tan\phi')\tan^2\left(\frac{\pi}{4} + \frac{\phi'}{2}\right)\exp(\pi\tan\phi')$$

Introducing the (dimensionless) factor $N_q = \tan^2\left(\frac{\pi}{4} + \frac{\phi'}{2}\right)\exp(\pi\tan\phi')$, then rearranging:

$$q_u = \sigma_o N_q + \gamma'B\tan\phi'(N_q - 1) \tag{4.49}$$

Moreover, if the foundation is built on a stiff heavily overconsolidated clay, then apparent cohesion can constitute a component of the long term drained shear strength of the soil, provided that its properly measured value is limited to a maximum of $15\,kN/m^2$ (refer to the discussion on cohesion in section 2.5.4). The effect of cohesion is to increase all normal stresses by an equal amount $c'\cot\phi'$; accordingly, equation 4.49 is modified:

$$q_u + c'\cot\phi' = (\sigma_0 + c'\cot\phi')\,N_q + \gamma'B\tan\phi'(N_q - 1)$$

which can be rewritten as:

$$q_u = \sigma_0 N_q + c'N_c + \frac{\gamma'B}{2}N_\gamma \tag{4.50}$$

with the bearing capacity factors:

$$N_q = \tan^2\left(\frac{\pi}{4} + \frac{\phi'}{2}\right)\exp(\pi\tan\phi') \tag{4.51a}$$

$$N_c = \cot\phi'(N_q - 1) \tag{4.51b}$$

$$N_\gamma = 2\tan\phi'(N_q - 1) \tag{4.51c}$$

Equation 4.50, together with equations 4.51, represent the basic classical bearing capacity equation of a strip footing with a width B and an infinite length, transmitting a normal effective stress σ'_0 to the soil at foundation level. While equations 4.51 can be used to calculate the bearing capacity factors N_c, N_q and N_γ, it is manifestly more straightforward to use the charts depicted in figure 4.26 to the same effect.

It is noticeable that, under undrained conditions (for which $\phi = 0$), equations 4.51 yield respectively $N_q = 1$, $N_c = (2 + \pi)$ and $N_\gamma = 0$. Accordingly, in the short term, the ultimate bearing capacity of a strip footing of infinite length, calculated from equation 4.50, is reduced to the following:

$$q_u = \sigma_0 + c_u N_c \tag{4.52}$$

In 1951, Skempton showed that the bearing capacity factor N_c in equation 4.52 depends not only on the shape of foundation, but also on its depth of embedment. He then produced the charts depicted in figure 4.27 from which N_c can be estimated. It is seen that for a strip footing of infinite length, N_c value varies between $(2 + \pi)$ at surface level and 7.5 for a depth to width ratio $D/B \geq 5$. Alternatively, a square or a circular foundation are characterised by a factor $N_c = 2\pi$ at surface level, increasing to $N_c = 9$ for a ratio $D/B \geq 5$.

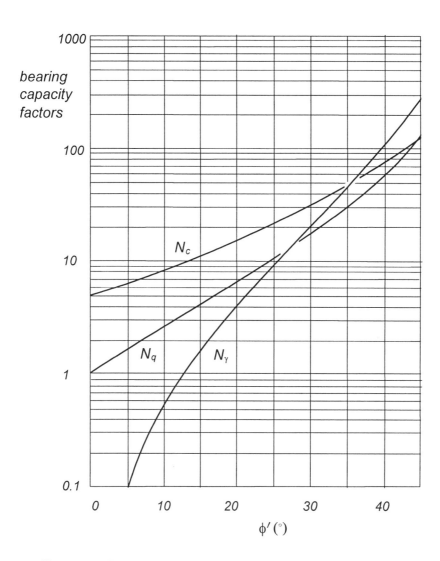

Figure 4.26: Bearing capacity factors for a strip footing of infinite length.

For a rectangular foundation with an area $A = L \times B$, $(L \geq B)$, an interpolation is needed, and in this respect, the following relationship can be used cautiously:

$$N_{c(\text{rectangle})} = N_{c(\text{square})}(0.84 + 0.16B/L) \tag{4.53}$$

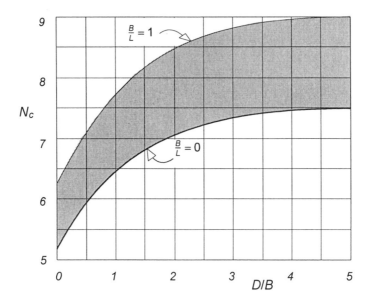

Figure 4.27: Bearing capacity factor N_c for undrained conditions.
(Reproduced by permission of the Building Research Establishment.)

4.8 Effects of foundation shape and depth and load inclination

Figure 4.27 illustrates the effects that the depth of embedment as well as the shape of the foundation have on the soil ultimate bearing capacity. Although the use of this figure is restricted to undrained short term conditions, its implications are significant in that one surely expects similar effects to affect equation 4.50 which should then be expressed in the following general form:

$$q_u = \sigma_o N_q s_q d_q + c' N_c s_c d_c + \gamma' \frac{B}{2} N_\gamma s_\gamma d_\gamma \qquad (4.54)$$

where the (empirically derived) correction factors s and d reflect the effects of foundation shape and depth respectively. Although several methods were suggested in the literature by which these factors can be estimated, the following relationships (Hansen, 1970, De Beer, 1970) can be used with caution:

- *shape factors*: $s_c = 1 + \dfrac{B}{L} \dfrac{N_q}{N_c}$ (4.55a)

$$s_q = 1 + \frac{B}{L} \tan \phi' \qquad (4.55b)$$

$$s_\gamma = 1 - 0.4 \frac{B}{L} \qquad (4.55c)$$

- *depth factors:* $d_c = 1 + 0.4\xi$ (4.55d)

$$d_q = 1 + \xi \tan \phi'\left(1 - \sin \phi'\right)$$ (4.55e)

$$d_\gamma = 1$$ (4.55f)

with $\xi = D/B$ if $D/B \le 1$, and $\xi = \tan^{-1}(D/B)$ if $D/B > 1$.

Moreover, if the foundation is subject to a load inclined at an angle with respect to the vertical as depicted in figure 4.28, then a fraction of the load will be transmitted horizontally and, accordingly, the three bearing capacity factors must be corrected to take account of the inclination effects. The respective correction factors can be evaluated in the following manner (Hanna and Meyerhof, 1981):

$$I_c = I_q = \left(1 - \frac{\beta^\circ}{90}\right)^2$$ (4.56a)

$$I_\gamma = \left(1 - \frac{\beta^\circ}{\phi'}\right)^2$$ (4.56b)

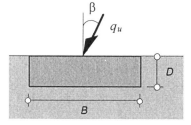

Figure 4.28: Effect on the bearing capacity of an inclined load.

It follows that, for a foundation of a *finite* shape, embedded at a depth D and subject to an inclined load, the general ultimate load capacity expression is:

$$q_u = \sigma'_o N_q s_q d_q I_q + c' N_c s_c d_c I_c + \gamma' \frac{B}{2} N_\gamma s_\gamma d_\gamma I_\gamma$$ (4.57)

Example 4.1

Assume that the foundation in figure 4.28 has a width $B = 2.5\,m$, a length $L = 4\,m$, and is embedded at a depth $D = 1.5\,m$ in a medium clay characterised in the short term by an undrained shear strength $c_u = 55\,kN/m^2$. Knowing that, under drained conditions, the clay has an angle of shearing resistance $\phi' = 21^\circ$ and an apparent cohesion

$c' = 5\,kN/m^2$, estimate the *allowable load per linear metre* that can be safely applied to the foundation at an angle $\beta = 12°$ with respect to the vertical, yielding a factor of safety $F = 3$ against shear failure. As far as the position of the water table is concerned, you may like to consider the three following scenarios : (a) the water is at the ground surface, (b) the water is at foundation level and (c) the water is several metres below foundation level. For the clay, it can be assumed that both saturated and bulk unit weights have the same value $\gamma = 20\,kN/m^3$.

- **Short term analysis**

For the undrained short term behaviour, the bearing capacity equation 4.52 applies provided that appropriate correction factors are used. Thus, taking account of the linear aspect of the *ultimate* load, the (rectangular) shape of foundation and the load inclination, it follows that:

$$q_u = L(\sigma_o + c_u N_{cr})\,l_c$$

- the total stress at foundation level is: $\sigma_o = \gamma D = 20 \times 1.5 = 30\,kN/m^2$;
- the bearing capacity factor for a square foundation with a ratio $D/B = 0.6$ is read from figure 4.27 on the graph corresponding to $B/L = 1$: $N_c \approx 7.2$. This value then has to be corrected (because of the rectangular shape of the foundation) through equation 4.53, whence:

$$N_{cr} = 7.2\left(0.84 + 0.16 \times \frac{2.5}{4}\right) = 6.8$$

- the correction factor l_c relating to the load inclination is calculated from equation 4.56a:

$$l_c = \left(1 - \frac{12}{90}\right)^2 = 0.75$$

So, the ultimate line load to which the foundation can be subjected in the short term is:

$$q_u = 4 \times (30 + 55 \times 6.8) \times 0.75 = 1212\,kN/m$$

Usually, the factor of safety against shear failure is defined as the ratio of the *net ultimate load* q_{un} to the *allowable net load* q_{an} applied to the foundation. The net ultimate and the net allowable loads are found by subtracting from the ultimate and allowable loads respectively the weight of soil above foundation level when applicable, thus:

$$q_{un} = q_u - L\gamma D = 1212 - 4 \times 20 \times 1.5 = 1092\,kN/m$$

Since a factor of safety of 3 is required in this instance, it follows that the allowable load per linear metre is:

$$\frac{q_{un}}{q_a - L\gamma D} = 3 \quad \Rightarrow \quad q_a = \frac{q_u - L\gamma D}{3} + L\gamma D$$

$$= \frac{1092}{3} + 4 \times 20 \times 1.5 = 484 \, kN/m.$$

• **Long term analysis**

For the long term analysis, effective stresses are used in conjunction with equation 4.57. Because the ultimate load is expressed per linear metre, it follows that:

$$q_u = L\left(\gamma' D N_q s_q d_q I_q + c' N_c s_c d_c I_c + \gamma' \frac{B}{2} N_\gamma s_\gamma d_\gamma I_\gamma\right)$$

γ' being the *effective* unit weight of soil. Prior to considering the position of the water table, let the different factors in the above equation be evaluated as follows:

• the bearing capacity factors are read from figure 4.26 for $\phi' = 21°$; thus:

$$N_q \approx 7, \; N_c \approx 17, \; N_\gamma \approx 5.$$

• the shape factors are calculated from equations 4.55(a)–(c); whence:

$$S_c = 1 + \frac{2.5}{4} \times \frac{7}{17} \approx 1.26, \quad S_q = 1 + \frac{2.5}{4}\tan 21 = 1.24,$$

$$S_\gamma = 1 - 0.4 \times \frac{2.5}{4} = 0.75$$

• the depth factors are computed from equations 4.55(d)–(f) in the knowledge that $\xi = 1.5/2.6 = 0.6$:

$$d_c = 1 + 0.4 \times 0.6 = 1.24, \quad d_q = 1 + 0.6\tan 21(1 - \sin 21) = 1.15,$$

$$d_\gamma = 1$$

• the inclination factors are determined using equations 9.56:

$$I_c = I_q = \left(1 - \frac{12}{90}\right)^2 = 0.75, \quad I_\gamma = \left(1 - \frac{12}{21}\right)^2 = 0.183$$

Inserting all these quantities in the bearing capacity equation, the result would then depend on the level of water, hence the following three distinct cases.

- (1) *The water table is at the ground surface* in which case the effective unit weight of soil is $\gamma' = \gamma_{sat} - \gamma_w = 10\,kN/m^3$ and, accordingly:

$$q_u = 4 \times (10 \times 1.5 \times 7 \times 1.24 \times 1.15 \times 0.75)$$
$$+4 \times (5 \times 17 \times 1.26 \times 1.24 \times 0.75)$$
$$+4 \times \left(\frac{10 \times 2.5}{2} \times 5 \times 0.75 \times 1 \times 0.183\right) = 881.9\,kN/m$$

Hence an allowable load per linear metre:

$$q_a = \frac{q_u - L\gamma D}{3} + L\gamma D = \frac{881.9 - 120}{3} + 120 = 374\,kN/m$$

- (2) *The water table is at foundation level (i.e. at a depth of 1.5 m).* In this case, the effective unit weight $\gamma' = 10\,kN/m^3$ is used in conjunction with the factor N_γ, while the effective stress σ'_o at foundation level is calculated using a unit weight $\gamma = 20\,kN/m^3$. Thence:

$$q_u = 4 \times (20 \times 1.5 \times 7 \times 1.24 \times 1.15 \times 0.75)$$
$$+4 \times (5 \times 17 \times 1.26 \times 1.24 \times 0.75)$$
$$+4 \times \left(\frac{10 \times 2.5}{2} \times 5 \times 0.75 \times 1 \times 0.183\right) = 1331.1\,kN/m$$

and the allowable load is in this case:

$$q_a = \frac{1331.1 - 120}{3} + 120 = 523.7\,kN/m$$

- (3) *The water table is well below foundation level.* An effective unit weight $\gamma' = 20\,kN/m^3$ applies, and the calculation yields:

$$q_u = 4 \times (20 \times 1.5 \times 7 \times 1.24 \times 1.15 \times 0.75)$$
$$+4 \times (5 \times 17 \times 1.26 \times 1.24 \times 0.75)$$
$$+4 \times \left(\frac{20 \times 2.5}{2} \times 5 \times 0.75 \times 1 \times 0.183\right) = 1365.4\,kN/m$$

leading to an allowable load:

$$q_a = \frac{1365.4 - 120}{3} + 120 = 535.3\,kN/m$$

The calculations are significant in many ways since it transpires that, in the long term, the water level has a detrimental effect on the bearing capacity of a foundation. It is seen that in this particular instance, were the clay to be totally submerged (*i.e.* the water level at the ground surface), the bearing capacity would be reduced by more than 35% compared with that corresponding to a water table well below foundation level. On the other hand, the bearing capacity in the short term depends to a large extent on the undrained shear strength of the clay and, once more, the calculations indicate that the short term bearing capacity, in this example, is more critical than the long term one unless the clay is waterlogged. This shows how crucial it is to manage the water level as far as the design of foundations is concerned.

4.9 Effects of load eccentricity

4.9.1 One way eccentricity

Consider the case of a shallow foundation subject to a moment $M_x = Qe$ as depicted in figure 4.29, where e represents the load eccentricity. Obviously, this type of loading is bound to affect the bearing capacity of foundation since the *effective* loaded area (*i.e.* the grey area in figure 4.29) is smaller in comparison with the actual foundation area $L \times B$. In fact, such foundations are designed in precisely the same way as described earlier, in other words both equations 4.52 and 4.57 still apply *provided that:*

- the width of foundation B in equations 4.52 (implicitly) and 4.53, as well as equation 4.57 is replaced by the effective width:

$$B' = B - 2e \tag{4.58}$$

- the effective width B' *must* be used in conjunction with equations 4.55(a)–(c) to evaluate the shape factors, the depth factors being unaffected.

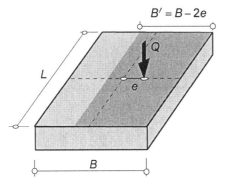

Figure 4.29: Effective width of an eccentrically loaded foundation.

A detailed examination of the calculations corresponding to this type of eccentricity (*i.e.* one way eccentricity) can be found in example 6.4, section 6.11 (chapter 6).

In assessing the stresses beneath the foundation base, a distribution such as the one illustrated in figure 4.30 can be assumed, notwithstanding the fact that the *actual* distribution might be slightly different. Based on the stress diagram in figure 4.30, it can easily be shown that the optimum values at either extremity of foundation are as follows:

$$q_{min} = \frac{Q}{BL} - \frac{B}{2}\frac{M}{I} \qquad (4.59a)$$

$$q_{max} = \frac{Q}{BL} + \frac{B}{2}\frac{M}{I} \qquad (4.59b)$$

the moment of inertia being $I = LB^3/12$, and the moment is, with reference to figure 4.30, $M = Qe$. Substituting for I and M in the above equations, it follows that:

$$q_{min} = \frac{Q}{BL}\left(1 - \frac{6e}{B}\right) \qquad (4.60a)$$

$$q_{max} = \frac{Q}{BL}\left(1 + \frac{6e}{L}\right) \qquad (4.60b)$$

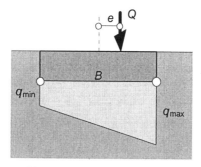

Figure 4.30: Assumed stress profile beneath an eccentrically loaded foundation.

Clearly, equation 4.60a implies that as soon as the eccentricity is larger than the value $B/6$, the quantity q_{min} becomes negative, meaning that the foundation starts to lift off the ground on one side. This can quickly give rise to a stress concentration that can cause a bearing capacity failure; hence, it is essential when designing a foundation with an eccentric loading, to ensure that the minimum stress beneath the foundation remains positive, in other words, the following criterion must be fulfilled:

$$e \leq \frac{B}{6} \qquad (4.61)$$

4.9.2 Two-way eccentricity

When a foundation is subject to a two-way eccentricity, then its effective area, that is the area affected by the load, will be similar to the dark area depicted in figure 4.31 *provided* that the two following criteria relating to eccentricity are not violated:

$$e_L \leq \frac{L}{6} \tag{4.62a}$$

$$e_B \leq \frac{B}{6} \tag{4.62b}$$

In this case, it can easily be shown that the effective width of foundation B' is such that:

$$B' = \frac{(B+B_1)}{2} + \frac{L_1(B-B_1)}{2L} \tag{4.63}$$

L being the actual length of foundation and B_1 and L_1 (refer to figure 4.31) can be determined from the charts established by Higher and Anders (1985) and reproduced in figures 4.32 and 4.33.

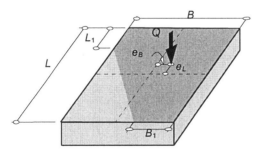

Figure 4.31: Effective area related to a two-way eccentricity load.

Obviously, the ultimate load capacity of a foundation that is subject to such loading conditions will be affected through the use of the effective width B' in the bearing capacity equations. Once more, remember that only the shape factors of equations 4.55(a)–(c) are affected by B'; the depth factors being calculated in conjunction with the *actual* width B. Thus, the ultimate total load that can be supported by a foundation is markedly reduced if the load in question is applied eccentrically as illustrated in figure 4.31, the reason being the decrease in the effective loaded area (refer to the dark area in figure 4.31). Since the total load is calculated from the ultimate pressure in the following way: $Q = A/q_u$, then any decrease in the area is bound to affect the loading capacity of the foundation.

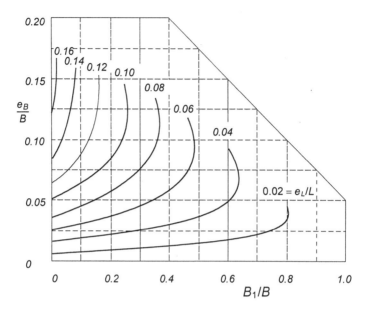

Figure 4.32: Higher and Anders charts for the determination of B_1.
(Reproduced by permission of the ASCE.)

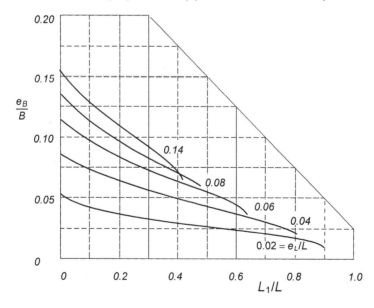

Figure 4.33 : Higher and Anders charts for the determination of L_1.
(Reproduced by permission of the ASCE.)

Example 4.2

Consider the case of a rectangular foundation, similar to that depicted in figure 4.31, with a width $B = 3.5\,m$, a length $L = 5\,m$, embedded at a depth $D = 1.8\,m$ in a dense sand characterised by an effective angle of shearing resistance $\phi' = 40°$ and a bulk unit weight $\gamma = 21\,kN/m^3$. The water level being well below the foundation base, calculate the maximum vertical load Q that can be applied eccentrically to the foundation. Assume the following eccentricities apply: $e_B = 0.5\,m$, $e_L = 0.7\,m$.

It is easy to check that the eccentricities do not violate the criteria set in equation 4.62. Prior to calculating the effective width of foundation B' from equation 4.63, the quantities B_1 and L_1 need to be determined. It is seen that:

$$\frac{e_L}{L} = \frac{0.7}{5} = 0.14 \quad \text{and} \quad \frac{e_B}{B} = \frac{0.5}{3.5} = 0.143$$

Accordingly, figures 4.32 and 4.33 yield respectively the values:

$$B_1/B \approx 0.075, \ L_1/L \approx 0.025$$

from which the following values are then obtained:

$$B_1 = 0.26\,m, \quad L_1 = 0.125\,m$$

Equation 4.63 can now be used to calculate B':

$$B' = \frac{1}{2}(3.5 + 0.26) + \frac{0.125}{2 \times 5}(3.5 - 0.26) = 1.92m$$

The effective area is thus: $A' = L \times B' = 5 \times 1.92 = 9.6\,m^2$ (compared with the *actual* area $A = 3.5 \times 5 = 17.5\,m^2$). Since the foundation is embedded in a cohesionless soil, and subject to a *vertical* load, albeit eccentrically, the bearing capacity equation 4.57 is then reduced to the following:

$$q_u = \gamma D N_q\,s_q\,d_q + \gamma\frac{B'}{2}N_\gamma\,s_\gamma\,d_\gamma$$

The bearing capacity factors corresponding to an angle $\phi' = 40°$ are read from figure 4.26:

$$N_q = 60, \quad N_\gamma \approx 105$$

The shape factors are calculated using the *effective width* B'. Thus, using equations 4.55(b)–(c), it follows that:

PROBLEMS

$$S_q = 1 + \frac{B'}{L}\tan\phi' = 1 + \frac{1.92}{5}\tan 40 = 1.32$$

$$S_\gamma = 1 - 0.4\frac{B'}{L} = 1 - 0.4 \times \frac{1.92}{5} = 0.85$$

The depth factors are calculated in conjunction with the *actual width B* from equations 4.55(e)–(f) knowing that $\xi = \frac{D}{B} = \frac{1.8}{3.5} = 0.514 < 1$:

$$d_q = 1 + \xi\tan\phi'(1 - \sin\phi') = 1 + 0.514\tan 40(1 - \sin 40) = 1.154$$

$$d_\gamma = 1$$

Whence the ultimate pressure:

$$q_u = 21 \times 1.8 \times 60 \times 1.32 \times 1.154 + \frac{21 \times 192}{2} \times 105 \times 0.85 \times 1$$
$$= 5254\,kN/m^2$$

The corresponding ultimate vertical load is thence obtained as follows:

$$Q = q_u A' = 5254 \times 9.6 = 50.438\,MN$$

If a factor of safety of 2.5 were required against shear failure, then the *allowable load* can be calculated in a way similar to that used in the previous example:

$$q_a = \frac{q_u - L\gamma D}{2.5} + L\gamma D = \frac{5254 - 5 \times 21 \times 1.8}{2.5} + 5 \times 21 \times 1.8$$

$$= 2215\,kN/m^2$$

Whence an allowable vertical load:

$$Q_a = q_a A' = 2215 \times 9.6 = 21.264\,MN$$

Problems

4.1 An excavation of depth H is to be made in a (dry) soil with a bulk unit weight γ and an undrained shear strength c_u. The excavation sides are prevented from collapsing through the use of struts.

(a) Consider the short term collapse mechanism depicted in figure p4.1a, then use the upper bound theorem to establish the expression of the ultimate pressure q_u needed to counteract the bottom heave of the excavation.

(*b*) Use the same upper bound theorem in conjunction with the long term collapse mechanism of figure *p4.1b*, and establish the relationship between the ratios H/B and q_u/q_o.

Ans: (a) $q_u = q_o (1 + \frac{H}{B}) + \gamma \frac{H^2}{2}(\frac{1}{B} + \frac{2}{H}) - 2c_u(1 + \frac{\pi}{2} + \frac{H}{B})$

(b) $\frac{H}{B} = \exp(-\frac{\pi}{2}\tan\phi')\left[\frac{q_u}{q_o}\tan^2(\frac{\pi}{4} + \frac{\phi'}{2})\exp(\pi\tan\phi') - 1\right]$

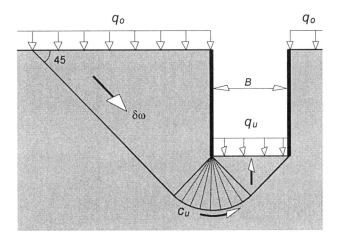

Figure p4.1a

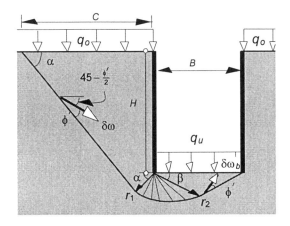

Figure p4.1b

4.2 Use the upper bound theorem and the collapse mechanism of figure p4.2 to establish the expression of the net ultimate pressure q_u that can be transmitted to the soil by the shallow foundation of width B.

Ans: $q_u = q_o \exp(\frac{\pi}{2} \tan \phi') \tan^2(\frac{\pi}{4} + \frac{\phi'}{2}) \left[\exp(\frac{\pi}{2} \tan \phi') + \frac{H}{B} \right]$

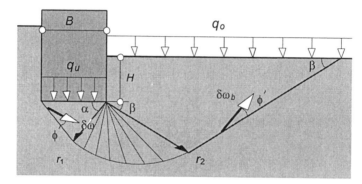

Figure p4.2

4.3 An excavation of depth H is carried out in a soil with a unit weight γ and an undrained shear strength c_u. Use the upper bound theorem in conjunction with the failure mechanism of figure p4.3, then establish the expression of the ultimate horizontal force P_1.

Ans: $P_1 = \gamma \frac{H^2}{2} \left(1 + \frac{2B}{H} \tan \alpha \right) - 2c_u H \left[1 + \frac{B}{H}(1 + \frac{\pi}{2}) \right]$

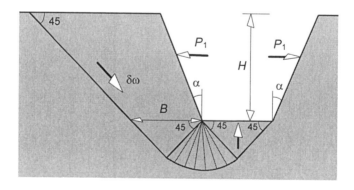

Figure p4.3

4.4   Consider the statically admissible stress field containing a stress
fan, depicted in figure p4.4. Assuming that the excavation is
undertaken in a (dry) clay with a bulk unit weight γ and an
effective angle of shearing resistance ϕ', use the lower bound
theorem to establish the expression for the ultimate heave
resistance q_u at the bottom of the excavation, then estimate its
magnitude for an angle $\phi' = 22°$.

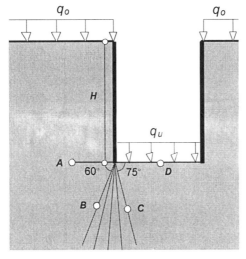

Figure p9.4

Ans: $$q_u = \frac{(q_0 + \gamma H)}{(1 - \sin\phi')\tan^2(\frac{\pi}{4} - \frac{\phi'}{2})}\left[1 + \sin\phi' + 0.845\exp\left(\frac{\pi}{2}\tan\phi'\right)\right]$$

$\phi' = 22°$ $\Rightarrow$ $q_u = 10.43(q_0 + \gamma H)$

4.5   A long retaining wall with a 3 m wide base is founded at a depth of
1.2 m in a silty sand. The analysis of static forces applied to the
wall yielded an eccentric resultant load $R = 400\,kN/m$, inclined at
an angle $\alpha = 20°$ with respect to the vertical as depicted in figure
p4.5. Above the ground water table situated at foundation level,
the sand has a bulk unit weight $\gamma = 18\,kN/m^3$, and below the
water, its saturated unit weight is $\gamma_{sat} = 19.8\,kN/m^3$.
The appropriate shear strength parameters of the sand are
$c' = 0$, $\phi' = 35°$. Calculate the eccentricity e if a factor of safety
against shear failure $F = 3$ is required.

Ans: $e \approx 0.49\,m$

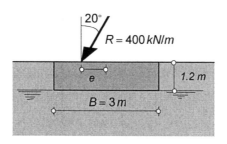

Figure p4.5

4.6 A rectangular foundation with a ratio $B/L = 0.8$, built at a depth $D = 2\,m$, is designed to support safely a net increase in vertical pressure of a magnitude $q_n = 150\,kN/m^2$, allowing for a factor of safety $F = 3$ against shear failure. The foundation is embedded in a thick layer of saturated firm clay having an undrained shear strength $c_u = 60\,kN/m^2$. Calculate the foundation size.

Ans: $B = 1.6\,m$, $L = 2\,m$

4.7 The foundation of a prop is embedded at a depth $D = 2.5\,m$ in a layer of saturated dense sand with an effective angle of shearing resistance $\phi' = 39°$ and a saturated unit weight $\gamma_{sat} = 20\,kN/m^3$. The prop is assumed to be transmitting a concentrated load $R = 5000\,kN$, inclined at an angle $\beta = 12°$ with respect to the vertical. The design of the foundation allows for a two-way eccentricity as depicted in figure p4.7, with $e_B = 0.3\,m$ and $e_L = 0.5\,m$.

(a) Estimate the ultimate bearing capacity of the foundation.

(b) Calculate the available factor of safety against shear failure.

Ans: (a) $q_u = 1682\,kN/m^2$, (b) $F = 4.56$

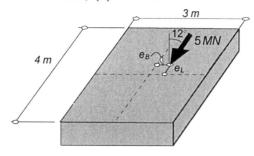

Figure p4.7

References

Bolton, M. D. (1991) *A Guide to Soil Mechanics*. M. D & K. Bolton, Cambridge.

Calladine, C. R. (1985) *Plasticity for Engineers*. Ellis Horwood Ltd, New York.

De Beer, E. E. (1970) *Experimental determination of the shape factors and bearing capacity factors of sands*. Géotechnique, 20 (4), pp. 387–411.

Hanna, A. M. and Meyerhof, G. G. (1981) *Experimental evaluation of bearing capacity of footings subjected to inclined loads*. Canadian Geotechnical Journal, 18 (4), pp. 599–603.

Hansen, J. B. (1970) *A Revised and Extended Formula for Bearing Capacity*. Danish Geotechnical Institute, Bulletin 28, Copenhagen.

Higher, W. H. and Anders J. C. (1985) *Dimensioning footings subjected to eccentric loads*. Journal of Geotechnical Engineering, ASCE, 111 (GT5), pp. 659–665.

Skempton, A. W. (1951) *The Bearing Capacity of Clays*. Proceedings of the Building Research Congress, London.

CHAPTER 5

Design of pile foundations

5.1 Type of piles

A *deep foundation* is defined as a foundation unit whose depth is at least five times larger than its width. Such a foundation unit provides support to an externally applied load through friction developing on its sides, better known as *skin* or *shaft friction*, and also through its *toe* or *base* as depicted in figure 5.1. The proportions of both *skin friction* and *base resistance* depend on the soil in which the pile is embedded, and the graphs on each side of figure 5.1 give an indication of how the overall axial load applied at the pile head is transferred to the soil along the pile shaft. For a pile embedded in a thick layer of soft clay, most of the resistance develops along the shaft, and the pile is referred to as a *floating pile*. However, when the pile is driven through a layer of soft clay, to be embedded in a much stiffer soil, then toe resistance is predominant and the pile is known as an *end bearing pile*.

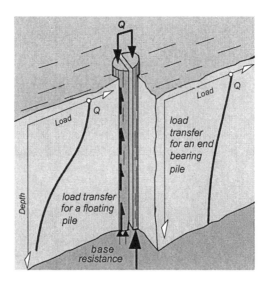

Figure 5.1: Axial load transfer through a piled foundation.

In both cases, both shaft friction and toe resistance must be calculated for the overall load capacity of the pile to be correctly evaluated, because the applied (axial) load is transferred from pile to soil through a combination of shaft friction and toe resistance. There is evidence that deep foundations were used by the Romans when oak and olive wood piles were considered imperishable when submerged in water. Perhaps the most famous site where wooden piles were used extensively is Venice, where some buildings are thought to be supported by 1100 year old wooden piles. However, since the mid-twentieth century, piles are almost exclusively made of concrete and steel.

Piles are classified into two categories as follows:

- **(a)** *Displacement piles (or driven piles)*

In the case of a *displacement pile*, the soil is moved laterally as the pile is driven into the ground and, obviously, the larger the cross-sectional area of the pile, the larger the volume of soil displaced to make room for the pile. Accordingly, a compaction process takes place in the vicinity of the pile, to an extent that a vertical soil movement can be observed at the ground surface were the pile to be driven into a dense granular material. The increased density during driving can be a mixed blessing, since it increases the shaft friction but, in the meantime, it can potentially impede the driving of the pile to the required depth. Also, *heave* may affect adjacent piles, particularly in dense sands. Piles can be of different cross-sectional areas as shown in figure 5.2, and they can be made of precast concrete, prestressed concrete, steel tubes or steel boxes.

The method of installation of displacement piles usually consists of using hydraulic diesel or compressed air hammers and, consequently, the pile head and toe should be protected so as to prevent any structural damage to the foundation. Obviously, the force needed to *drive* the pile to the desired depth *exceeds* the load the pile is designed to carry safely. Moreover, the driving generates tensile stresses within the pile due to wave reflections off its tip and, therefore, concrete piles must be designed to withstand these excess stresses. Tip reflections are a particular problem in clays where end resistance is small and reflections can be very large.

On the other hand, piles installed in sands can be driven using vibration methods, in which case, care must be taken so as to minimise the structural damage to neighbouring buildings since vibration can cause quicksand conditions to occur. In particular, vibration has important effects in looser sands where it causes a *volume decrease*. Also, piles with diameters of less than the nominal value of 250 *mm*, known as *micropiles*, can be jacked into the ground (usually hydraulically) against a fixed reaction.

 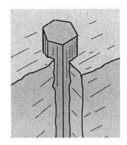 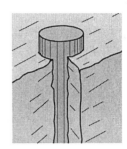

Figure 5.2: Some displacement piles.

Some of the most widely used types of displacement piles and their installation techniques are briefly introduced in the following.

- *Prefabricated concrete piles*: these are constituted of reinforced concrete, and can be prestressed. These piles are installed either by driving or by vibration. Piles with diameters of between 200 *mm* and 600 *mm* can be prefabricated into up to 14 *m* long elements which are then driven *in situ* through jacking against a fixed reaction. During this process the different elements can be prestressed. For plain reinforced concrete piles, jointing systems allow installation of very long piles in some ground conditions.
- *Steel piles*: these are made of steel with a minor copper content (usually less than 0.5%), and may be jacked into the ground against a fixed reaction. They may also be driven using conventional hammers.
- *Driven and cast-in-place piles* (also known as *Franki piles*): these are plugged tubes, with a fabricated steel or a reinforced concrete shoe and a protected head, driven by a hammer to the required depth. The tube is then filled with concrete. A steel reinforcement cage is always used (reinforcement serves the purpose of resisting *heave forces* when adjacent piles are driven). In most cases, the tube is withdrawn during concreting.
- *Steel piles coated with concrete*: steel tubes, steel H-sections or steel boxes, with steel plates larger than their cross-sectional areas welded at their bases are driven whilst concrete of high workability is poured to fill the void space including that created by the protruding base plate. Such a process requires that the external steel area is covered by at least a 40 *mm* thick concrete coat. Note that this type of piles is not common.
- *Screwed and cast-in-place piles*: the process consists of obtaining a threaded hole by pushing a rotating drilling screw into the ground as depicted in figure 5.3. On reaching the required depth, the drilling equipment is then withdrawn through rotation in the opposite direction, while fresh concrete is poured into the hole. This process leads to a substantial increase in the carrying capacity of the pile (Imbo, 1984,

Bustamente and Gianeselli, 1995). This type of *Franki* pile is especially suited for clays (excluding very soft and boulder clays).

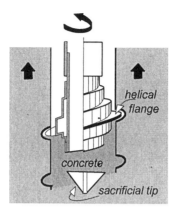

Figure 5.3: 'Atlas' screwed and cast in place pile.

• ***Open base piles***: these are of relatively small cross-sectional areas such as *steel H-sections*, *open end steel tubes* and *boxes* (see figure 5.4), and are mainly used *offshore*. In particular, *open end concrete shell piles* consist of elements of concrete shells, with a length of between 1.5 *m* and 3 *m*, an internal diameter of between 0.7 *m* and 0.9 *m* and a wall thickness of about 150 *mm*, driven with an open base to the required depth, then prestressed *in situ*. Sometimes, the upper layer of the soil plug inside the tube can be drilled using a rotating cutter, so as to facilitate the driving.

Regardless of their (cross-sectional) size, these piles, known as *low displacement piles*, offer a small cross-section to the soil and are easy to drive because, in this case, less compaction develops along the shaft during driving, thus lessening the friction between pile and soil. The reduced friction is an obvious advantage when the required depth of embedment is substantial.

  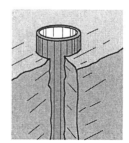

Figure 5.4: Low displacement piles.

• *(b) Non-displacement piles (bored piles)*

For a non-displacement pile, a borehole with a diameter corresponding to that of the pile is first excavated, then a concrete pile is cast *in situ*. For *small diameter piles* (up to 600 *mm*), boreholes are often executed using rigs of the type used for site investigations. Larger diameter boreholes are usually executed using rotary drilling methods (see Fleming *et al.* (1992) for instance). The two main techniques used in conjunction with bored piles consist of *augering* and *grabbing*, the choice of which depends on soil conditions and pile dimensions. Hence, some *heavy duty rotary augers* can drill pile shafts with diameters of 4.5 *m* and depths of up to 70 m (Tomlinson, 1995). Depending on soil conditions, the borehole may have to be supported so as to prevent its collapse. A full casing can be used during drilling, then withdrawn during 'concreting' of the pile. Also, a *bentonite slurry* can provide lateral support to the walls of a borehole (refer to figure 5.5), due to its *high density* and *thixotropic properties* (*i.e.* it forms a gel at rest and becomes a fluid if rapidly agitated). Bentonite consists largely of montmorillonite, a clay mineral known for its expansive properties as introduced in chapter 1. *Bentonite slurry* is made of a suspension of 5% bentonite (by weight) in water, thus forming a mud with a unit weight $\gamma_b \approx 11\,kN/m^3$, greater than that of water ($\gamma_w \approx 10\,kN/m^3$). This slurry is characterised by thixotropic properties, in that its high viscosity under low stresses decreases as the stresses are increased. For these properties, bentonite slurry is widely used in the construction industry to provide lateral support to the walls of an excavation while preventing any water ingress.

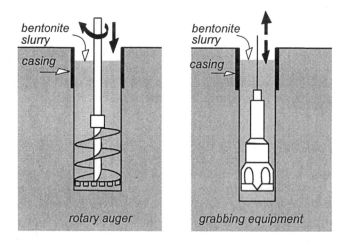

Figure 5.5: Augering and grabbing of pile shafts.

When the soil conditions are such that rotary augers cannot be used economically (drilling through boulder clays or very coarse gravel for example), then a *grabbing rig* is often preferred (see figure 5.5). This technique is used especially in conjunction with the construction of *diaphragm walls* (which are discussed in detail in chapter 7) and *barettes* which are piles with large cross-sectional areas with different shapes as illustrated in figure 5.6. Generally, the cross-sectional dimensions of a barette are such that $2\,m \le e \le 3\,m$, and $0.5\,m \le b \le 1.5\,m$. Bentonite slurry is usually used as a support for the trench walls as depicted in figure 5.5. On achieving the required depth, a reinforcing steel cage is placed inside the borehole (or the trench in the case of a barette) then concrete is pumped through a *trémie* pipe (refer to figure 5.7).

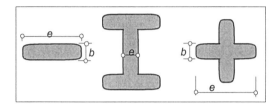

Figure 5.6: Barettes dimensions.

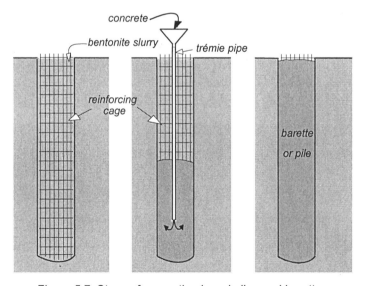

Figure 5.7: Steps of concreting bored piles and barettes.

Relatively small diameter bored piles (up to 1.5 *m* in diameter) can be executed using *short flight* or *continuous flight augers*. In particular, technologically advanced continuous flight augers are available, and figure

5.8 depicts the steps related to the execution of a bored pile using the *Starsol* rig developed and operated by *Solétanche*. On reaching the final depth, the auger is gradually withdrawn while concrete is injected under controlled pressure through the telescopic *trémie* pipe. Once concreting is finished, steel reinforcement is then pushed into the freshly poured concrete. Notice that the maximum size of concrete aggregates is limited to 20 *mm*; moreover, a plasticising agent is usually mixed with concrete so as to improve what Tomlinson (1995) refers to as 'pumpability' (*sic*).

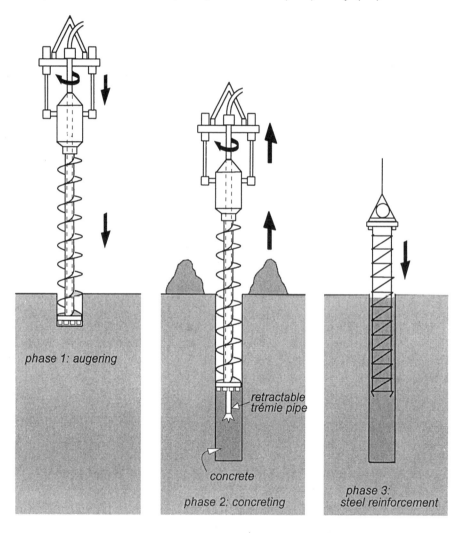

Figure 5.8: Starsol rig—Solétanche.
(Reproduced by permission of Solétanche.)

Other systems are operated under full and continuous computer control, so that the construction process becomes almost automatic. This form of construction appears to lead to better and more consistent pile performance. Special cases of deep foundations include the following.

- *Hand excavated deep shafts* are used where drilling equipment cannot be operated due to obstructed soil conditions or to a lack of access. For obvious safety reasons, the shaft is lined as the depth progresses. This method of drilling can be cost effective and offers an *ad hoc* solution to the inspection of the shaft base before concreting,

- *Open-well caissons* are used in conjunction with water bearing strata ranging from soft clays to gravels. They are, however, unsuitable for boulder clays which are difficult to excavate by grabbing. The sinking of the caisson under its own weight occurs as the soil is excavated by grabbing from within the shaft. There are instances in which corrective measures may be required to ensure the verticality of the caisson as it is sunk. Once the required depth is reached, the bottom of the well is then sealed by pouring a thick layer of concrete. The well can thereafter be filled with water, sand or concrete. *Pneumatic caissons*, as opposed to open well caissons, are excavated by hand under air pressure and, accordingly, stricter safety regulations apply depending on the level of air pressure used, which should not exceed $350\,kN/m^2$. A detailed analysis of excavation under air pressure is presented in conjunction with tunnelling in cohesive soils in section 8.2.

There are no rules, as such, for the *selection* of a particular type of pile. Rather, some recommendations based mostly on common sense can be advocated. The selection of a type of pile is closely related to the type of soil, the type of structure to be supported (bridges, high rise buildings, quays *etc.*), and to the magnitude and nature of loading transmitted to the soil (*i.e.* axial loading and/or horizontal loading). Generally, the contractor has a major say in the selection of pile type, depending on the following.

- The type of technology available (driving, augering, continuous flight augering or grabbing equipment). In particular, the continuous flight augering method accounts for about 40% of the bored pile market (1999 estimate).
- The site conditions [onshore or offshore, soil strata, and groundwater conditions are major factors affecting the selection of piles (steel or concrete piles, driven or bored, barettes, deep shafts, caissons *etc.*)].
- The cost of piling.

Piles with diameters exceeding 1 *m* are usually used for large projects (*i.e.* bridges, very tall buildings *etc.*). The length of a pile is dictated by the need to generate enough skin friction and/or base resistance to support the structural load. Bored and cast-in-place piles and barettes are reinforced wholly or partially. The depth of reinforcement depends on soil conditions, lateral and eccentric loading conditions, and the requirements of the construction process.

5.2 Pile testing

It is now becoming a common practice to check cast-in-place piles and barettes *selectively* for major defects that may arise, for instance, from the inclusion of soil during concreting or from lack of cover to steel reinforcement. This process involves the undertaking of *integrity tests* which are sometimes limited to a few preselected piles for reasons of cost effectiveness. Obviously, because of the limited number of tested piles, there is always a possibility that some defective piles may not be detected. The nature of these non-destructive tests can be acoustic, seismic, dynamic or radiometric. The principles involved consist of measuring pulses transmitted through the pile (case of acoustic and radiometric tests), or waves reflected from the pile base (case of seismic and dynamic tests). Signals thus measured can be interpreted to check, for example, major pile defects, the length of pile or the pile–soil contact at the pile base. Further technical details on how these tests are actually undertaken, and on the way they are interpreted can be found in Fleming *et al.* (1992).

Piles are also tested for their carrying capacity using *in situ* full scale *load tests*. These tests must be considered carefully because they can be expensive. They may involve the use of sophisticated instruments and complex testing set ups. Preliminary load tests are undertaken *prior* to the construction of the actual deep foundation. They consist of applying incremental loads to a pile using the set up depicted schematically in figure 5.9. The pile settlement is monitored against the applied load until the occurrence of failure, or until a specified load has been reached. By definition, the *ultimate overall load at failure* is that at which the *full soil resistance* is mobilised. It is usual practice to apply one or more unload–reload cycles well before the (estimated) ultimate load is reached. However, the usefulness of several unload–reload cycles is debatable since they involve different stress paths to those of the normal incremental loads. Also, each load increment is maintained *constant* for about 60 *min* during loading and 5 *min* during unloading, before the next increment is applied. In this respect, it is important to bear in mind that the *constancy* of applied load is vital to permit useful analysis of test results. Because piles are sometimes load-tested until the occurrence of failure and to stress levels which may damage the pile structure, they cannot then be part of the actual foundation and, accordingly, preliminary load tests are undertaken prior to the construction of the foundation. On the other hand, unless the soil in which the pile is driven is highly permeable (sand or gravel), pile driving is bound to generate excess porewater pressures in the vicinity of the pile. If the pile is driven through a highly overconsolidated clay, then negative excess porewater pressures are generated (refer to section 2.5.4) meaning that, with time, the porewater pressure *increases* and the effective stress around the pile shaft (*i.e.* the skin friction) *decreases* until a large enough volume of water is absorbed by the soil matrix around the pile shaft so that the excess porewater pressure becomes zero. Alternatively, if the pile is driven through a normally consolidated clay, then positive excess porewater pressure is produced and, given time, the porewater pressure *decreases* and the effective stress (and hence the friction applied around the pile shaft) *increases*. As a result, load tests must allow for these adjustments to take place and, hence, a knowledge of dissipation rates may be necessary.

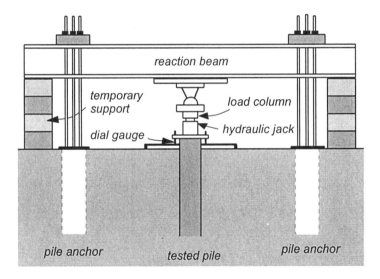

Figure 5.9: Set up used in conjunction with axial load testing of piles.

Depending on the type of pile instrumentation and the testing method, a load test can yield:

- the ultimate shaft resistance of the pile and the corresponding settlement (*i.e.* penetration);
- the penetration corresponding to the ultimate base carrying capacity of the pile;
- the overall load and settlement behaviour;
- the distribution of the unit skin friction along the pile shaft (which depends on the availability and accuracy of instrumentation).

Figure 5.10 depicts a typical load-penetration curve along the pile shaft and at the pile base in the case of a bored and cast-in-place or a driven pile. The graph shows, in particular, that the settlement S_s corresponding to the shaft friction at failure Q_s is noticeably smaller than the settlement S_f needed to mobilise the ultimate base resistance Q_b of the pile. Also noticeable is the difference in the carrying capacity of the pile along the shaft and at the base (the grey area in figure 5.10). Shaft capacity usually predominates in clay soils and base load does so in sands.

The pile must be designed so that not only is the structural load carried safely, but also the settlement is kept within an acceptable limit. In other words, the *safe load* or the *working load* must be a *fraction* of the ultimate carrying capacity Q_u in figure 5.10. In any case, the overall settlement under the working load Q_a must be kept smaller than S_s in figure 5.10 by a reasonable *margin of safety*. In this respect, it is advised to use the lesser of the following two loads as the working load in the case of bored and cast-in-place piles:

$$Q_a = \frac{Q_u}{2.5} \tag{5.1}$$

or

$$Q_a = Q_s + \frac{Q_b}{3} \tag{5.2}$$

Notice that Burland *et al.* (1966) advocated the use of an overall factor of safety of 2 in equation 5.1 (instead of 2.5). The use of such a working load in conjunction with bored and cast-in-place piles ensures that the overall settlement does not constitute any cause for concern since its magnitude S is kept well within the acceptable limits of shaft settlement as illustrated in figure 5.11. At the end of a test, it is seen that on removing the load, a *rebound* of the pile head is measured (soil recovery plus elastic component of settlement that consist of the axial displacement between points A and B in figure 5.11). The *residual settlement* under the applied load corresponds to the total settlement minus the rebound. However, equations 5.1 and 5.2 should be applied cautiously, and a degree of conservatism is even advised by using these equations in conjunction with driven piles (for which the skin friction and base resistance can be increased due to soil compaction in the vicinity of piles during driving). For bored and cast-in-place piles, Tomlinson recommends using a smaller working load Q_a (*i.e.* larger factors of safety), corresponding to the lesser of the two following values:

$$Q_a = \frac{Q_u}{2.5} \tag{5.3}$$

or

$$Q_a = \frac{Q_s}{1.5} + \frac{Q_b}{3.5} \tag{5.4}$$

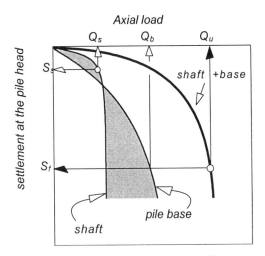

Figure 5.10: Typical load-penetration curves
for a driven or bored and cast-in-place pile.

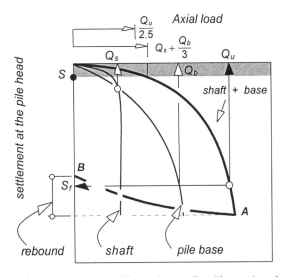

Figure 5.11: Typical overall settlement under
working load (bored and cast-in-place piles).

Ample experimental evidence indicates that the settlement of small
diameter piles (up to 600 mm) under working loads calculated from
equation 5.3 rarely exceeds 10 mm (see Tomlinson (1995), for instance).
The pile can also be instrumented along the shaft with *extensometers*,
which are reusable strain gauges utilised for measuring the local axial

deformations $\Delta l/l$ of a pile under a constant load increment. These deformations are then used, in conjunction with appropriate calibration graphs, to determine the load distribution along the pile shaft and at its base, as well as the changes in skin friction along the shaft as the loading proceeds. Results corresponding to a full scale load test, undertaken on a screwed and cast-in-place pile are depicted in figure 5.12 (Bustamente and Gianeselli, 1997). The pile, with a diameter of $360\,mm$ and a length of $8.5\,m$, was installed in a site near *Lille* in the North of France characterised by a $5\,m$ thick layer of sandy clay overlying a thick layer of dense clayey sand. The entire operation of pile execution, that is drilling, concreting and inclusion of an $8.5\,m$ long steel reinforcement cage took less than 15 *min*.

In particular, figure 5.12*a* indicates that just over one third of the full load $Q = 1500\,kN$ is transferred to the pile base, whereas nearly $Q/6$ is resisted by skin friction along portion C of the pile (refer to shaded areas in figure 5.12*a*). Figure 5.12*b* on the other hand, shows that skin friction increases initially with settlement, then reaches limiting values as the settlement approaches the magnitude at which failure occurs. More importantly, the same figure indicates that skin friction is not uniform along the pile shaft. It is seen that the friction developed along portion D is much higher than that generated along portions A and B due to the mechanism of load transfer from pile to soil (see figure 5.1). This remark is all the more important since the ultimate loads Q_s, Q_b and Q_u in figure 5.10 are not always determined from load tests. As mentioned earlier, such tests may be expensive and may only justifiably be used in conjunction with large projects. Alternatively, the ultimate loads can be estimated using the *static method* of design, provided that representative soil parameters are available, and a somewhat larger factor of safety is used to estimate the working (safe) load. Also, *back analysis* of normal pile load tests carried out to near failure constitutes another very useful way of design (Fleming, 1992, England and Fleming, 1994). Prior to developing both methods, it is essential to realise that they do not constitute the only alternative way of pile design. In terms of design methods in general (including those applied to pile design), there are many regional variations which differ from country to country. The reader is therefore urged to appreciate the need to explore other methods of design and to make himself (herself) familiar with regional or even sometimes local variations. It is worth reiterating what was written in the preface to the extent that Geotechnics is not an exact science, rather, it can be described as an art in which the artist (*i.e.* the engineer) has to rely sometimes, if only partly, on his or her intuition (*i.e.* judgement). Consequently, the fact that different methods of design almost invariably yield different results for the same problem does not imply that all methods, other than method A with an outcome nearest to the measured results, are wrong. Rather, it shows that under the circumstances, method A is more suitable. Different conclusions may possibly be drawn were the circumstances to change.

There is often a need to utilise more than one method of design so that any aberrations can be discarded, bearing in mind that in the vast majority of cases in geotechnical design, the aim is limited to predicting a solution within $x\%$ of the behaviour observed in the field and to use adequate factors of safety (sometimes a solution within 50% either side of the exact measured solution can be deemed very acceptable). This explains the need to adjust the same method of design so that regional or even local variations of soil conditions are taken into account.

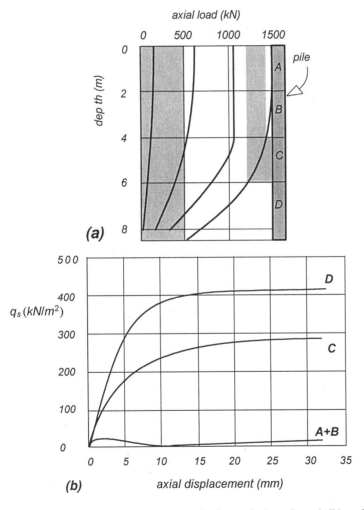

Figure 5.12: (a) Load transfer from pile to soil, and (b) variation of skin friction with axial displacement along the pile shaft (From Bustamente and Gianeselli (1997), by permission of the Laboratoire Central des Ponts et Chaussées.)

5.3 Ultimate loading capacity of axially loaded single piles using the static method

5.3.1 General considerations

In the static method of analysis, the *net ultimate loading capacity* of a single vertical pile, subject to an *axial load,* is evaluated as follows (refer to figure 5.13):

$$Q_u = Q_s + Q_b - W \qquad (5.5)$$

with

Q_u: ultimate loading capacity
Q_s: ultimate skin friction
Q_b: ultimate base resistance
W: weight of pile.

Note that, in many cases, W can safely be discarded since its effect on Q_u is relatively minor.

The (safe) working load related to the ultimate load of equation 5.5 can be estimated using, for example, a *minimum overall factor of safety F* = 3. Accordingly:

$$Q_a = \frac{Q_s + Q_b}{3} - W \qquad (5.6)$$

As mentioned earlier, the least favourable conditions for the ultimate carrying capacity may depend on the excess porewater pressure generated during pile execution. Thus, if a pile were driven through a thick layer of saturated sand, for instance, then no excess porewater pressure will be engendered because of the high permeability of such a soil. Consequently, provided that the water table remains relatively unaltered, the ultimate carrying capacity of the pile would be similar in the short term (that is a few days after pile installation) and in the long term (*i.e.*years after the pile execution). In other words, the state of effective stresses applied to the pile does not alter with time, and hence the analysis should be undertaken under *drained conditions* in terms of *effective stresses.*

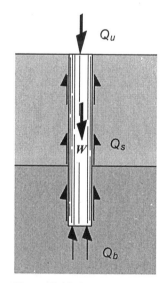

Figure 5.13: Load transfer from pile to soil.

On the other hand, if the pile were driven or bored and cast in place in a clayey soil, then its ultimate carrying capacity may initially depend on the nature of excess porewater pressure generated in the vicinity of the pile during installation. Because the pile must be designed to withstand the most unfavourable loading conditions when the soil develops the least resistance, the following possibilities arise.

(1) • The clay is heavily overconsolidated, hence pile installation generates negative excess porewater pressure, thus causing the effective stresses in the vicinity of the pile (and therefore the friction on the pile shaft and the soil resistance at the pile base) to *increase.* The negative water pressure may take some time to dissipate (the time can be measured in days or even weeks in the case of a single pile, and can sometimes be expressed in years in the case of large pilegroups), during which, the porewater pressure gradually increases and the effective stresses *decrease* until zero excess water pressure is reached. Accordingly, the least favourable soil resistance (*i.e.* the smallest effective stresses) may occur in the *long term* when all excess negative porewater pressure has dissipated. Hence the critical carrying capacity of the pile must be calculated under *drained conditions* in terms of *effective stresses.*

(2) • The pile is installed through a normally consolidated clay, in which case, positive excess porewater pressure is engendered, leading to a *decrease* in the effective stresses around the pile immediately after its installation. With time, as the excess water pressure slowly dissipates, the porewater pressure decreases and the effective stresses increase. Accordingly, the smallest effective stresses, or the least soil resistance to the load applied at the pile head, occur in the *short term* when the excess porewater pressure is hardly changed, and the critical carrying capacity of the pile must therefore be evaluated under *undrained conditions* in terms of *total stresses.*

(3) • The clay in which the pile is driven or bored and cast in place is lightly overconsolidated, and pile installation generates relatively small excess porewater pressure. In this case, the critical carrying capacity of the pile may occur either in the long term or in the short term, and therefore both *drained* and *undrained conditions* ought to be checked, in that the design should be undertaken using both *total stresses* and *effective stresses*, so that the least favourable conditions are found.

(4) • The pile is installed through multi-layered clay soil, whereby the top layer is still undergoing a process of consolidation. This implies that an excess porewater pressure already exists within the soil matrix of the top layer and, consequently, any extra excess porewater pressure

generated by pile installation is bound to induce a differential consolidation settlement between the pile and the top clay layer. This process generates a down force around the pile shaft in the consolidating clay layer known as *negative skin friction*. Because consolidation is a long term process (refer to Azizi, 2007), the final settlement of the top layer occurs when all excess porewater pressure has dissipated and, hence, the critical carrying capacity of the pile occurs in the long term. Accordingly, whenever a negative skin friction is predicted, pile design must be undertaken under *drained conditions* in terms of *effective stresses*.

5.3.2 Undrained carrying capacity of single piles embedded in clays

Under undrained conditions, the net ultimate carrying capacity of an axially loaded single pile is calculated from equation 5.5. In the short term, the *ultimate skin friction* of a pile embedded in a homogeneous isotropic clay is evaluated as follows:

$$Q_s = A_s \alpha c_u \tag{5.7}$$

with

$A_s = \pi d L$ shaft area (*d* and *L* are pile diameter and length respectively)

c_u : *average* undrained shear strength of the clay along the pile shaft

α : adhesion factor.

The *adhesion factor* corresponds to the ratio of the unit skin friction mobilised on the pile shaft to the undrained shear strength c_u of undisturbed clay. Because the process of pile driving or boring and casting in place is bound to disturb the soil, the skin friction developed in the short term around the pile shaft will only be a *fraction* of c_u, depending on the nature of the soil strata and pile dimensions. Naturally, one would expect the magnitude of skin friction developed around the shaft of a pile driven into a thick layer of a stiff overconsolidated clay to be different from that mobilised around the shaft of the same pile driven through a layer of soft clay and just reaching the top of an underlying layer of gravel for instance.

Reasonable estimates of the adhesion factor can be cautiously obtained from the useful graphs compiled by Tomlinson (1995) and Weltman and Healy (1978), and reproduced in figures 5.14 and 5.15. In particular, the difference in behaviour exhibited in figures 5.14(a), (b) and (c) reflects the degree of clay disturbance generated during pile installation.

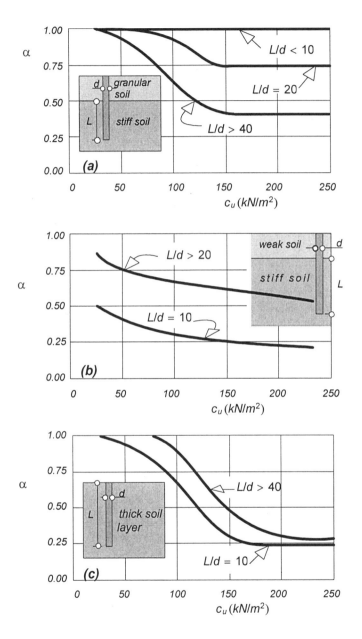

Figure 5.14: Adhesion factors applied to different soil strata: (a) granular soil overlying stiff soil; (b) weak soil underlain by stiff soil; (c) uniform layer of soil (from Tomlinson (1995), reproduced by permission).

It is seen that in figure 5.14(*a*) the pile is initially *driven* through a granular soil, and some granular frictional material is bound to 'adhere' to the pile shaft as it penetrates the clay layer. The skin friction mobilised around the shaft is thus maximised by the adhering thin layer of granular material, as long as the depth of embedment *L* within the clay layer remains modest ($L/d < 10$; *d*: pile diameter). This positive effect decreases gradually as the depth of embedment *L* increases (see graphs corresponding to $L/d = 20$, and $L/d > 40$ in figure 5.14(*a*)). Adhesion factors for intermediate values of *L/d* can be interpolated from the three graphs. In figure 5.14(*b*), the pile is *driven* through a layer of soft soil overlying a layer of stiff soil. Under such circumstances, a process similar to that described previously develops with an opposite effect. In fact, while the pile is driven through the soft soil, a thin layer of soft material adheres to the shaft. As the pile embedment extends into the stiff soil, the soft material is gradually 'peeled', thus increasing the skin friction (*i.e.* the adhesion factor). Figure 5.14(*c*) reflects the fact that, for piles *driven* into a thick layer of soil, a smaller degree of clay disturbance (hence a larger adhesion factor) is induced by a larger depth of embedment. Bear in mind, however, that the empirical relationships in figure 5.14 are meant for driven piles and, as stated earlier, driving a pile through a stiff clay carries the risk of damaging the pile section due to wave reflection. Consequently, driving deep piles in firm or stiff clay soils is often not recommended. Moreover, the graphs in figures 5.14 and 5.15 should be used with caution since the magnitude of the adhesion factor is affected by the pile surface roughness. This emphasises the need for alternative methods of design (such as the use of an effective stress analysis) to be explored.

Figure 5.15 on the other hand applies to piles bored and cast-in-place, driven or driven and cast-in-place in a boulder clay or a glacial till.

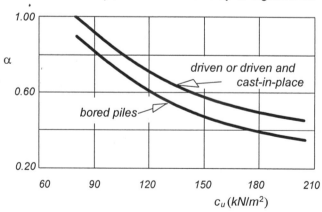

Figure 5.15: Adhesion factors for piles installed in boulder clays and glacial tills (from Weltman and Healy (1978), reproduced by permission).

If the soil properties vary with depth, then equation 5.7 would be expressed as follows:

$$Q_s = \int_0^L p\,\alpha\,c_u\,dz \qquad (5.8)$$

with L: pile length

         p: pile perimeter (which can also vary with depth).

The *ultimate base resistance* of the pile is calculated from the bearing capacity equation 4.50 established earlier:

$$Q_b = A_b(c_u N_c + \gamma L N_q + \tfrac{1}{2}\gamma\,d\,N_\gamma) \qquad (5.9)$$

with

A_b : cross-sectional area of the pile base, which includes the soil plug in the case of a steel tube pile or a H-section pile (see figure 5.16)

L: pile length d : pile diameter (or equivalent).

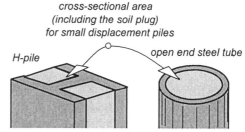

Figure 5.16: Cross-sectional areas used in conjunction with equation 5.8.

However, for undrained conditions, a clay is characterised by an angle of shearing resistance $\phi_u = 0$, in which case both equations 4.51a and c (refer to section 4.7) yield the bearing capacity factors $N_q = 1$ and $N_\gamma = 0$ respectively. Moreover, when the pile is driven through a layer of soft clay in a way that its base reaches a much higher bearing capacity stratum, Fleming *et al.* (1992) suggest that a linear interpolation should be made between a value $N_c = 6$ for the case of the pile base just reaching the stiff stratum, up to $N_c = 9$ where the pile base penetrates the stiff layer by three diameters or more as illustrated in figure 5.17.

On substitution for the values $N_q = 1$ and $N_\gamma = 0$ into equation 5.9, it follows that:

$$Q_b = A_b(N_c\,c_u + \gamma L) \qquad (5.10)$$

Notice that the quantity $A_b\gamma L$ in equation 5.10 represents the total weight of soil at pile base level, and can be assumed, for all practical purposes, to be equal to the weight of pile W. Consequently, equation 5.10 is rewritten as follows:

$$Q_b - W = N_c c_u A_b \qquad (5.11)$$

and, according to equation 5.5, the short term *ultimate loading capacity* of the pile is in this case:

$$Q_u = Q_s + Q_b - W = c_u(\alpha A_s + N_c A_b) \tag{5.12}$$

where A_s is the area of the pile shaft, and A_b represents the cross-sectional area of the pile base.

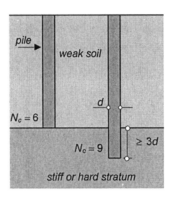

Figure 5.17: Short term effects of pile embedment on the bearing capacity factor N_c.

5.3.3 Drained carrying capacity of single piles embedded in clays

When a pile is embedded in a *stiff overconsolidated clay*, the long term *net ultimate loading capacity* calculated from equation 5.5 corresponds to the critical value for which the pile should be designed. Therefore, an effective stress analysis is required. Under drained conditions, the *ultimate skin friction* is calculated as follows:

$$Q_s = \int_0^L p\sigma_v' K \tan \delta \, dz \tag{5.13}$$

with

     σ_v' : vertical (overburden) effective stress *prior* to pile installation
     p: pile perimeter
     δ: friction angle of pile–soil interface which is dependent on the surface roughness of the pile, usually in the range $0.75\phi' \leq \delta \leq \phi'$ for steel or concrete piles, ϕ' being the effective angle of shearing resistance of the clay (Fleming *et al.*, 1992).

As for the coefficient of earth pressure K in equation 5.13, Poulos and Davis (1980) related it to the overconsolidation ratio *OCR* of the clay in the following manner:

$$K \approx (1 - \sin \phi')(OCR)^{1/2} \tag{5.14}$$

The *ultimate base resistance* of the pile is calculated from the bearing capacity equation 4.50, in which the drained cohesion of the clay is usually assumed to be $c' = 0$; whence:

$$Q_b = A_b(\sigma'_{vb}N_q + \frac{1}{2}\gamma'dN_\gamma) \approx A_b\sigma'_{vb}N_q \qquad (5.15)$$

The quantity $\frac{1}{2}\gamma'dN_\gamma$ being negligible.

σ'_{vb} corresponds to the vertical effective stress at pile base level *prior* to pile installation, and the bearing capacity factor N_q varies with the soil angle of shearing resistance ϕ' as per figure 5.18 corresponding to average values compiled by Poulos and Davies (1980) and based on the work of Berezantzev *et al.* (1961). Thence the *net ultimate loading capacity* under drained conditions, for piles embedded in clays characterised by $c' = 0$:

$$Q_u = Q_s + Q_b - W = A_b\sigma'_{vb}N_q - W + \int_0^L pK\sigma'_v \tan\delta\, dz \qquad (5.16)$$

in which the quantity W corresponds to the *effective weight* of the pile.

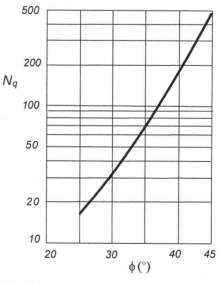

Figure 5.18 : *Bearing capacity factor for drained analysis of piles in clays (Berezantzev et al. (1961), redrawn from Poulos and Davis, 1980).*

Example 5.1

A circular concrete pile with a diameter $d = 520\,mm$ is driven through a thick layer of soft saturated normally consolidated clay (see figure 5.19) having an undrained shear strength $c_u = 18\,kN/m^2$ at the ground surface, increasing with depth at a rate of $0.5\,kN/m^2$ per metre. The drained behaviour of the clay is characterised by an angle $\phi' = 20°$ and $c' = 0$. Estimate the length of pile required to carry safely a working vertical load $Q_a = 200\,kN$. The unit weight of concrete is $\gamma_c = 24\,kN/m^3$ and, for water, use $\gamma_w = 10\,kN/m^3$. Assume an overall factor of safety $F = 4$ applies.

This example is used to illustrate the fact that piles installed through a normally consolidated clay are characterised by a smaller carrying capacity in the short term. Accordingly, the prediction, or rather the expectation, is that a shorter pile is required in the long term (*i.e.* the least favourable carrying capacity conditions occur in the short term, for which the pile must be designed). First, consider the *short term* conditions where the clay behaviour is undrained. The undrained shear strength varies from 18 kN/m^2 at the top of the clay layer to $(18 + \frac{L}{2})$ kN/m^2 at the pile base, with an *average* value across the pile shaft of:

$$c_u = \left(18 + \frac{L}{4}\right) kN/m^2$$

The adhesion factor, estimated from figure 5.14c, is $\alpha \approx 1$. Because the bearing capacity factor $N_c = 9$ in this case, equation 5.12 then yields:

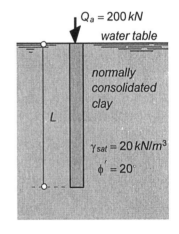

$Q_a = 200\,kN$

water table

normally consolidated clay

L

$\gamma_{sat} = 20\,kN/m^3$

$\phi' = 20°$

$$Q_u = \pi dL\alpha\left(18 + \frac{L}{4}\right) + \pi\frac{d^2}{4}N_c\left(18 + \frac{L}{2}\right)$$

Because an overall factor of safety $F = 4$ is assumed, the magnitude of the ultimate load is then:
$$Q_u = 4Q_a = 4 \times 200 = 800\,kN$$

Substituting for $Q_u = 800\,kN$ and $d = 0.52\,m$ in the previous equation, the following quadratic can easily be established:

Figure 5.19: Soil characteristics.

$$0.408L^2 + 30.36L - 765.6 = 0$$

leading to a pile length $L \approx 19.9\,m$.

Now consider *the long term* behaviour when the excess porewater pressure will have dissipated. Under such circumstances, a drained analysis must be undertaken, and the net ultimate loading capacity is calculated from equation 5.16:

$$Q_u = A_b \sigma'_{vb} N_q - W + pK \tan \delta \int_0^L \sigma'_v \, dz$$

- the pile cross sectional area: $A_b = \pi \dfrac{d^2}{4} = 0.212 \, m^2$,

- the vertical *effective* stress at pile base level:
  $\sigma'_{vb} = (\gamma_{sat} - \gamma_w) L = 10L$,

- the bearing capacity factor corresponding to an angle $\phi' = 20°$ is according to figure 5.18: $N_q \approx 10$,

- the coefficient of earth pressure is calculated from equation 5.14, with $OCR = 1$, and $\delta = 0.75\phi' = 15°$. Hence the *constant* quantity:

  $pK \tan \delta = \pi d (1 - \sin 20) \tan 15 = 0.288 \, m$.

- the quantity corresponding to $\int_0^L \sigma'_v \, dz$ is in fact the shaded area in figure 5.20: $A = \frac{1}{2}(L \times \gamma' L) = 5L^2$.

- the *effective* weight of the pile is:

$$W = \pi \frac{d^2}{4} L \gamma'_c = \pi \frac{d^2}{4} L(\gamma_c - \gamma_w) = 2.97L$$

γ_c being the unit weight of concrete.

Finally, knowing that $Q_u = 800 \, kN$, and substituting for all the above quantities into equation 5.16 then rearranging yields the following quadratic:

$$1.44L^2 + 18.23L - 800 = 0$$

whose solution is $L \approx 18.07 \, m$.

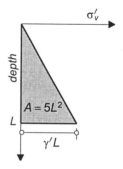

Figure 5.20: Integration of σ'_v along the pile shaft.

A quick comparison of results suggests that, as expected, the short term conditions are *the least favourable*.

Example 5.2

A 20 *m* deep *H-section* steel pile is driven in an 18 *m* thick layer of stiff clay underlain by a thick layer of hard clay. Both clays are overconsolidated, and the *average* values of the undrained shear strength are:

- stiff clay: $c_u = 120\,kN/m^2$
- hard clay: $c_u = 400\,kN/m^2$.

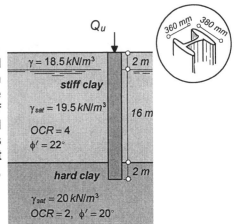

The water table is 2 m beneath the ground surface and the soil properties are as indicated in figure 5.21. In estimating the ultimate loading capacity Q_u of the pile, assume that the steel cross-sectional area of the pile is $S = 22 \times 10^{-3}\,m^2$ and the steel unit weight is $\gamma = 77\,kN/m^3$. For water, use $\gamma_w = 10\,kN/m^3$.

Figure 5.21: Soil conditions.

The reader is reminded that for this type of pile, the *total* cross-sectional area includes the soil plug as illustrated in figure 5.16. Furthermore, based on the analysis related to porewater pressure generation during pile driving, it is expected that, in this case, the least pile carrying capacity would occur in the long term.

For *undrained short term* conditions, the ultimate loading capacity is calculated from equation 9.5. Because the pile is driven through two different layers of clay, the *ultimate skin friction* has to be evaluated separately for both layers, hence:

- for the stiff clay (from the ground surface to a depth of 18 m), figure 5.14b yields $\alpha = 0.65$ for $c_u = 120\,kN/m^2$. Therefore:

$$Q_{s1} = A_s \alpha c_u = 2\,(0.36 + 0.38) \times 18 \times 0.65 \times 120 \approx 2078\,kN$$

- between 18 m and 20 m (hard clay), an interpolation of the graph in figure 5.14b yields $\alpha \approx 0.24$ for $c_u = 400\,kN/m^2$, and:

$$Q_{s2} = 2(0.36 + 0.38) \times 2 \times 0.24 \times 400 = 284\,kN$$

The *net ultimate base resistance* of the pile is calculated from equation 5.11:

$$Q_b - W = 9A_b c_u = 9(0.36 \times 0.38) \times 400 = 492\,kN$$

so that the short term *net ultimate loading capacity* of the pile is:

$$Q_u = Q_s + Q_b - W$$

$$= 2078 + 284 + 492 = 2854\,kN$$

The *long term* (drained) analysis necessitates the use of equation 5.16 to calculate the ultimate loading capacity:

$$Q_u = A_b \sigma'_{vb} N_q - W + pK \tan \delta \int_0^L \sigma'_v\,dz$$

- the cross-sectional area of the pile (including the soil plug) is:

$$A_b = 0.38 \times 0.36 = 0.1368\,m^2,$$

- the vertical *effective* stress at the pile base is:

$$\sigma'_{vb} = 2 \times 18.5 + 16 \times 9.5 + 2 \times 10 = 209\,kN/m^2,$$

- the bearing capacity factor corresponding to an angle $\phi' = 20°$ is, according to figure 5.18, $N_q \approx 10$,

- the coefficient of earth pressure K is calculated from equation 5.14:

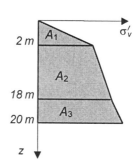

  - for the stiff clay: $K_1 = (1 - \sin 22)\sqrt{4} = 1.25$
  $\delta_1 = 0.75 \times 22 = 16.5°$
  - for the hard clay: $K_2 = (1 - \sin 20)\sqrt{2} = 0.93$
  $\delta_2 = 0.75 \times 20 = 15°$

- the sum of the shaded areas in figure 5.22 corresponds to:

$$\int_0^L \sigma'_v\,dz = A_1 + A_2 + A_3$$

Figure 5.22: Integration of σ'_v along the pile shaft.

with: $A_1 = \frac{1}{2}(18.5 \times 2 \times 2) = 37\,kN/m$

$$A_2 = (18.5 \times 2 \times 16) + \frac{1}{2}(9.5 \times 16 \times 16) = 1808\,kN/m$$

$$A_3 = 2[(18.5 \times 2) + (9.5 \times 16)] + \frac{1}{2}(2 \times 2 \times 10) = 398\,kN/m$$

The total *skin friction* is therefore:

$$Q_s = p[K_1 \tan \delta_1 (A_1 + A_2) + K_2 \tan \delta_2 A_3]$$

$$= 2 \times (0.36 + 0.38)$$

$$\times [1.25 \times (37 + 1808) \times \tan 16.5 + 0.93 \times 398 \times \tan 15]$$

$$= 1158 \, kN$$

and the *base resistance* of the pile is:

$$Q_b = A_b \sigma'_{vb} N_q = 0.1368 \times 209 \times 10 = 286 \, kN$$

The *effective* weight of the pile is the combined effective weights of the steel and soil plug. Considering the depth of the water table indicated in figure 5.21:
- the effective weight of steel is:

$$W_1 = 22 \times 10^{-3}(2 \times 77 + 18 \times 67) = 30 \, kN$$

- the effective weight of soil plug (assuming that the plug has a cross-sectional area $S_p = 0.36 \times 0.38 \, m^2$) is:

$$W_2 = (0.36 \times 0.38)[(2 \times 18.5) + (16 \times 9.5) + (2 \times 10)] = 29 \, kN$$

Whence the pile effective weight: $W = 30 + 29 = 59 \, kN$

The long term *ultimate loading capacity* of the pile can now be calculated:

$$Q_u = 1158 + 286 - 59 \approx 1385 \, kN$$

The *long term* ultimate carrying capacity is, as predicted, *smaller* than the short term one, and in this particular case it is seen that with time, the pile loading capacity decreases by more than 50%, compared with the initial short term capacity.

5.3.4 Carrying capacity of single piles embedded in sand

The analysis of piles embedded in sand is undertaken in terms of effective stresses, where the long term *net ultimate loading capacity* is calculated from equation 5.5:

$$Q_u = Q_s + Q_b - W \tag{5.17}$$

The ultimate skin friction Q_s is evaluated according to the equation:

$$Q_s = \int_0^L p\sigma'_v K \tan\delta \, dz \qquad\qquad (5.18)$$

with

p: pile perimeter
σ'_v: vertical effective stress (prior to pile installation)
d: pile/soil friction angle
K: coefficient of earth pressure.

The pile/soil friction angle depends on the pile material, and can be estimated as follows (Kulhawy, 1984):

- smooth steel/sand $\qquad\qquad \delta = 0.5\phi'$ to $0.7\phi'$ $\qquad$ (5.19a)
- rough steel/sand $\qquad\qquad \delta = 0.7\phi'$ to $0.9\phi'$ $\qquad$ (5.19b)
- prescast concrete/sand $\qquad \delta = 0.8\phi'$ to ϕ' $\qquad$ (5.19c)
- cast-in-place concrete/sand $\quad \delta = \phi'$ $\qquad$ (5.19d)

Moreover, the coefficient of earth pressure K is related to pile installation technique, and can be estimated from the coefficient of earth pressure at rest $K_o = (1 - \sin\phi')$ in the following way (Kulhawy, 1984):

- large displacement driven piles:

$$K = K_o \text{ to } 2K_o \qquad\qquad (5.20a)$$

- small displacement driven piles:

$$K = 0.75K_o \text{ to } 1.75K_o \qquad\qquad (5.20b)$$
- bored and cast-in-place piles:

$$K = 0.71K_o \text{ to } K_o \qquad\qquad (5.20c)$$

- jacked piles:

$$K = 0.5K_o \text{ to } 0.7K_o \qquad\qquad (5.20d)$$

The reader is reminded that according to equation 5.18, the ultimate skin friction developed around a pile shaft *embedded in a uniform sand* increases linearly with depth. However, suggestions made by different authors implying that the skin friction may reach an upper limit at penetration depths between 10d and 20d (d being the pile diameter) have constituted the basis of a common practice for some time (see for example Vesic, 1969,70; Meyerhof, 1976). Accordingly, some authors advocate the use of an upper limit to the unit skin friction $q_s = \bar{\sigma}'_v K \tan\delta$ (where $\bar{\sigma}'_v$ represents the average effective vertical pressure along the pile shaft) beyond a *critical depth* of about 20d.

Nevertheless, the notion of *critical depth* has been called into question lately by Fellenius and Altaee (1995), who argued that the critical depth is nothing but a 'fallacy' (*sic*) that derives from the misinterpretation of pile test measurements, and which can lead to unsafe designs. According to the same authors, the load distribution along a pile shaft during a full scale test *must* take into account the *residual loads* (*i.e.* loads generated by wave reflections or negative skin friction *prior* to pile testing). Failing that, the shape of the corresponding graph appears (erroneously) linear below what is commonly referred to as the critical depth. Similarly, neglecting the stress scale effects during the interpretation of model scale test results can equally be misleading.

Although this contentious issue is still a matter for debate, it is useful to remember that, in practice, driving a pile in a dense sand would induce a higher degree of compaction and therefore a higher density around the pile shaft, leading to early pile refusal (*i.e.* impossibility of further driving the pile into the sand). The refusal may develop for a depth of embedment into the dense sand of as little as 2*d* or 3*d*, in which case, the debate related to the depth of embedment of a pile driven through a loose sand layer and into an underlying dense sand layer becomes irrelevant. In any case, caution must be exercised when using equation 5.18.

The *ultimate base resistance* Q_b, on the other hand, is calculated according to equation 5.15:

$$Q_b = A_b \sigma'_{vb} N_q$$

where A_b is the cross-sectional area of pile, σ'_{vb} the effective vertical stress (prior to pile installation) at pile base level, and N_q represents the bearing capacity factor that depends on the state of sand, and which can be cautiously estimated from figure 5.18 in which the angle ϕ corresponds to the following:

- for driven piles (Kishida, 1967):

$$\phi = \frac{\phi' + 40}{2}$$ (5.21*a*)

- for bored piles (Poulos and Davis, 1980):

$$\phi = \phi' - 3°$$ (5.21*b*)

For driven piles, the *unit base resistance* q (*i.e.* the quantity $N_q \sigma'_{vb}$ developed at pile base level) is related to the type of sand and can reach a value of up to 25 *MN/m²* in the case of dense sands. Once more, it cannot be emphasised enough that the depth of embedment is controlled by pile refusal, and that under such circumstances, there is not much evidence for a critical depth beyond which q can be assigned a constant value.

Example 5.3

An open end rough steel tube pile with an external diameter $d = 400\,mm$ and a wall thickness of 5 mm is driven to a depth $L = 8\,m$, through a soil consisting of a 5 m thick layer of loose sand overlying a thick layer of medium dense sand. The water table is 1.5 m beneath the ground surface and the soil characteristics are as indicated in figure 5.23.

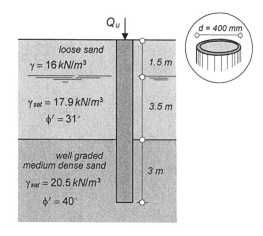

Figure 5.23: Soil characteristics.

In estimating the net ultimate loading capacity of the pile, assume a coefficient of earth pressure $K = 1.2K_o$, a soil/pile friction angle $\delta = 0.75\phi'$, a steel unit weight $\gamma = 77\,kN/m^3$ and a unit weight of water $\gamma_w \approx 10\,kN/m^3$.

- The *net ultimate loading capacity* being: $Q_u = Q_s + Q_b - W$

- *The ultimate skin friction:* $Q_s = pK \tan\delta \int_0^L \sigma'_v\,dz$

with:
- $p = 0.4 \times \pi$ (pile perimeter)
- $K_1 = 1.2K_o = 1.2(1 - \sin 31)$ (loose sand)
- $K_2 = 1.2(1 - \sin 40)$ (medium dense sand)
- $\delta_1 = 0.75 \times 31 = 23°$
- $\delta_2 = 0.75 \times 40 = 30°$.

The sum of the areas represented in figure 5.24 is:

$$\int_0^8 \sigma'_v\,dz = A_1 + A_2 + A_3 + A_4$$

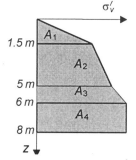

Figure 5.24: Integration of σ'_v along the pile shaft.

with: $A_1 = \frac{1}{2}(1.5 \times 1.5 \times 16) = 18 \, kN/m$

$A_2 = (1.5 \times 16 \times 3.5) + \frac{1}{2}(3.5 \times 3.5 \times 7.9) = 132 \, kN/m$

$A_3 = (1.5 \times 16) + (3.5 \times 7.9) + \frac{1}{2}(1 \times 10.5) = 57 \, kN/m$

$A_4 = 2[(1.5 \times 16) + (3.5 \times 7.9) + (1 \times 10.5)] = 124 \, kN/m$

Whence the *ultimate skin friction* of the pile:

$$Q_s = 0.4\pi[K_1 \tan\delta_1(A_1 + A_2) + K_2 \tan\delta_2(A_3 + A_4)]$$

$$= 0.4\pi[0.58 \times 0.42 \times (18 + 132) + 0.43 \times 0.58 \times (57 + 124)]$$

$$\approx 103 \, kN$$

The effective weight W of pile is the sum of the effective weight of steel W_1 and that of the soil plug W_2.

- the cross-sectional area of steel: $A_s = \frac{\pi}{4}(0.4^2 - 0.39^2) = 6.2 \times 10^{-3} \, m^2$
- the cross-sectional area of soil plug: $A_p = \pi\frac{0.39^2}{4} = 0.119 \, m^2$

It follows that:

$$W = A_s(1.5 \times 77 + 6.5 \times 67) + A_p(1.5 \times 16 + 3.5 \times 7.9 + 3 \times 10.5) = 13 \, kN$$

The *ultimate base resistance* of the pile is estimated from equations 5.15:

$$Q_b = A_bN_q\sigma'_v$$

- the cross-sectional area of the pile tip (including the soil plug) is:
  $$A_b = \pi\frac{0.4^2}{4} = 0.125 \, m^2$$

- at the pile base: $\sigma'_v = 1.5 \times 16 + 3.5 \times 7.9 + 3 \times 10.5 = 83.1 \, kN/m^2$
- the bearing capacity factor for dense sand is read from figure 5.18:
  medium dense sand: $\phi = \frac{40+40}{2} = 40° \Rightarrow N_q \approx 180$

Accordingly, the *base resistance* is such that:

$$Q_b = 180 \times 83.1 \times 0.125 = 1870 \, kN$$

Finally, the *ultimate loading capacity* of the pile is therefore:

$$Q_u = 103 + 1870 - 13 = 1960 \, kN$$

5.4 Negative skin friction

The negative skin friction occurs when a pile (or a group of piles) is installed through a layer of clay undergoing a consolidation process. In some cases, the structural loads transmitted to the ground during construction can generate time dependent settlements that can trigger a negative skin friction in the upper part of a pile shaft. If the rate of settlement of the (loaded) pile is smaller than the rate of consolidation settlement of the clay, then a downward (negative) friction force (Q_n in figure 5.25) develops on the pile shaft reducing, markedly sometimes, the carrying capacity of the pile. As consolidation develops with time, a drained analysis is therefore required in conjunction with negative skin friction. Figure 5.25 implies that the maximum displacement of the consolidating clay takes place at the top of the layer, and that the amount of settlement reduces with depth. The *neutral depth* z_f, below which no relative settlement occurs, can be estimated using the one-dimensional consolidation model (see Azizi, 2007 for instance). In practice, z_f can be taken as the depth at which a consolidation settlement $S_c = 0.01d$ is obtained (*d* being the pile diameter or equivalent).

Referring to figure 5.25, the ultimate loading capacity of the pile can be estimated as follows:

$$Q_u = Q_b + Q'_s - Q_n - W \qquad (5.22)$$

The related quantities in equation 5.22 are such that:

- the base resistance:

$$Q_b = A_b \sigma'_{vb} N_q \qquad (5.23a)$$

- the *effective* skin friction:

$$Q'_s = pK \tan\delta \int_{z_f}^{L} \sigma'_v \, dz \qquad (5.23b)$$

- the *negative* skin friction:

$$Q_n = pK \tan\delta \int_{0}^{z_f} \sigma'_v \, dz \qquad (5.23c)$$

Note that with respect to equations 5.23, the bearing capacity factor N_q is calculated in the usual way using figure 5.18. The angle of soil/pile friction is such that $0.75\phi' \leq \delta \leq \phi'$, the same value being used to evaluate the *effective* and *negative* skin frictions. Finally the coefficient of earth pressure can be estimated from equation 5.14, adapted for normally consolidated clays (*i.e.* $OCR = 1$):

$$K = (1 - \sin \phi')$$

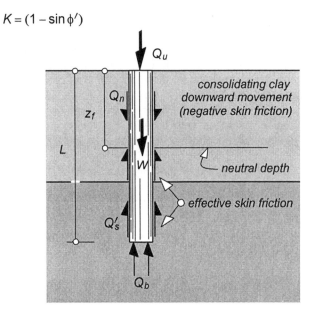

Figure 5.25: Negative skin friction due to a consolidating clay layer.

The (safe) *working load* that can be applied to a pile subject to a negative skin friction can now be calculated in the following manner using an overall factor of safety F :

$$Q_a = \frac{Q_b + Q'_s - 1.5Q_n}{F} - W \qquad (5.24)$$

A factor of 1.5 is used in conjunction with Q_n to cover any uncertainty related to the calculation of such a quantity. Also, notice that according to equation 5.22, the ultimate carrying capacity of the pile is affected, not only by the development of negative skin friction, but also by a reduction in the effective (or positive) shaft resistance.

The negative skin friction (or the downdrag) may be reduced by coating the pile with soft asphalt over the section within the consolidating layer (so reducing the value of δ). However, in practice, slip coats are expensive, difficult to apply and can get stripped off in upper frictional soils as in the case of fill materials. It is often more economical to provide extra loading capacity by making the pile longer.

Example 5.4

A square concrete pile, $0.4\,m \times 0.4\,m$ in cross-section is required to carry a *working* vertical load $Q_a = 800\,kN$ in the soil conditions illustrated in figure 5.26. It is predicted that consolidation settlement of the clay, triggered by the sand fill layer, becomes negligible at a depth $z_f = 4.5\,m$ below the ground surface.

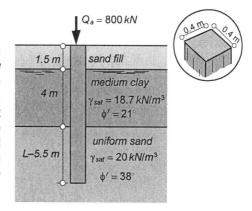

Figure 5.26: Soil conditions.

Determine the length L of the pile that satisfies the requirement of an overall factor of safety $F = 3$. The unit weight of concrete is $\gamma_c = 24\,kN/m^3$ and for water, $\gamma_w \approx 10\,kN/m^3$. Also, assume the following coefficients of earth pressure apply:

- sand fill and clay: $K = K_o = (1 - \sin\phi')$
- uniform sand: $K = 1.5K_o$

The sand fill has the following properties: $\gamma = 17\,kN/m^3$, $\phi' = 30°$.

The allowable and ultimate loading capacities are related through equation 5.24, accordingly:

$$Q_a = \frac{Q_b + Q'_s - 1.5Q_n}{3} - W = 800\,kN$$

On the other hand, the ultimate loading capacity is calculated from equation 5.22:

$$Q_u = Q_b + Q'_s - Q_n - W$$

- *The base resistance:* $Q_b = A_b\sigma'_{vb}Nq$
  - the cross sectional area of the pile: $A_b = (0.4 \times 0.4) = 0.16\,m^2$
  - the bearing capacity factor for an angle $\phi = \frac{38+40}{2} = 39°$ is read from figure 5.18: $N_q \approx 155$.
  - the *effective* vertical stress at the pile tip level is, according to figure 5.26: $\sigma'_{vb} = (1.5 \times 17) + (4 \times 8.7) + (L - 5.5) \times 10$

It follows that: $Q_b = (248L + 131.4)\,kN$

- *The effective shaft resistance*: $Q'_s = pK \tan \delta \int_{z_f}^{L} \sigma_v \, dz$

where:
- $p = 2(0.4 + 0.4) \, m$ (pile perimeter)
- $K_1 = (1 - \sin 30) = 0.5$ (sand fill)
- $K_2 = (1 - \sin 21) = 0.64$ (clay)
- $K_3 = 1.5(1 - \sin 38) = 0.58$ (uniform sand)
- $\delta_1 = 0.75 \times 30 = 22.5°$ (sand fill)
- $\delta_2 = 0.75 \times 21 = 16°$ (clay)
- $\delta_3 = 0.75 \times 38 = 28.5°$ (uniform sand).

Furthermore, it can be seen that according to figure 5.27:

$$\int_{z_f}^{L} \sigma'_v \, dz = A_3 + A_4$$

with
$$A_3 = 1 \times (17 \times 1.5 + 8.7 \times 3) + \frac{1}{2}(1 \times 8.7 \times 1) = 56 \, kN/m$$
$$A_4 = (L - 5.5) \times (17 \times 1.5 + 8.7 \times 4) + \frac{1}{2}(L - 5.5) \times (L - 5.5) \times 10$$
$$= (5L^2 + 5.3L - 180.4) \, kN/m$$

Consequently: $Q'_s = p \, (K_2 \tan \delta_2 . A_3 + K_3 \tan \delta_3 . A_4)$

$$= 2.52L^2 + 2.67L - 74.5$$

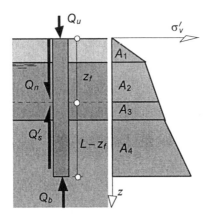

Figure 5.27: Integration of σ'_v along the pile shaft.

- *The negative shaft friction*:

$$Q_n = pK \tan \delta \int_0^{z_f} \sigma'_v \, dz = p(K_1 A_1 \tan \delta_1 + K_2 A_2 \tan \delta_2)$$

where: $A_1 = \frac{1}{2}(1.5 \times 1.5 \times 17) = 19\,kN/m$

$A_2 = (3 \times 1.5 \times 17) + \frac{1}{2}(3 \times 8.7 \times 3) = 116\,kN/m$

Whence: $Q_n = 40.4\,kN$

• *The effective weight of pile*:

$$W = A_b[1.5\gamma_c + (L - 1.5)(\gamma_c - \gamma_w)]$$

$$= 0.4 \times 0.4 \times [1.5 \times 24 + (L - 1.5) \times 14] = (2.24L + 2.4)\,kN$$

The *allowable loading capacity* of the pile is therefore:

$$Q_a = \frac{Q_b + Q_s' - 1.5Q_n}{3} - W = (0.84L^2 + 81.32L - 3.63)\,kN$$

Thus, substituting for the value $Q_a = 800\,kN$ into the above equation then rearranging, it follows that:

$$L^2 + 96.8L - 956.7 = 0$$

leading to a length $L = 9.04\,m$, that is a depth of embedment into the dense sand of about $3.5\,m$.

5.5 Ultimate carrying capacity of pile groups

5.5.1 Group effect

Piles are usually used in groups related through a *pilecap* above, at, or below the ground surface (see figure 5.29) and as such, the behaviour of a pile within a group in terms of carrying capacity or settlement, for instance, is different from that of an isolated pile subject to the same loading conditions. The difference in behaviour is due to the *group effect* generated by:

- a higher degree of soil disturbance during the installation of a group of piles, as opposed to a relatively small degree of disturbance for an isolated pile;

- the loading and subsequent displacement of a pile within a group which is affected by the loading of adjacent piles. Because the size of the area of stressed soil beneath a single pile is relatively small compared with that developed at the base of a pile group (refer to figure 5.28), the ensuing settlement will be markedly different.

Consequently, the carrying capacity of a pile group is *not necessarily* equal to the sum of the capacities of individual piles within the group taken in isolation. At this stage, one must distinguish between a *free standing group* where the pilecap is *above* the soil surface as depicted in figure 5.29a, and a *piled foundation* for which piles are joined by a pilecap *at* or *below* the ground surface (refer to figure 5.29b). Notice that a piled foundation is in fact a combined foundation since the pilecap plays the role of a shallow foundation supported by piles. *Often, however, the pilecap sits on fill or soft ground which may be unreliable in terms of bearing capacity.*

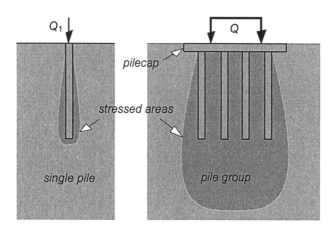

Figure 5.28: Effect of pile groups on the spreading of stressed soil areas.

In both cases, the ratio of the ultimate loading capacity of the group to that of individual piles within the group, considered in isolation, is sometimes referred to as the *efficiency factor:*

$$\eta = \frac{Q_{ug}}{\sum\limits_{i=1}^{n} Q_u} \qquad (5.25)$$

with

Q_{ug} : ultimate loading capacity of the group
Q_u : ultimate loading capacity of an isolated single pile within the group n: total number of piles within the group.

The value of η depends on the type of foundation soil, the method of pile installation (displacement or non-displacement piles) and the ratio s/d where s represents the centre-to-centre spacing between two adjacent piles within the group as depicted in figure 5.29, and d is the pile diameter. Practical considerations related to pile installation dictate that the minimum value of s/d for driven piles is around 2.5 (about 2 for bored piles), and although no upper limit exists for this ratio, one has to bear in mind that the higher its value, the thicker the pilecap must be, and so in practice s/d arely exceeds 8. Also, the spacing s indicated in figure 5.29b can have a different value in each direction.

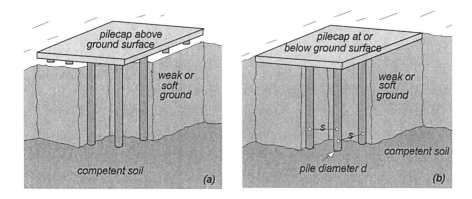

Figure 5.29: (a) Free standing group, (b) piled foundation.

From a physical view point, the efficiency factor η reflects the change in density of the material in which the piles are embedded. For example, if a group of piles is *driven* in a *loose sand* at a relatively close spacing, $s/d < 3$ say, the sand compaction in the vicinity of piles increases as the group expands. As the density of the sand gradually increases within the group compound, the loading capacity of each individual pile within the group becomes larger than that of an isolated pile. Hence, the efficiency factor related to a pile group driven in a loose sand is usually larger than unity and can be as high as 2.5 or 3 when $s/d \approx 2$. As the ratio s/d increases, the compaction effect becomes less significant. On the opposite side, when a group of piles is *driven* into a *dense sand*, dilation ensues causing the sand to loosen as a result of the sand particles being rearranged as pile driving proceeds. Once more, the loosening depends on the ratio s/d: the larger its value the smaller the loosening effect. In practice, the depth of embedment to which a single pile can be driven into a dense sand is limited because of the increase in soil density during driving. The limitation in the depth of embedment is accentuated by the group effect in the case of a pile group, due to a larger increase in density as the stressed sand area spreads around the group (refer to figure 5.28). However, there seems to be some confusion as to the use of the efficiency factor η, and in this respect, it is strongly advised to follow the suggestion made by Fleming *et al.* (1992), specifying that *the factor η should in no way be used to estimate the ultimate loading capacity of a pile group*. Instead, the ultimate capacities related to appropriate modes of failure must be assessed independently, and the *least favourable conditions* adopted with an adequate factor of safety.

Also, because of the large stressed area generated beneath the base of a pile group (see figure 5.28), provision must be made to check that the ensuing *settlement* under the working load is tolerable. It must be emphasised that while the ultimate loading capacity of a pile group is an important design parameter, its relevance depends on the amount of settlement needed to mobilise fully the base resistance of the group. This settlement can be very high and therefore unacceptable, in which case, it may be necessary to carry the entire load by skin friction, and totally overlook the end bearing of the group. It is useful to bear in mind that the amount of settlement occurring before the end bearing is fully mobilised is usually much larger than that needed to develop the full skin friction (as illustrated in figure 5.10 in the case of single piles).

5.5.2 Carrying capacity of piled foundations embedded in clay: undrained analysis

A piled foundation is a combination of a shallow foundation represented by the pilecap and a deep foundation represented by the group of piles as illustrated in figure 5.29(*b*). The carrying capacity of such a foundation can be estimated by assessing the two following modes of failure.

- *Mode 1* whereby piles within the group may fail individually, thus causing a redistribution of the applied load as per figure 5.30(*a*).

- *Mode 2* in which the block of soil containing the piles fails once the shear stresses on the sides of the block exceed the ultimate strength of the soil as depicted in figure 5.30(*b*).

An analysis of the type developed by Poulos and Davis (1980) is adopted in what follows, in that for a piled foundation containing n piles, the ultimate loading capacity corresponds to the *smaller* of the following two quantities:

Q_1: the sum of the ultimate loading capacities of individual piles plus that of the pilecap

Q_2: the ultimate loading capacity of the block containing the piles plus that of the portion of the pilecap outside the perimeter of the block.

Often, the contribution of the pilecap to the bearing capacity of the group is ignored because a large deflection of the cap is usually required before its

bearing capacity is fully mobilised. Since sites are often disturbed during pile installation, it is advisable to be cautious and not to presume that the pilecap will always be effective. In the following analysis of piled foundations, the pilecap is assumed to be fully effective in order to cover the few cases where such an assumption can be justified. For the majority of cases, however, the contribution of the pilecap should be set to zero.

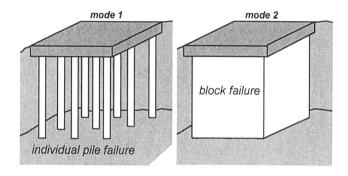

Figure 5.30: Modes of failure for a piled foundation.

• The ultimate loading capacity Q_1 can be estimated in the short term (i.e. under undrained conditions) as follows:

$$Q_1 = nQ_u + Q'_c - W_c \qquad (5.26)$$

with
- n: total number of piles within the group
- Q_u: ultimate loading capacity of a single pile as per equation 5.12

- $Q'_c = A'_c(N_{cc}c_u + \gamma D)$: ultimate loading capacity of the pilecap

- $A'_c = A_c - nA_b$: effective area of pilecap as depicted in figure 5.31
- A_c: pilecap area
- A_b: cross-sectional area of a single pile
- D: depth below ground surface of pilecap
- W_c: total weight of pilecap.

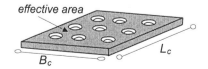

Figure 5.31: Effective area of pilecap.

- The bearing capacity factor for the pilecap is calculated as follows (Skempton, 1951):

$$N_{cc} = (2 + \pi)\left(1 + 0.2\frac{B_c}{L_c}\right) \tag{5.27}$$

- *The ultimate loading capacity Q_2 under undrained conditions is calculated in the following way:*

$$Q_2 = Q_{sb} + Q_{bb} + Q_c'' - nW_p - W_c - W_s \tag{5.28}$$

with

- $Q_{sb} = p_b L c_u$: ultimate side resistance of the block
- $p_b = 2(b + e)$: block perimeter
- $Q_{bb} = A_{bb}[c_u N_{cb} + \gamma(L + D)]$: ultimate base resistance of the block
- $A_{bb} = be$: cross-sectional area of the block (see figure 5.32)
- L: block depth
- D: depth of the pilecap below ground level
  - γ: total unit weight of soil in which the group is embedded.
- The bearing capacity factor at the base of the block is estimated as follows (Skempton, 1951) [L, b, e as per figure 5.32 ($e > b$)]:

$$N_{cb} \approx 5\left(1 + 0.2\frac{b}{e}\right)\left(1 + \frac{L}{12b}\right) \tag{5.29}$$

$Q_c'' = (A_c - A_{bb})(c_u N_{cc} + \gamma D)$: bearing capacity of the portion of the pilecap situated outside the block (refer to figure 5.32)

with

- A_c : area of pilecap
- N_{cc}: bearing capacity factor at pilecap level
- $W_s = (A_{bb} - NA_b)\gamma L$: total weight of soil within the block.

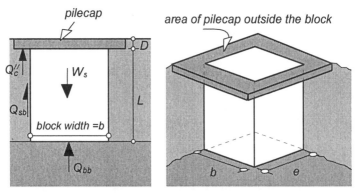

Figure 5.32: Dimensions used in conjunction with the design of piled foundations.

It is useful to reiterate that the ultimate load capacity of the group Q_{ug} adopted for design is the *lesser* of Q_1 and Q_2 and, in this respect, the ultimate load capacity Q_2 is usually smaller than Q_1 for ratios $s/d < 3$.

Example 5.5

A group of 8×10 square concrete piles is driven through a 12 m saturated soft clay layer, underlain by a thick slightly overconsolidated stiff clay as depicted in figure 5.33. Both layers have the following parameters:

- *soft clay:* $c_{uav} = 18 \, kN/m^2$, $\gamma_{sat1} = 19 \, kN/m^3$
- *stiff clay:* $c_{uav} = 90 \, kN/m^2$, $\gamma_{ssat2} = 20 \, kN/m^3$

(c_{uav} is the average undrained shear strength). Each pile is 18 m long and has a cross-sectional area of $(0.5 \times 0.5) \, m^2$. The group is characterised by a ratio $s/d = 3$, and the pilecap is 1.2 m thick and has an area of $(13 \times 16) \, m^2$. Estimate the allowable loading capacity of the group if an overall factor of safety $F = 3$ is used. For concrete, use $\gamma_c = 24 \, kN/m^3$.

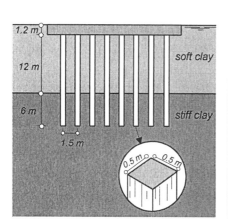
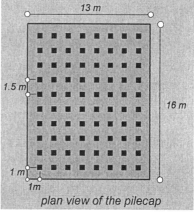

Figure 5.33: Soil characteristics and pile dimensions.

Considering the modes of failure described previously, the ultimate loading capacity of the group corresponds to the smaller of the two quantities Q_1 and Q_2.

- Q_1 is calculated using equation 5.26: $Q_1 = nQ_u + Q'_c - W_c$ ($n = 80$, total number of piles in the group).

Taking into account the layered nature of soil, the *ultimate loading capacity* Q_u of a single pile is calculated from equation 5.12, in which the adhesion factors of both soft and stiff clay layers are read from figure 5.14(b), and have the respective values $\alpha_1 \approx 1$, $\alpha_2 \approx 0.7$. Referring to the dimensions in figure 5.33, it follows that (p being the pile perimeter):

$$Q_u = p(\alpha_1 c_{u1} L_1 + \alpha_2 c_{u2} L_2) + 9 A_b c_{u2}$$

$$= 2 \times (0.5 + 0.5) \times (1 \times 18 \times 12 + 0.7 \times 90 \times 6)$$

$$+ 9 \times 0.5 \times 0.5 \times 90 \approx 1391 \, kN$$

• The ultimate loading capacity of the pilecap:

$$Q'_c = (A_c - n A_b)(N_{cc} c_{u1} + \gamma_{sat1} D)$$

With the bearing capacity factor calculated from equation 5.27:

$$N_{cc} = (2 + \pi)\left(1 + 0.2 \times \frac{13}{16}\right) \approx 6$$

and the depth of pilecap below the ground surface $D = 1.2 \, m$ (refer to figure 5.32), it is seen that:

$$Q'_c = (16 \times 13 - 80 \times 0.5 \times 0.5) \times (6 \times 18 + 19 \times 1.2)$$
$$= 24,590 \, kN$$

On the other hand, the total weight of pilecap is:

$$W_c = 16 \times 13 \times 1.2 \times 24 = 5990 \, kN$$

Thus the ensuing first estimate of the ultimate loading capacity of the group:

$$Q_1 = 80 \times 1391 + 24590 - 5990 = 129,880 \, kN \quad (129.88 \, MN)$$

• The ultimate loading capacity corresponding to the block failure mode is estimated from equation 9.28:

$$Q_2 = Q_{sb} + Q_{bb} + Q''_c - n W_p - W_c - W_s$$

Notice that for this mode of failure, the block in question is 14 m long and 11 m wide as seen in figure 5.33. Therefore:

• the block perimeter: $p_b = 2 \times (11 + 14) = 50 \, m$
• the block cross-sectional area: $A_{bb} = 11 \times 14 = 154 \, m^2$
• the ultimate side resistance:

$$Q_{sb} = p_b(c_{u1}L_1 + c_{u2}L_2) = 50 \times (18 \times 12 + 90 \times 6)$$

$$= 37,800 \, kN$$

- the ultimate base resistance:

$$Q_{bb} = A_{bb}[c_{u2}N_{cb} + \gamma_{sat1}(L_1 + D) + \gamma_{sat2}L_2]$$

with the bearing capacity factor calculated from equation 5.29:

$$N_{cb} = 5 \times (1 + 0.2 \times \frac{11}{14})(1 + \frac{18}{12 \times 11}) \approx 6.6$$

Whence:

$$Q_{bb} = 154 \times [90 \times 6.6 + 19 \times (12 + 1.2) + 20 \times 6] = 148,579 \, kN$$

- The bearing capacity of the portion of pilecap situated outside the block (see figure 5.32):

$$Q_c'' = (A_c - A_{bb})(c_{u1}N_{cc} + \gamma_{sat1}D)$$
$$= (16 \times 13 - 154) \times (18 \times 6 + 19 \times 1.2) = 7063 \, kN$$

Moreover, the total weight of all piles within the group is:

$$nW_p = 80 \times 0.5 \times 0.5 \times 18 \times 24 = 8640 \, kN$$

and the total weight of soil within the block:

$$W_s = (A_{bb} - NA_b)(\gamma_{sat1}L_1 + \gamma_{sat2}L_2)$$
$$= (154 - 80 \times 0.5 \times 0.5) \times (19 \times 12 + 20 \times 6) = 46,632 kN$$

Hence the second estimate of the ultimate carrying capacity of the group under undrained conditions:

$$Q_2 = 37800 + 148579 + 7063 - 8640 - 5990 - 46632 = 132,180 \, kN$$

A quick comparison between the two ultimate loading capacities shows that the single pile failure mode is more critical than the block failure; hence the *ultimate loading capacity* of the pile group:

$$Q_{ug} = Q_1 = nQ_u + Q_c' - W = 129,880 \, kN$$

The *allowable loading capacity* is therefore:

$$Q_{ag} = \frac{nQ_u + Q_c'}{F} - W = \frac{1391 \times 80 + 24590}{3} - 5990 = 39,300 \, kN$$

Note that the loading capacity of pile groups may sometimes be restricted by settlement requirements rather than a simple factor of safety as in the case of the above example.

5.5.3 Design of free standing pile groups embedded in clay

For a free standing group, the pilecap is above the ground surface and does not as such contribute towards the loading capacity of the group except for its weight as illustrated in figure 5.34. The ultimate capacity of the group can then be estimated in a way similar to that used for piled foundations. That is to say, the ultimate loading capacity of the group is taken as the smaller of Q_1 and Q_2 (Terzaghi and Peck, 1967) whereby:

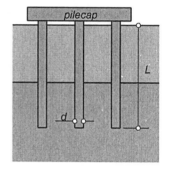

Figure 5.34: Free standing group.

$$Q_1 = nQ_u - W_c \tag{5.30}$$

$$Q_2 = Q_{sb} + Q_{bb} - nW_p - W_c - W_s \tag{5.31}$$

the different quantities having the same meaning (and are calculated in the same way) as in equations 5.26 and 5.28.

Example 5.6

Consider what would have been the ultimate loading capacity of the pile group in the previous example 5.5, had the pilecap been a small distance above the ground. Manifestly, the calculations already undertaken in the previous example are valid and can be used in conjunction with both equations 5.30 and 5.31. Accordingly:

$$Q_1 = 80 \times 1391 - 5990 = 105,290 \; kN$$

$$Q_2 = 37800 + 148570 - 8640 - 5990 - 46632 = 125,108 \; kN$$

Thence the ultimate loading capacity of the free standing group:

$$Q_{ug} = Q_1 = nQ_u - W = 105,290 \; kN$$

so that the allowable load, calculated using the same factor of safety $F = 3$, is:

$$Q_{ag} = \frac{n\,Q_u}{3} - W = \frac{80 \times 1391}{3} - 5990 = 31,103\,kN$$

that is a decrease of around 21% with respect to the allowable load in the case of piled foundation.

5.5.4 Design of pile groups in sand: drained analysis

An effective stress analysis of a pile group embedded in non-cohesive soils can be undertaken in a way similar *in principle* to that used for clays under drained conditions. Considering the two modes of failure adopted previously where piles can fail either individually or as a block. The ultimate loading capacity of a pile group driven through a non-cohesive soil can be taken as *the lesser* of the two quantities:

$$Q_1 = nQ_u + Q_c' - W_c \tag{5.32}$$

$$Q_2 = Q_{bb} + Q_{sb} + Q_c'' - nW_p - W_c - W_s \tag{5.33}$$

with
- *n*:   total number of piles in the group
- Q_u: ultimate loading capacity of a single pile as calculated from equation 5.16
- $Q_c' = (A_c - nA_b)\left(\gamma' D N_q' + 0.4\gamma' B_c N_\gamma'\right)$
- $Q_{bb} = A_{bb}\left(\sigma_{vb}' N_q' + 0.4\gamma' b N_\gamma'\right)$ (refer to figure 5.35)
- $Q_{sb} = p_b \int_0^L K_o \tan\phi' \sigma_v' dz$: side friction of the block
- $Q_c'' = (A_c - A_{bb})\left(\gamma' D N_q' + 0.4\gamma' B_c N_\gamma'\right)$
- γ' : relevant *effective* unit weight of soil
- W_p : effective weight of a single pile
- W_c : effective weight of pilecap
- W_s : effective weight of soil within the block
- σ_{vb}': effective overburden stress at the base of the block.

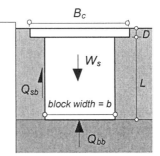

Figure 5.35: Dimensions used in conjunction with drained analysis.

The bearing capacity factors N_q' and N_γ' can be read from the graphs in figure 5.36 which take into account the localised shear failure (Terzaghi,

1943, Vesic, 1969). (They are *different* from those corresponding to figure 4.26, section 4.7.)

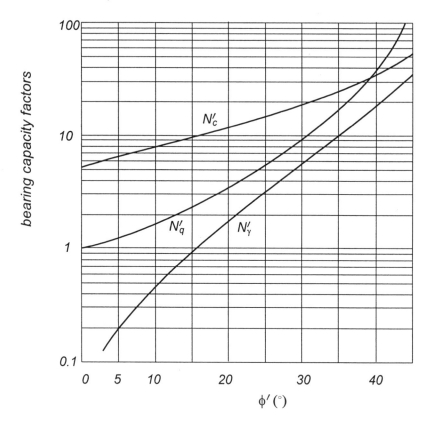

Figure 5.36: Bearing capacity factors used in conjunction with piles.

Example 5.7

A small group of 3×3 piles with a square pilecap is needed to support an ultimate load Q_{ug} (see figure 5.37). The dimensions of each individual tubular pile as well as the soil strata in which the group is driven are identical to those used in example 5.3. The loose sand is characterised by a bulk unit weight $\gamma = 16\,kN/m^3$, a saturated unit weight $\gamma_{sat} = 17.9\,kN/m^3$, and an effective angle of friction $\phi' = 31°$. The dense sand on the other hand has $\gamma_{sat} = 20.5\,kN/m^3$ and $\phi' = 40°$.

Estimate the allowable loading capacity of the group knowing that an overall factor of safety $F = 3$ is required.

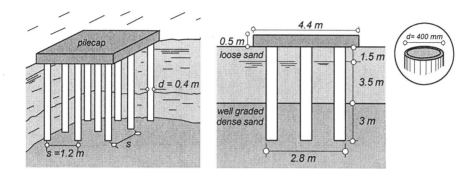

Figure 5.37: Group dimensions and soil conditions.

First, use equation 5.32 to assess the ultimate loading capacity Q_1:

$$Q_1 = nQ_u + Q_c' - W_c$$

- $Q_u = 1566\,kN$: ultimate loading capacity of a single pile calculated in example 5.3
- $Q_c' = (A_c - nA_b)\left(\gamma'DN_q' + 0.4\gamma'B_cN_\gamma'\right)$
- $D = 0$ since the pilecap is on the ground surface (see figure 5.37)

For the pilecap:
- $A_c = (4.4 \times 4.4) = 19.36\,m^2$ and $B_c = 4.4\,m$

The cross-sectional area of a single pile is:
- $A_b = \pi\dfrac{0.4^2}{4} \approx 0.126\,m^2$

Moreover, the bearing capacity factor, read from figure 5.36 for an angle $\phi' = 31°$ is $N_\gamma' \approx 6.2$. Whence:

$$Q_c' = (19.36 - 9 \times 0.126) \times (0.4 \times 16 \times 4.4 \times 6.2) = 3182\,kN$$

The effective weight of pilecap being:

$$W_c = 24 \times 4.4 \times 4.4 \times 0.5 = 232\,kN$$

and therefore the first estimate of the ultimate loading capacity of the group is as follows:

$$Q_1 = 9 \times 1566 + 3182 - 232 = 17,044\,kN$$

Next, the quantity Q_2 is calculated from equation 5.33:

$$Q_2 = Q_{bb} + Q_{sb} + Q_c'' - nW_p - W_c - W_s$$

with:

$$Q_{bb} = A_{bb}\left(\sigma_{vb}' N_q' + 0.4\gamma' bN_\gamma'\right)$$

The block area being $A_{bb} = (2.8 \times 2.8) = 7.84\, m^2$, and its width is $b = 2.8\, m$. Furthermore, the effective overburden stress at the base of the block is as follows:

$$\sigma_{vb}' = (1.5 \times 16 + 3.5 \times 7.9 + 3 \times 10.5) = 83\, kN/m^2$$

The following bearing capacity factors are read from figure 5.36 for $\phi' = 40°$: $N_q' \approx 40$ and $N_\gamma' \approx 18$. Whence:

$$Q_{bb} = 7.84 \times (83 \times 40 + 0.4 \times 10.5 \times 2.8 \times 18) = 27,688\, kN$$

Now, the side friction of the block is estimated as follows:

$$Q_{sb} = p_b \int_0^L K_o \tan\phi' \sigma_v'\, dz$$

with:

- $K_{o1} = (1 - \sin 31) = 0.48$ for loose sand
- $K_{o2} = (1 - \sin 40) = 0.36$ for dense sand.

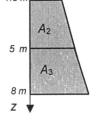

1.5 m A_1

A_2

5 m

A_3

8 m

z

Figure 5.38: Integration of σ_v' along the block sides.

The sum of the shaded areas in figure 5.38 is:

$$\int_0^L \sigma_v'\, dz = A_1 + A_2 + A_3$$

where: $A_1 = \frac{1}{2}(1.5 \times 1.5 \times 16) = 18\, kN/m$

$$A_2 = (1.5 \times 16 \times 3.5) + \frac{1}{2}(3.5 \times 3.5 \times 6) = 120.75\, kN/m$$

$$A_3 = 3 \times (1.5 \times 16 + 3.5 \times 6) + \frac{1}{2}(3 \times 3 \times 10.5) = 182.25\, kN/m$$

Thus:

$$Q_{sb} = 2(2.8 + 2.8)[0.48(18 + 120.75)\tan 31 + 0.36 \times 182.25 \tan 40]$$

$$= 1065\, kN$$

On the other hand:

$$Q_c'' = (A_c - A_{bb})\left(\gamma' D N_q' + 0.4\gamma' B_c N_\gamma'\right) \quad (note \; D = 0)$$

$$= (19.36 - 7.84)(0.4 \times 16 \times 4.4 \times 6.2) = 2011\,kN$$

The effective weight of a single pile was calculated earlier in example 5.3, whence the total effective weight of piles within the group is:

$$nW_p = 9 \times 13 = 117\,kN$$

The effective weight of soil within the block being:

$$W_s = (A_{bb} - nA_b)\gamma'L$$

$$= (7.84 - 9 \times 0.126) \times (16 \times 1.5 + 6 \times 3.5 + 3 \times 10.5) = 513\,kN$$

Hence the second estimate of the ultimate loading capacity of the group is:

$$Q_2 = 27688 + 1065 + 2011 - 117 - 232 - 513 = 29,902\,kN$$

Since Q_1 is smaller than Q_2, the ultimate loading capacity of the group is therefore:

$$Q_{ug} = Q_1 = nQ_u + Q_c' - W_c = 17,044\,kN$$

Using a factor of safety $F = 3$, the allowable loading capacity of the group is therefore:

$$Q_{ag} = \frac{nQ_u + Q_c'}{3} - W_c = \frac{9 \times 1566 + 3182}{3} - 232 \approx 5527\,kN$$

5.5.5 Negative skin friction on pile groups

As in the case of an isolated pile, a pile group may be subjected to a negative skin friction if it is embedded through a layer of consolidating soil. An effective stress analysis is dictated by the time dependent nature of consolidation. For a pile group, the group action arising from installing a cluster of piles has a limiting effect on the development of negative skin friction. In other words, the total negative skin friction force acting within the compound of a group of n piles is usually smaller than the sum of negative skin friction forces acting on the same number of isolated piles. However, it is difficult to determine accurately a negative skin force within a pile group. To overcome this difficulty, an upper limit can be imposed by stating that the total negative skin friction force cannot be larger than the force on the sides of the block of consolidating soil enclosed within the pile group, augmented by its weight as illustrated in figure 5.39.

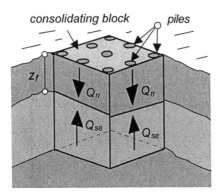

Figure 5.39: Development of negative skin friction along the block sides.

The negative skin friction force can therefore be taken as *the lesser* of the two following quantities:

$$Q_{n1} = np \int_0^{z_f} K \tan \delta \, \sigma_v' \, dz \tag{5.34}$$

$$Q_{n2} = (A_{bb} - nA_b)\gamma \, z_f + p_b \int_0^{z_f} K_o \tan \phi' \, \sigma_v' \, dz \tag{5.35}$$

with
- n: total number of piles within the group
- p: pile perimeter
- p_b: block perimeter
- A_{bb}:   cross-sectional area of the block
- A_b: pile cross sectional area
- z_f: depth below which no negative skin friction occurs.

Example 5.8

A group of piles is required to support a structure transmitting an allowable load $Q_{ag} = 12.5\,MN$. A total of 31 circular concrete piles are driven in an arrangement characterised by a centre to centre spacing of 1.2 *m*. The 0.4 *m* diameter piles are related on the ground surface through a pilecap having a cross-sectional area $A_c = 57\,m^2$ and weighing 684 *kN*. The block of soil (represented by broken lines in figure 5.40) has a cross-sectional area $A_{bb} = 54.9\,m^2$ and a perimeter $p_b = 22.8\,m$. The piles are installed through a 6 *m* thick layer of firm clay overlying a deep layer of stiff, lightly overconsolidated clay. Well before the pile installation and for reasons totally unrelated to the foundation, the water table, originally at the ground surface level, had to be permanently lowered by 2 *m*, causing the upper clay layer to undergo a consolidation process due to the increase in effective stresses. It can be assumed that a resulting negative skin friction will develop around the shaft areas of piles down to a depth $z_f = 3.5\,m$ (neutral depth in figure 5.40). The soil properties are as follows:

- firm clay: $\gamma = 18.5\,kN/m^3$, $\gamma_{sat} = 19.5\,kN/m^3$, $\phi' = 24°$, $c' = 0$
- stiff clay: $\gamma_{sat} = 20\,kN/m^3$, $\phi' = 22°$, $c' = 0$

and the pile/soil friction angle can be taken as $\delta = 0.75\phi'$. Estimate the length L of individual piles required to carry the aforementioned load allowing for an overall factor of safety $F = 3$.

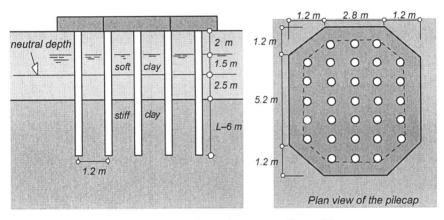

Figure 5.40: Group dimensions and soil conditions.

Because of the consolidation process involved, a long term effective stress analysis must be undertaken. The negative skin friction exerted on the group down to a depth $z_f = 3.5\,m$ is assessed according to equations 5.34 and 5.35. Thus:

$$Q_{n1} = np \int_0^{z_f} K \tan\delta\, \sigma_v'\, dz$$

where

- $n = 31$: total number of piles within the group
- $p = 0.4\pi = 1.26\,m$: pile perimeter
- $K = (1 - \sin 24) = 0.59$
- $\delta = 0.75 \times 24 = 18°$ and hence $\tan\delta = 0.32$

- $\int_0^{3.5} \sigma_v'\, dz = A_1 + A_2$ (see figure 5.41).

- $A_1 = 37\,kN/m$, $A_2 = 66.2\,kN/m$

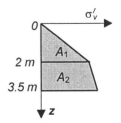

Figure 5.41: Integration of σ_v' along the block sides

Whence the quantity:

$$Q_{n1} = 31 \times 1.26 \times 0.59 \times 0.32 \times (37 + 66.2) = 761 \, kN$$

Equation 5.35 is now used, in turn, to estimate the negative skin friction:

$$Q_{n2} = (A_{bb} - nA_b)\gamma' z_f + p_b \int_0^{z_f} K_o \tan\phi' \sigma_v' \, dz$$

with

- $A_{bb} = 54.9 \, m^2$: cross-sectional area of the block
- $A_b = \pi \frac{0.4^2}{4} = 0.1256 \, m^2$: cross-sectional area of a pile
- $p_b = 22.8 \, m$: block perimeter
- $K_o = (1 - \sin 24) = 0.59$
- $\phi' = 24°$.

Hence:

$$Q_{n2} = (54.9 - 31 \times 0.1256)(18.5 \times 2 + 9.5 \times 1.5)$$

$$+ (22.8 \times 0.59 \times 0.445) \times (37 + 66.2) = 3231 \, kN$$

Since the smaller of the two values Q_{n1} and Q_{n2} applies, it follows that the negative skin friction is:

$$Q_n = 761 \, kN$$

Next, adopting the two modes of failure of the previous example 5.7, the ultimate loading capacity of the group is therefore the *smaller* of the two values Q_1 (calculated using equation 5.32) and Q_2 (estimated from equation 5.33).

For the first mode of failure (*i.e.* individual pile failure within the group), the ultimate loading capacity of the group is:

$$Q_1 = nQ_u + Q_c' - Q_n - W_c$$

- *The ultimate loading capacity of an isolated pile:*

$$Q_u = Q_b + Q_s - W_p.$$

  - The base resistance of a single pile:

$$Q_b = A_b N_q \sigma_{vb}' = 0.1256 \times 36 \times [18.5 \times 2 + 4 \times 9.5 + 10(L - 6)]$$
$$= (67.8 + 45.2L) \, kN$$

N.B. at the base of the pile, $\phi' = 22°$, and according to equation 5.21a, $\phi = (22 + 40)/2 = 31°$ so that figure 5.18 yields a bearing capacity factor of $N_q \approx 36$.

- The shaft resistance of an isolated pile:

$$Q_s = p \int_{z_f}^{L} K \tan \delta \, \sigma'_v \, dz$$

where:
- $K_1 = (1 - \sin 24) = 0.59,\quad \delta_1 = 0.75 \times 24 = 18°$ (firm clay)
- $K_2 = (1 - \sin 22) = 0.63,\quad \delta_2 = 0.75 \times 22 = 16.5°$ (stiff clay)

- $\int_{3.5}^{L} \sigma'_v \, dz = A_3 + A_4$ (refer to figure 5.42)

- $A_3 \approx 158 \, kN/m$
- $A_4 = (5L^2 + 15L - 270) \, kN/m$

Hence:

$$Q_s = \pi \times 0.4 \times (K_1 \times A_3 \times \tan \delta_1 + K_2 \times A_4 \times \tan \delta_2)$$
$$= (1.17L^2 + 3.51L - 25.2) \, kN$$

- The effective weight of a single pile:

$$W_p = 0.1256 \times (2 \times 24 + 14 \times [L-2]) = (1.76L + 2.51) \, kN$$

It follows that the ultimate loading capacity of an isolated pile is:

$$Q_u = Q_s + Q_b - W_p = (1.17L^2 + 47L + 40) \, kN$$

The ultimate loading capacity of the pilecap:

$$Q'_c = (A_c - nA_b) \times 0.4\gamma' B_c N'_\gamma$$

with:
- $A_c = 57 \, m^2$:   area of the pilecap
- $B_c = 5.2 \, m$:   width of the pilecap
- $N'_\gamma \approx 2.8$:   (see figure 5.36, $\phi' = 24°$)

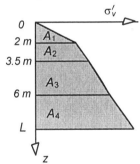

Figure 5.42: Integration of σ'_v along the block sides.

Accordingly: $Q'_c = (57 - 31 \times 0.1256) \times 0.4 \times 18.5 \times 5.2 \times 2.8 = 5722 \, kN$

Knowing that the weight of the pilecap is $W_c = 684 \, kN$, the ultimate loading capacity of the group corresponding to the first mode of failure is therefore:

$$Q_1 = nQ_u + Q_c - Q_n - W_c = (36.3L^2 + 1457L + 5517) \, kN$$

The group is subjected to an *allowable load* $Q_{ag} = 12,500 \, kN$, so that using a factor of safety of 3, Q_{ag} can then be expressed as follows:

$$Q_{ag} = nQ_a + \frac{Q_c'}{3} - Q_n - W_c \qquad (5.36)$$

in which the allowable load on an *isolated* pile is:

$$Q_a = \frac{Q_s + Q_b}{3} - W_p$$

But the ultimate loading capacity of the pile group is:

$$Q_1 = nQ_u + Q_c' - Q_n - W_c$$

$$= n(Q_s + Q_b - W_p) + Q_c' - Q_n - W_c \qquad (5.37)$$

Thus, subtracting equation 5.36 from equation 5.37 then rearranging, it is straightforward to establish that:

$$Q_{ag} = Q_1 - \frac{2}{3}[n(Q_s + Q_b) + Q_c'] \qquad (5.38)$$

Substituting for all relevant quantities into equation 5.38, the following quadratic is then obtained:

$$L^2 + 37.1L - 963.5 = 0$$

leading to a pile length: $L_1 = 17.6\,m$.

For the second mode of failure (*i.e.* block failure), the ultimate load capacity of the group is:

$$Q_2 = Q_{bb} + Q_{sb} + Q_c'' - Q_n - nW_p - W_c - W_s \qquad (5.39)$$

• *The ultimate base resistance of the block:*

$$Q_{bb} = A_{bb}\left(\sigma_{vb}' N_q' + 0.4\gamma' bN_\gamma'\right)$$

with   • $A_{bb} = 54.9\,m^2$: cross-sectional area of the block

• $N_q' \approx 4.6$, $N_\gamma' \approx 2.1$ (figure 9.36, $\phi' = 22°$)

• $b = 5.2\,m$: width of the block.

Thus:

$$Q_{bb} = 54.9 \times (4.6 \times [18.5 \times 2 + 9.5 \times 4 + 10(L - 6)])$$

$$+ 54.9 \times (0.4 \times 10 \times 5.2 \times 2.1) = (2525.4L + 6186)\,kN$$

- *The ultimate side friction force of the block:*

$$Q_{sb} = p_b \int_{z_f}^{L} K \tan \phi' \, \sigma'_v \, dz$$

$$= 22.8 \times (K_1 A_3 \tan 24 + K_2 A_4 \tan 22)$$

with

- $K_1 = (1 - \sin 24) = 0.59, \quad K_2 = (1 - \sin 22) = 0.63$

- A_3, A_4 as per figure 5.42.

so that: $Q_{sb} = (29L^2 + 87L - 621) \, kN$

- *The ultimate loading capacity of the pilecap portion outside the block:*

$$Q_c'' = (A_c - A_{bb}) \times 0.4\gamma' B_c N'_\gamma$$
$$= (57 - 54.9) \times 0.4 \times 18.5 \times 5.2 \times 2.8 = 226.3 \, kN$$

- *The effective weight of soil within the block:*

$$W_s = (A_{bb} - n.A_b)\gamma'L$$
$$= (54.9 - 31 \times 0.1256) \times (18.5 \times 2 + 9.5 \times 4 + 10 \times [L - 6])$$
$$= (510L + 765) \, kN$$

Substituting for the different quantities in equation 5.39, the ensuing expression of the ultimate loading capacity Q_2 can easily be established:

$$Q_2 = (29L^2 + 2048L + 3504) \, kN$$

The *allowable loading capacity* of the group is now calculated as follows:

$$Q_{ag} = \frac{1}{3}(Q_{bb} + Q_{sb} + Q_c'') - Q_n - nW_p - W_c - W_s \tag{5.40}$$

Hence, if equation 5.40 were subtracted from equation 5.39, it follows that:

$$Q_{ag} = Q_2 - \frac{2}{3}(Q_{bb} + Q_{sb} + Q_c'') \tag{5.41}$$

so that a substitution for the different quantities into equation 5.41 results in the quadratic:

$$L^2 + 31.6L - 1325.5 = 0$$

the solution of which is $L_2 \approx 23.9 \, m$.

A comparison between the two modes of failure indicates that the block failure is more critical than individual pile failure and, accordingly, the required pile's length is $L \approx 23.9\,m$.

5.6 Settlement of single piles and pile groups

The settlement of a deep foundation generated by a working load is usually difficult to predict because of the many variables upon which settlement depends. In fact, the magnitude of settlement of such a foundation is related to:

- the magnitude of applied load;
- the pile–soil interaction in terms of relative stiffness;
- the pile shape (straight sides, enlarged base) and dimensions (ratio L/d);
- the soil strata and its behaviour in terms of stiffness, density, compressibility, non-linearity;
- the group dimensions and the interaction between piles within the group (group depth and spacing ratio s/d).

Empirical, semi-empirical, analytical, and *numerical* methods have been advocated by different authors to estimate the settlement of deep foundations. As mentioned earlier (refer to section 5.2), the settlement of a single pile subject to axial loading is usually very small *provided* that an adequate factor of safety is used to reduce the ultimate load. In this respect, results relating to a comprehensive full scale load testing programme, undertaken over a period of years in different sites on different types of piles with a shaft length of between 6 *m* and 45 *m,* and diameters varying from 0.3 *m* to 1.5 *m* (LCPC-SETRA, 1985) indicate that, in all but a very few cases, the settlement under the working load measured at the pile head, rarely exceeds 10 *mm*.

A *crude estimate* of settlement at the head of a single pile with a diameter *d,* subject to a working Q_a can be obtained from the following *empirical relationships* (Frank, 1995):

- *bored piles:* $0.003d \le S \le 0.01d$ (5.42)
- *driven piles:* $0.008d \le S \le 0.012d$ (5.43)

Other methods of analysis of single pile settlement include the following:
- **The elastic methods** (Poulos and Davis, 1980): this is an analytical method based on the assumption that the *isotropic* soil in which the pile is embedded is characterised by a *linear elastic* behaviour. Such assumptions may quickly become unrealistic since the behaviour of most soils is non-linear and, accordingly, caution is advocated when using such a method.

• *The load transfer method*, better known as the (*t, z*) method (Meyer *et al.*, 1975, Vijayergiya, 1977, Frank and Zhao, 1982): this can easily accommodate non-linear soil behaviour and different soil conditions. However, this somewhat complex method requires that graphs corresponding to the variation of unit skin friction with settlement are known along the pile shaft at different depths. Representative graphs are often difficult to determine, and settlement predictions should therefore be considered carefully.

• *Numerical techniques* such as finite difference and finite element methods (refer to chapter 9) can always be used to estimate settlement. One has to bear in mind, however, that the outcome of a numerical analysis depends entirely on the quality of the input in terms of soil parameters.

Alternatively, settlement of single piles can be predicted from the *modified hyperbolic method* (Fleming, 1992). The method, originally developed by Chin (1970, 1972, 1983), is based on the idea that the load–settlement graphs for a pile shaft and its base can be closely represented by hyperbolic functions. Both the *ultimate shaft load* Q_{su} *and the ultimate base resistance* Q_{bu} correspond to the *asymptotic values* depicted in figure 5.43(a) (Terzaghi, 1943). Under these circumstances, both graphs can then be linearised by plotting the variation of the quantity S/Q *versus* the settlement S as shown in figure 5.43(b). The method was further refined by Fleming (1992) who showed that the total settlement predictions of the original Chin method were distorted by the *elastic shortening* of the pile body. Fleming then suggested a simplified technique by which the elastic pile deformation can be determined with sufficient accuracy, subtracting it thereafter from the settlement prior to plotting the graphs of figure 5.43. Based on the dimensions shown in figure 5.44, the elastic shortening of the pile depends on the magnitude of the *applied load* Q, compared with the *ultimate shaft friction* Q_{su}.

Thus, if $Q \le Q_{su}$, the elastic deformation of the pile body corresponds to the sum of the pile shortening along the *free or low friction depth* L_o, and that developed along the depth L_a of *the active shaft*, leading to the following expression:

$$S_e = \frac{4}{\pi} \frac{Q(L_o + K_e L_a)}{d_s^2 E_c} \tag{5.44}$$

If, on the other hand, the applied load Q exceeds the ultimate shaft friction, an additional shortening of the active length L_a occurs, which must then be added to the elastic deformation of equation 5.44. Accordingly, for $Q > Q_{su}$:

$$S_e = \frac{4}{\pi} \frac{1}{d_s^2 E_c} [Q(L_o + L_a) - L_a Q_{su}(1 - K_e)] \tag{5.45}$$

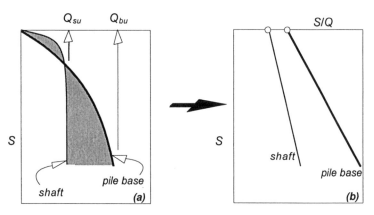

Figure 5.43: (a) Hyperbolic and (b) linearised settlement graphs.

The different quantities in both equations are such that:

- d_s: pile shaft diameter
- E_c: stiffness modulus of the pile material whose value can be linearly interpolated between the values $E_c = 26 \times 10^6 \, kN/m^2$ for a concrete specified strength of $20 \, N/mm^2$, and $E_c = 40 \times 10^6 \, kN/m^2$ for a concrete strength of $40 \, N/mm^2$
- L_o, L_s as per figure 5.44
- K_e ratio of the equivalent shaft length to the active shaft length L_a. Its value can be taken as $K_e = 0.5$ when a uniform friction develops along L_a or when the pile is installed in a sand or a gravel. For piles in a clay characterised by a strength increasing with depth, $K_e = 0.45$ can be adopted.

The settlement of the *rigid pile* can now be calculated knowing that the sum of the shaft friction and base resistance corresponds to the total load applied at the pile head:

$$Q = Q_s + Q_b \tag{5.46}$$

Because the pile is rigid, the total settlement at the pile head is identical to the settlement occurring along the pile shaft, as well as that measured at the pile base:

$$S_t = S_s = S_b \tag{5.47}$$

Moreover, it can easily be shown that, by virtue of the linear graphs in figure 5.43(*b*), the settlement along the pile shaft can be calculated as follows:

$$S_s = \frac{M_s \, d_s \, Q_s}{(Q_{su} - Q_s)}$$ (5.48)

with

- M_s: a dimensionless soil/shaft flexibility factor
- d_s: pile shaft diameter
- Q_s: shaft friction
- Q_{su}: long term (*i.e.* drained) *ultimate* shaft friction determined from the static method (refer to sections 5.3.3 and 5.3.4).

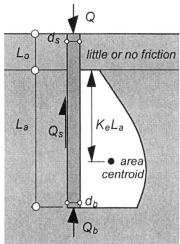

Figure 5.44: Pile dimensions related to the calculation of pile elastic shortening.

The equation of settlement at the pile base derived by Fleming is based on the settlement formula of a circular footing, in which the *secant soil modulus* corresponds to the load $Q_{bu}/4$:

$$S_b = \frac{0.6 Q_{bu} \, Q_b}{d_b E_b (Q_{bu} - Q_b)}$$ (5.49)

with
- d_b: diameter of the pile base
- Q_b: base resistance
- Q_{bu}: ultimate base resistance
- E_b: soil secant modulus corresponding to $Q_{bu}/4$.

Hence, taking equations 5.49 and 5.48 to be equal, and using the total load from equation 5.46, it can readily be shown that the *total settlement of the rigid pile* is as follows:

$$S_t = \frac{-g \pm \sqrt{(g^2 - 4fh)}}{2f}$$ (5.50)

with only the positive value considered. The variables in equation 5.50 are such that:

$$f = \eta(Q - \alpha) - \beta \qquad (5.51a)$$

$$g = Q(\delta + \lambda\eta) - \alpha\delta - \beta\lambda \qquad (5.51b)$$

$$h = \lambda\delta Q \qquad (5.51c)$$

where $\alpha = Q_{su}$, $\beta = d_b E_b Q_{bu}$, $\lambda = M_s d_s$, $\delta = 0.6 Q_{bu}$, and $\eta = d_b E_b$.

The overall settlement of the pile consists therefore of the component of total settlement calculated from equation 5.50 and the elastic shortening of the pile determined from equations 5.44 or 5.45, whichever is appropriate. The soil modulus below the base E_b is related to the soil characteristics and is highly sensitive to pile construction techniques. Fleming (1992) advocates that it is highly desirable for this key parameter to be determined from full scale tests whereby piles are loaded to the point where a substantial amount of base resistance is mobilised. Failing that, E_b can be *cautiously* selected from the following range of values related to the type of soil and pile installation technique. In all cases of bored piles, the pile base is assumed to be *well cleaned*.

- *Bored piles in clays*

clay consistency	$E_b (kN/m^2)$
very soft	<3000
soft	3000 to 6000
firm	6000 to 15,000
stiff	15,000 to 25,000
very stiff	25,000 to 40,000
hard	>40,000

- *Bored piles in sands and gravel*

soil type	$E_b (kN/m^2)$
very loose	<15,000
loose	15,000 to 30,000
medium dense	30,000 to 100,000
dense	100,000 to 200,000
very dense	>200,000

- *Bored piles in marls, shales and mudstones*

soil type	$E_b(kN/m^2)$
unweathered	150,000 to 250,000
relatively weathered	80,000 to 150,000
weathered	50,000 to 80,000
highly weathered	10,000 to 50,000

- *Bored piles in chalk*

chalk type	$E_b(kN/m^2)$
unstructured	<100,000
chalk with apertures > 3	100,000 to 200,000
apertures < 3 mm	150,000 to 250,000
closed discontinuities	>250,000

For piles driven without an enlarged base, the above relevant values apply. When the pile base is *enlarged*, then the above values must be multipied by a factor of 1.5. As regards the shaft/soil flexibility factor M_s, a comprehensive database amassed by *Cementation Piling and Foundations Limited* indicates that the variation of this *dimensionless factor* is remarkably small, and that its values are invariably between 0.001 and 0.0015. Moreover, these values seem to be unaffected by the type of pile or the nature of soil.

Example 5.9

Consider the pile of example 5.3, for which the different quantities have been calculated, neglecting the weight of pile:

$$Q_{s_u} \approx 100\,kN, \quad Q_{bu} = 1870\,kN, \quad Q_u = 1970\,kN.$$

Assuming that the pile is made of concrete, and that the depth along which little or no friction develops is $L_o = 1.5\,m$, so that $L_a = 6.5\,m$, calculate the elastic shortening and the settlement of the rigid pile knowing that:

$$K_e = 0.5, \quad M_s = 0.001, \quad E_c = 3 \times 10^7\,kN/m^2,$$
$$E_b = 2 \times 10^5\,kN/m^2, \quad d_s = d_b = 0.4\,m$$

The following calculations are undertaken for an applied load $Q = 600\,kN$. Because $Q > Q_{su} = 100\,kN$, the elastic shortening of the pile is calculated from equation 5.45:

$$S_e = \frac{4}{\pi} \times \frac{1}{0.4^2 \times 3 \times 10^7} [600 \times 8 - 6.5 \times 100 \times (1 - 0.5)] \approx 1.2mm$$

Next, the rigid pile settlement is evaluated using equation 5.50. The intermediate variables are as follows:

- $\alpha = Q_{su} = 100\,kN$

- $\beta = d_b E_b Q_{bu} = 0.4 \times 2 \times 10^5 \times 1870 = 149.6 \times 10^6\,kN^2/m$

- $\lambda = M_s d_s = 0.001 \times 0.4 = 4 \times 10^{-4}\,m$

- $\delta = 0.6 Q_{bu} = 0.6 \times 1870 = 1122\,kN$

- $\eta = d_b E_b = 0.4 \times 2 \times 10^5 = 8 \times 10^4\,kN/m$

Whence:

$$\begin{aligned} g &= Q(\delta + \lambda\eta) - \alpha\delta - \beta\lambda \\ &= 600 \times (1122 + 8 \times 10^4 \times 4 \times 10^{-4}) - 100 \times 1122 \\ &\quad -4 \times 10^{-4} \times 149.6 \times 10^6 \; = 520.36 \times 10^3\,kN^2 \end{aligned}$$

$$\begin{aligned} f &= \eta(Q - \alpha) - \beta \\ &= 8 \times 10^4 \times (600 - 100) - 149.6 \times 10^6 \; = -109.6 \times 10^6\,kN^2/m \end{aligned}$$

$$h = \lambda\delta Q = 4 \times 10^{-4} \times 1122 \times 600 = 269.3\,kN^2 m$$

Accordingly, the settlement of the rigid pile corresponding to the positive quantity calculated from equation 5.50 is:

$$\begin{aligned} S_t &= \frac{520.36 \times 10^3 \pm 10^3 \sqrt{(520.36)^2 + 4 \times 109.6 \times 269.3}}{2 \times 109.6 \times 10^6} \\ &= 5.22 \times 10^{-3}\,m \end{aligned}$$

If similar calculations are undertaken for different loads, the results can then be plotted in terms of load–settlement and are depicted in figure 5.45. The graph can be used to select a safe working load instead of the usual factor of safety related to the ultimate load as in the static method of design. Figure 5.45 indicates that loads of up to 800 kN can safely be carried out by the pile. The above calculations may appear to be tedious, however, the formulae can easily be programmed, and commercial software packages based on this method are available.

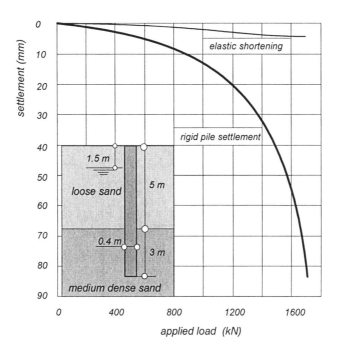

Figure 5.45: Load–settlement analysis using the hyperbolic method.

Example 5.10

Assuming the *driven* pile in example 5.2 is made of concrete with a circular cross-section corresponding to a diameter $d = 0.38\,m$, all other things being equal. The different pile characteristics are as follows:

$$E_c = 3 \times 10^7\ kN/m^2, \quad E_b = 6 \times 10^4\ kN/m^2, \quad M_s = 0.001,$$
$$K_e = 0.45, \quad L_o = 2\,m, \quad L_a = 18\,m$$

Neglecting the self weight of the pile, and considering the ultimate loads calculated in example 5.2:

$$Q_{su} = 1178\,kN, \quad Q_{bu} = 286\,kN, \quad Q_u = 1464\,kN$$

The calculation of both the pile elastic shortening and its settlement can then be undertaken in the same way using equations 5.44 or 5.45 (whichever is appropriate) and 5.50. The ensuing results, plotted in figure 5.46, indicate that the pile can safely support a load of up to $800\,kN$ for which the elastic shortening $(2.4\,mm)$ is 3.2 times larger than the actual total settlement of the pile $(\approx 0.75\,mm)$.

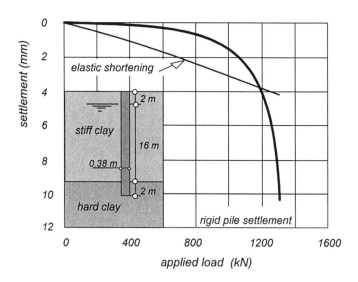

Figure 5.46: Total settlement of a single pile driven in clay.

Interestingly, both examples 5.9 and 5.10 reflect the effects of soil type on the overall settlement of single piles. The ultimate base resistance in example 5.9 (Q_{bu} = 1870 kN) was predominant compared with the ultimate shaft friction (Q_{su} = 100 kN), hence the relatively large settlement calculated before the end bearing is mobilised. In contrast, a much smaller settlement is induced by the full mobilisation of the shaft resistance in example 5.10 (Q_{su} = 1178 kN), which is much larger than the end bearing (Q_{bu} = 286 kN).

The hyperbolic method can be used in the same way to determine the load/settlement behaviour of pile groups and shallow foundations. Nevertheless, it ought to be emphasised that in practice, problems related to pile group design arise from the *differential settlement* of individual piles within the group rather than from the uniform settlement of the group *en masse.* It has been mentioned earlier that the contribution of the pilecap to the loading capacity of a pile group is usually discarded since large displacements are required to mobilise such a contribution in full. This implies that individual piles within a group are subjected to *different* loading through the pilecap, thus inducing different settlements depending on the position of each pile within the group compound. The potentially dangerous excessive differential settlement between individual piles may result in one or more piles failing, increasing in the process (markedly and suddenly) the load on adjacent piles. The hyperbolic method is well suited to predict reliably the amount of differential settlement, so that any potential problems can be remedied prior to the group being fully operational.

5.7 Design of Laterally loaded piles.

5.7.1 Introduction.

Lateral loading of piles occurs especially in conjunction with bridges, flyovers and retaining structures founded on piles. The loading can be classified into two categories :

- *active lateral loading* : when the pile head is directly subject to an *actual* horizontal load H_o or a bending moment M_o
- *passive lateral loading* for which the pile is subject to a lateral thrust generated by a surcharge load adjacent to the pile as depicted in figure 5.47.

In either case, the solution in terms of displacement, bending moments, shear stress and lateral pressure distributions depends on the soil/structure interaction, in other words on both soil and pile stiffness characteristics. In the following analysis, *only* the case of *active loading* will be considered. The soil/structure interaction is clearly depicted in figure 5.48 whereby the resistance to the active load is provided by the pile stiffness *and* the soil reaction per unit length (that is, the *force per unit length* generated within the soil mass by the active load). While the pile stiffness can be assumed constant along the pile shaft, the soil stiffness on the other hand depends generally on the depth of embedment. The figure shows that at a given depth z, the relationship between the soil reaction P and the lateral displacement y (*i.e.* the pile deflection) is non-linear; furthermore, the nature of the relationship varies with depth.

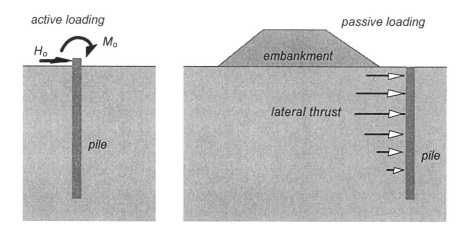

Figure 5.47. Active and passive lateral loading of piles

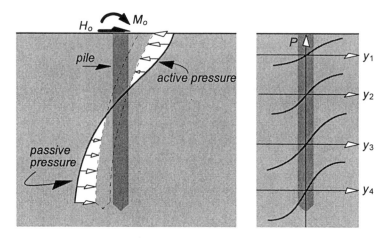

Figure 5.48: Soil/structure interaction along the pile shaft.

Assuming (P,y) graphs are known at different levels, then for a selected depth such as z_3 in figure 5.48, the slope at a given displacement is defined as the *modulus of subgrade reaction* (Reese & Matlock, 1956, Davisson & Gill, 1963):

$$K = \frac{P}{y} \qquad (5.52)$$

where : • P is the soil reaction per unit length (kN/m),
   • y represents the lateral displacement (m) corresponding to P,
   • K is the subgrade reaction modulus (kN/m^2).

Notice that sometimes, equation 5.52 is presented as follows :

$$p = k_h.y \qquad (5.53)$$

with   • $p = \frac{P}{d}$: the soil reaction *pressure* (kN/m^2), d being the pile diameter (or width if not circular),

   • $k_h = \frac{K}{d}$: modulus of subgrade reaction (kN/m^3).

In practice, reliable estimates of (P,y) graphs along selected depths of embedment can be obtained from *in situ* tests such as self-boring pressuremeter test (Azizi, 2007). Consequently, the following method of design of laterally loaded single piles, based on (P,y) analysis, is deemed to yield satisfactory results that compare favourably with the outcome of more numerical techniques such as finite element analysis.

5.7.2 The subgrade reaction method (also known as Winkler model).

In this method, first developed by Winkler (1867), the pile is assumed to be a vertical thin strip and the soil is modelled as a series of unconnected linearly-elastic springs (see figure 5.49). As such, the model does not allow for any shear stress to be transferred, and the stiffness parameters depend on foundation size. However, parameters such as non-linearity, non-homogeneity, and variation of stiffness with depth can be accommodated, thus making the model one of the most widely used in engineering practice.

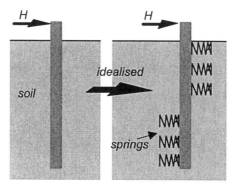

Figure 5.49: Spring idealisation related to subgrade reaction model.

The subgrade reaction modulus K of equation 5.52 is not a material constant; rather, it depends on the stiffness and width of the pile, and on loading conditions. The variation can be expressed as follows :

$$K = n_h . d \left(\frac{z}{d}\right)^n \tag{5.54}$$

where d represents the pile diameter (or width), n_h is the *rate of increase* of subgrade reaction with depth and the exponent n is assumed to vary from zero for overconsolidated clays to one for sands (Elson, 1984 , Poulos & Davis, 1980). The behaviour of the pile, assumed to act as a thin strip, is governed by the beam equation :

$$E_p I_p \frac{d^4 y}{dz^4} = -p.d \tag{5.55}$$

in which
- E_p: modulus of elasticity of pile,
- I_p: moment of inertia of pile section,
- d : pile diameter (or width),
- z : depth in soil.

Thus, substituting for the quantity $p.d$ from equation 5.53 into equation 5.55, then rearranging :

$$E_p I_p \frac{d^4 y}{dz^4} + k_h\, d.y = 0 \qquad (5.56)$$

This fourth order differential equation can easily be solved numerically using a finite difference formulation. Alternatively, an analytical solution to equation 5.56 can be derived, depending on the modulus of subgrade reaction.

A • Case of constant subgrade reaction modulus

For overconsolidated clays, the subgrade reaction modulus K may be assumed constant throughout the depth of embedment of the pile (*i.e.* the exponent n in equation 5.54 is zero). Accordingly, the general solution to equation 5.56 takes the form :

$$y = \exp\left(\frac{z}{l_c}\right)\left[A\cos\frac{z}{l_c} + B\sin\frac{z}{l_c}\right] + \exp\left(-\frac{z}{l_c}\right)\left[C\cos\frac{z}{l_c} + D\sin\frac{z}{l_c}\right] \qquad (5.57)$$

$$l_c = \left[\frac{4E_p I_p}{k_h\, d}\right]^{1/4} \qquad (5.58)$$

l_c reflects the stiffness of the pile relative to that of the soil and is thought of as a characteristic length of the pile. The constants of integration A, B, C, and D can be determined from two boundary conditions at the pile head and two more at the pile tip. Of particular interest, depending on the condition of fixity, a pile is referred to as:

- *fixed head* if the pile head is free to translate but not rotate,

- *free head* if the pile head is free to translate and rotate at the same time as depicted in figure 5.50.

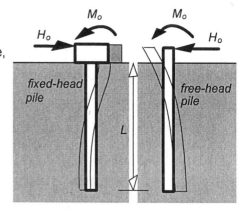

Figure 5.50 : Boundary conditions relating to laterally loaded piles.

Moreover, the profile of deflection, soil reaction and bending moment relate, not only to the conditions of fixity at the pile head, but also on the depth of embedment L, and on the type of soil in which the pile is inserted these effects being depicted in figures 5.51 & 5.52 in the case of a cohesionless soil. Thus, depending on their length, laterally loaded piles are classified into two categories :

- *long or flexible piles* when the depth of embedment (L in figure 5.50) in proportion to the characteristic length (l_c from equation 5.58) is such that $L \geq 2.5l_c$ for a *free head* pile or $L \geq 1.5l_c$ for a *fixed head* pile,

- *short or rigid piles* if $L \leq 1.5l_c$ in the case of a *free head* pile, or $L \leq 0.5l_c$ for a *fixed head* pile.

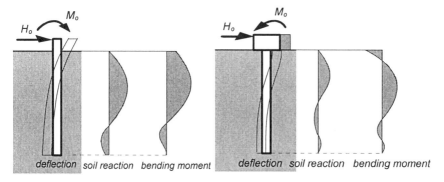

Figure 5.51: Profile of deflection, soil reaction and bending moment for a long pile in a cohesionless soil.

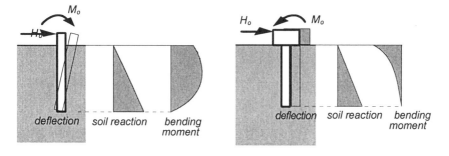

Figure 5.52: Profile of deflection, soil reaction and bending moment for a short pile in a cohesionless soil.

Based on equation 5.57, and provided the four integration constants are known, the following quantities can thence be found at any depth z in a straightforward way :

- *the slope along the pile shaft:* $\qquad \theta = \dfrac{dy}{dz}$ (5.59a)

- *the pile bending moment :* $\qquad M = E_p I_p \dfrac{d\theta}{dz} = E_p I_p \dfrac{d^2 y}{dz^2}$ (5.59b)

- *the shear load along the pile shaft:* $\qquad V = \dfrac{dM}{dz} = E_p I_p \dfrac{d^3 y}{dz^3}$ (5.59c)

- *the reaction pressure (equation 5.55) :* $p = -\dfrac{E_p I_p}{d}\dfrac{d^4 y}{dz^4}$ (5.59d)

Matlock and Reese (1960) derived similar equations from a dimensional analysis of a pile subject at its head to a horizontal load H_o and a bending moment M_o (refer to figure 5.50). These equations allow for the following quantities to be calculated at any depth z :

- *the lateral deflection:* $\qquad y = \dfrac{H_o T^3}{E_p I_p} A_y + \dfrac{M_o T^2}{E_p I_p} B_y$ (5.60a)

- *the slope:* $\qquad \theta = \dfrac{H_o T^2}{E_p I_p} A_s + \dfrac{M_o T}{E_p I_p} B_s$ (5.60b)

- *the pile bending moment :* $\qquad M = H_o T A_m + M_o B_m$ (5.60c)

- *the vertical load shear:* $\qquad V = H_o A_v + \dfrac{M_o}{T} B_v$ (5.60d)

- *the soil reaction per unit length:* $P = \dfrac{H_o}{T} A_r + \dfrac{M_o}{T^2} B_r$ (5.60e)

where the characteristic length T corresponding to a *constant* subgrade reaction modulus is defined as follows :

$$T = \left[\dfrac{E_p I_p}{k_h d} \right]^{1/4} = \dfrac{l_c}{\sqrt{2}} \qquad\qquad (5.61)$$

and A and B are coefficients related to the boundary conditions. Thus, for a *long flexible pile* (*i.e.* when $L \geq 2.5 l_c$ for a free head pile or $L \geq 1.5 l_c$ for a fixed head pile), A and B are calculated as follows:

$$A_y = \sqrt{2}\,\exp\left(-\dfrac{z}{l_c}\right) \cos\dfrac{z}{l_c}, \qquad B_y = \exp\left(-\dfrac{z}{l_c}\right)\left[\cos\dfrac{z}{l_c} - \sin\dfrac{z}{l_c} \right] \qquad (5.62a)$$

$$A_s = -\exp\left(-\dfrac{z}{l_c}\right)\left[\cos\dfrac{z}{l_c} + \sin\dfrac{z}{l_c} \right], \qquad B_s = -\sqrt{2}\,\exp\left(-\dfrac{z}{l_c}\right)\cos\dfrac{z}{l_c} \qquad (5.62b)$$

$$A_m = \sqrt{2} \, \exp\left(-\frac{z}{l_c}\right) \sin\frac{z}{l_c}, \qquad B_m = \exp\left(-\frac{z}{l_c}\right)\left[\cos\frac{z}{l_c} + \sin\frac{z}{l_c}\right] \qquad (5.62c)$$

$$A_v = -\exp\left(-\frac{z}{l_c}\right)\left[\cos\frac{z}{l_c} - \sin\frac{z}{l_c}\right], \quad B_v = -\sqrt{2} \, \exp\left(-\frac{z}{l_c}\right)\sin\frac{z}{l_c} \qquad (5.62d)$$

$$A_r = A_y, \qquad B_r = B_y \qquad (5.62e)$$

Notice that by using both parameters A_s and B_s (equation 5.62b) in conjunction with equation 5.60b, it is straightforward to show that at the ground surface (*i.e.* $z = 0$), the case of a *long fixed head pile* ($\theta = 0$, $\beta L > 1.5$) is equivalent to the case of a *free head pile* subject at its head to a moment $M_o = -H_o Tl\sqrt{2}$.

For a *short rigid pile* with an embedment depth L, subject at its head to horizontal load H_o with an eccentricity e above the ground surface as illustrated in figure 5.53, Poulos and Davis (1981) suggest to use the following limiting solutions to estimate the horizontal displacement and rotation at the ground surface :

• *free head rigid pile* $(L \le 1.5l_c)$:

$$y = \frac{4H_o\left(1 + \frac{1.5e}{L}\right)}{k_h \, dL} \qquad (5.63)$$

$$\theta = \frac{6H_o\left(1 + \frac{2e}{L}\right)}{k_h \, dL^2} \qquad (5.64)$$

• *fixed head rigid pile* $(L \le 0.5l_c)$:

$$y = \frac{H_o}{k_h \, dL} \qquad (5.65)$$

For *intermediate piles*, that is when $2.5l_c \le L \le 1.5l_c$ for a free head pile or when $1.5l_c \le L \le 0.5l_c$ for a fixed head pile, a modified form of equation 5.55 can be cautiously used (Frank, 1995), whereby the lateral displacement y at a given depth z is expressed as follows :

$$y(z) = y(z = 0) + z.\frac{dy}{dz}(z = 0) \qquad (5.66)$$

Equations 9.56 can thence be used to estimate the variation with depth of different parameters.

Example 5.11

A steel tube pile with a moment of inertia $I_p = 1.23 \times 10^{-4} m^4$ and a modulus of elasticity $E = 250\,GN/m^2$ is embedded in a stiff clay characterised by a constant subgrade reaction modulus $k_h = 20\,MN/m^3$. The free head pile having a diameter of 0.5m and an embedment length of 8m, is subject to a horizontal force $H_o = 300\,kN$ applied 1.2m above the ground surface. Calculate the slope, bending moment and soil reaction at the ground surface; also, determine the deflection profile along the pile shaft.

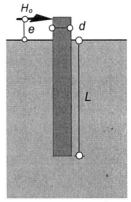

Figure 5.53: Loading
conditions for a short pile

First, let us determine if the pile is *long* or *short* by calculating the characteristic length I_c using equation 5.58:

$$I_c = \left[\frac{4 E_p I_p}{k_h . d} \right]^{1/4} = \left[\frac{4 \times 250 \times 10^6 \times 1.23 \times 10^{-4}}{0.5 \times 20 \times 10^3} \right]^{1/4} = 1.87m$$

whence : $\dfrac{L}{I_c} = \dfrac{8}{1.87} = 4.27 > 2.5$

Consequently, we are dealing with a *long flexible pile*. The slope, bending moment and soil reaction are calculated from equations 5.60b, c & e. Prior to any calculations, one needs to determine all the constant quantities used in conjunction with equations 5.60 :

$E_p I_p = 250 \times 123 = 30750\,kNm^2$, $T = \dfrac{I_c}{\sqrt{2}} = \dfrac{1.87}{\sqrt{2}} = 1.32m$,

$M_o = 1.2 H_0 = 1.2 \times 300 = 360\,kNm$.

At the ground surface $z = 0$ and equations 5.62b, c & e then yield the following coefficients respectively :

$A_s = -1.00$, $B_s = -1.42$, $A_m = 0.00$, $B_m = 1.00$, $A_r = 1.42$, $B_v = 1.00$.

Whence the slope at ground level (equation 5.60b) :

$$\theta = \frac{T}{E_p I_p} (A_s H_o T + B_s M_o) = \frac{1.32}{30750} \times (-300 \times 1.32 - 1.42 \times 360)$$

$$= -0.0389\,radians\ (-2.2°).$$

The bending moment at $z = 0$ (equation 5.60c) :

$$M = 360 \times 1 = 360 \, kNm.$$

The soil reaction at ground level (equation 5.60e):

$$p = \frac{300}{1.32} \times 1.42 + \frac{360}{1.32^2} \times 1 = 529 \, kN/m.$$

The deflection profile with depth is calculated in a similar way using the constants A_y and B_y in conjunction with equation 5.60a, so that for instance, the deflection at a depth $z = 2m$ is computed as follows:

$$A_y = \sqrt{2} \, \exp\left(\frac{-2}{1.87}\right) \cos \frac{2}{1.87} = 0.234,$$

$$B_y = \exp\left(\frac{-2}{1.87}\right)\left[\cos \frac{2}{1.87} - \sin \frac{2}{1.87}\right] = -0.136$$

(Notice that the ratios used in conjunction with sine and cosine functions are expressed in *radians*). Substituting into equation 5.60a :

$$y_{(z=2)} = \frac{T^2}{E_p I_p} (A_y T H_o + M_o B_y)$$

$$= \frac{1.32^2}{30750} \times (0.234 \times 1.32 \times 300 - 0.136 \times 360) = 2.47 \times 10^{-3} m.$$

The calculations can hence be undertaken on a spreadsheet; the corresponding results being plotted in figure 5.54.

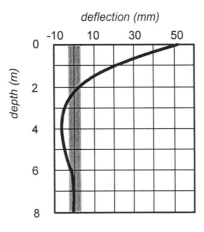

Figure 5.54: Deflection profile.

Example 5.12

A free head steel tube pile with a diameter of *0.3m* and a flexural stiffness $E_p I_p = 65,000 \, kNm^2$ is embedded *4m* in the same soil conditions described in the previous example 5.11, and subject to the same horizontal load at *1.2 m* above the ground surface. In this case, the pile stiffness has changed, and the new characteristic length is thence:

$$I_c = \left[\frac{4 \times 65 \times 10^3}{0.3 \times 20 \times 10^3} \right]^{1/4} = 2.56m.$$

Whence the ratio $\dfrac{L}{I_c} = \dfrac{4}{2.56} = 1.56 < 2.5$, indicating that the pile is *short (or rigid)*. Consequently, the deflection at ground level can be estimated from equation 5.63:

$$y_{(z=0)} = \frac{4H_o \left(1 + \frac{1.5e}{L} \right)}{k_h \, dL} = \frac{4 \times 300 \times \left(1 + \frac{1.5 \times 1.2}{4} \right)}{20 \times 10^3 \times 0.3 \times 4} = 72.5 \, mm.$$

Equation 5.64 on the other hand is used to calculate the slope at ground level :

$$\theta = \frac{6H_o \left(1 + \frac{2e}{L} \right)}{k_h \, dL^2} = \frac{6 \times 300 \times \left(1 + \frac{2 \times 1.2}{4} \right)}{20 \times 10^3 \times 0.3 \times 4^2} = 0.03 \, radians \quad (1.72°)$$

B • *Case of k_h varying linearly with depth.*

For normally consolidated clays and for most sands, the modulus of subgrade reaction may be considered to vary linearly with depth (*i.e.* the exponent *n* in equation 5.64 is one) :

$$K = n_h.z \quad\quad\quad\quad\quad\quad\quad (5.67)$$

In which case, a closed form solution to equation 5.56 is not available. However, the ensuing differential equation can be solved numerically, and in this respect, the solutions obtained using a finite difference technique (Elson, 1984) are deemed satisfactory provided that values of subgrade reaction modulus appropriate to the soil behaviour are used. Non-dimensional coefficients A and B that can be used in conjunction with equations 5.60 a-c to calculate the deflection and bending moments with depth are given in tables 5.1 to 5.9 reproduced from Elson (1984). These coefficients are expressed in terms of :

- a (dimensionless) depth factor: $Z = \dfrac{z}{T^*}$ (5.68)
- a length factor: $Z_{max} = \dfrac{L}{T^*}$ (5.69)

with the characteristic length, in this case :

$$T^* = \left[\frac{E_p I_p}{n_h} \right]^{1/5}$$ (5.70)

Table 5.1: $Z_{max} = 1.0$

Coefficients A & B for a pile in a Winkler medium									
Z	A_y	A_s	A_m	A_v	A_r	B_y	B_s	B_m	B_v	B_r
0.0	17.66	-23.78	0.00	1.00	0.00	23.20	-35.48	1.00	0.00	0.00
0.1	15.28	-23.78	0.11	0.93	-1.53	19.65	-35.38	1.00	-0.10	-1.97
0.2	12.90	-23.76	0.18	0.69	-2.58	16.12	-35.28	0.98	-0.39	-3.22
0.3	10.52	-23.74	0.25	0.41	-3.16	12.60	-35.18	0.93	-0.75	-3.78
0.4	8.15	-23.71	0.27	0.06	-3.26	9.09	-35.09	0.83	-1.15	-3.63
0.5	5.78	-23.69	0.26	-0.24	-2.89	5.58	-35.01	0.70	-1.48	-2.79
0.6	3.41	-23.66	0.22	-0.52	-2.05	2.08	-34.95	0.53	-1.71	-1.25
0.7	1.05	-23.64	0.16	-0.65	-0.73	-1.41	-34.91	0.35	-1.73	0.99
0.8	-1.32	-23.63	0.09	-0.66	1.05	-4.90	-34.88	0.19	-1.51	3.92
0.9	-3.68	-23.63	0.02	-0.44	3.31	-8.39	-34.87	0.05	-0.94	7.55
1.0	-6.04	-23.63	0.00	0.00	6.04	-11.87	-34.87	0.00	0.00	11.87

Table 5.2: $Z_{max} = 1.5$

Coefficients A & B for a pile in a Winkler medium									
Z	A_y	A_s	A_m	A_v	A_r	B_y	B_s	B_m	B_v	B_r
0.0	7.97	-7.25	0.00	1.00	0.00	7.20	-7.72	1.00	0.00	0.00
0.1	7.25	-7.25	0.10	0.96	-0.73	6.43	-7.62	1.00	-0.04	-0.64
0.2	6.52	-7.23	0.19	0.86	-1.30	5.67	-7.52	0.99	-0.13	-1.13
0.3	5.80	-7.21	0.27	0.70	-1.74	4.92	-7.42	0.97	-0.26	-1.48
0.4	5.08	-7.18	0.33	0.51	-2.03	4.19	-7.32	0.94	-0.42	-1.67
0.5	4.36	-7.14	0.37	0.29	-2.18	3.46	-7.23	0.89	-0.60	-1.73
0.6	3.65	-7.10	0.39	0.07	-2.19	2.74	-7.15	0.82	-0.77	-1.64
0.7	2.94	-7.06	0.39	-0.14	-2.06	2.03	-7.07	0.74	-0.93	-1.42
0.8	2.24	-7.02	0.36	-0.34	-1.79	1.33	-7.00	0.63	-1.05	-1.06
0.9	1.54	-6.99	0.32	-0.50	-1.39	0.63	-6.94	0.52	-1.14	-0.57
1.0	0.84	-6.96	0.26	-0.62	-0.84	-0.06	-6.89	0.41	-1.17	0.06
1.1	0.15	-6.94	0.19	-0.67	-0.16	-0.75	-6.86	0.29	-1.13	0.82
1.2	-0.55	-6.92	0.13	-0.65	0.65	-1.43	-6.84	0.18	-1.00	1.72
1.3	-1.24	-6.91	0.07	-0.54	1.61	-2.12	-6.82	0.09	-0.78	2.75
1.4	-1.93	-6.91	0.02	-0.33	2.70	-2.80	-6.82	0.02	-0.45	3.92
1.5	-2.62	-6.91	0.00	0.00	3.93	-3.48	-6.82	0.00	0.00	5.22

Table 5.3: $Z_{max} = 2.0$

					Coefficients A & B for a pile in a Winkler medium				
Z	A_y	A_s	A_m	A_v	A_r	B_y	B_s	B_m	B_v	B_r
0.0	4.71	-3.40	0.00	1.00	0.00	3.39	-3.20	1.00	0.00	0.00
0.1	4.36	-3.40	0.10	0.98	-0.44	3.07	-3.10	1.00	-0.02	-0.31
0.2	4.03	-3.38	0.20	0.91	-0.81	2.77	-3.00	1.00	-0.06	-0.55
0.3	3.69	-3.36	0.28	0.82	-1.11	2.47	-2.90	0.99	-0.13	-0.74
0.4	3.35	-3.33	0.36	0.69	-1.34	2.19	-2.80	0.97	-0.21	-0.87
0.5	3.02	-3.29	0.42	0.55	-1.51	1.91	-2.70	0.95	-0.30	-0.96
0.6	2.70	-3.24	0.47	0.39	-1.62	1.65	-2.61	0.91	-0.40	-0.99
0.7	2.37	-3.19	0.50	0.23	-1.66	1.39	-2.52	0.87	-0.50	-0.97
0.8	2.06	-3.14	0.51	0.06	-1.65	1.14	-2.44	0.81	-0.60	-0.91
0.9	1.75	-3.09	0.51	-0.10	-1.57	0.90	-2.36	0.75	-0.68	-0.81
1.0	1.44	-3.04	0.49	-0.26	-1.44	0.67	-2.29	0.68	-0.76	-0.67
1.1	1.14	-2.99	0.46	-0.39	-1.25	0.45	-2.22	0.60	-0.82	-0.49
1.2	0.84	-2.95	0.41	-0.51	-1.01	0.23	-2.17	0.51	-0.86	-0.27
1.3	0.55	-2.91	0.36	-0.59	-0.71	0.01	-2.12	0.42	-0.87	-0.01
1.4	0.26	-2.88	0.30	-0.65	-0.36	-0.20	-2.08	0.34	-0.86	0.28
1.5	-0.03	-2.85	0.23	-0.67	0.04	-0.41	-2.05	0.25	-0.82	0.61
1.6	-0.31	-2.83	0.16	-0.64	0.50	-0.61	-2.03	0.17	-0.74	0.98
1.7	-0.59	-2.82	0.10	-0.57	1.01	-0.81	-2.02	0.11	-0.62	1.38
1.8	-0.88	-2.81	0.05	-0.44	1.58	-1.01	-2.01	0.05	-0.46	1.82
1.9	-1.16	-2.81	0.01	-0.25	2.20	-1.21	-2.01	0.01	-0.25	2.31
2.0	-1.44	-2.81	0.00	0.00	2.87	-1.42	-2.01	0.00	0.00	2.83

Table 5.4: $Z_{max} = 2.5$

Coefficients A & B for a pile in a Winkler medium :										
Z	A_y	A_s	A_m	A_v	A_r	B_y	B_s	B_m	B_v	B_r
0.0	3.31	-2.17	0.00	1.00	0.00	2.16	-2.10	1.00	0.00	0.00
0.1	3.10	-2.16	0.10	0.98	-0.31	1.95	-2.00	1.00	-0.01	-0.20
0.2	2.88	-2.15	0.20	0.94	-0.58	1.76	-1.90	1.00	-0.04	-0.35
0.3	2.67	-2.12	0.29	0.87	-0.80	1.57	-1.80	0.99	-0.08	-0.47
0.4	2.46	-2.09	0.37	0.78	-0.98	1.40	-1.70	0.98	-0.13	-0.56
0.5	2.25	-2.05	0.44	0.67	-1.12	1.23	-1.60	0.97	-0.19	-0.62
0.6	2.05	-2.00	0.50	0.55	-1.23	1.08	-1.51	0.94	-0.26	-0.65
0.7	1.85	-1.95	0.55	0.43	-1.29	0.93	-1.42	0.91	-0.32	-0.65
0.8	1.66	-1.89	0.59	0.29	-1.33	0.79	-1.33	0.88	-0.39	-0.64
0.9	1.47	-1.83	0.61	0.16	-1.32	0.66	-1.24	0.84	-0.45	-0.60
1.0	1.29	-1.77	0.62	0.03	-1.29	0.55	-1.16	0.79	-0.51	-0.55
1.1	1.12	-1.71	0.62	-0.10	-1.23	0.43	-1.08	0.74	-0.56	-0.48
1.2	0.95	-1.64	0.60	-0.22	-1.14	0.33	-1.01	0.68	-0.60	-0.40
1.3	0.79	-1.59	0.58	-0.33	-1.02	0.23	-0.95	0.62	-0.64	-0.30
1.4	0.63	-1.53	0.54	-0.42	-0.89	0.14	-0.89	0.55	-0.66	-0.20
1.5	0.48	-1.48	0.49	-0.50	-0.72	0.05	-0.84	0.48	-0.68	-0.08
1.6	0.34	-1.43	0.44	-0.57	-0.54	-0.03	-0.79	0.41	-0.68	0.04
1.7	0.20	-1.39	0.38	-0.61	-0.33	-0.10	-0.75	0.35	-0.67	0.18
1.8	0.06	-1.36	0.32	-0.63	-0.11	-0.18	-0.72	0.28	-0.64	0.32
1.9	-0.07	-1.33	0.25	-0.63	0.14	-0.25	-0.70	0.22	-0.61	0.47
2.0	-0.21	-1.31	0.19	-0.60	0.41	-0.32	-0.68	0.16	-0.55	0.64
2.1	-0.34	-1.29	0.13	-0.55	0.71	-0.38	-0.67	0.11	-0.48	0.81
2.2	-0.46	-1.28	0.08	-0.46	1.02	-0.45	-0.66	0.06	-0.39	0.99
2.3	-0.59	-1.27	0.04	-0.34	1.36	-0.52	-0.65	0.03	-0.28	1.19
2.4	-0.72	-1.27	0.01	-0.19	1.72	-0.58	-0.65	0.01	-0.15	1.40
2.5	-0.85	-1.27	0.00	0.00	2.11	-0.65	-0.65	0.00	0.00	1.62

Table 5.5: $Z_{max} = 3.0$

Z	A_y	A_s	A_m	A_v	A_r	B_y	B_s	B_m	B_v	B_r
Coefficients A & B for a pile in a Winkler medium :									
0.0	2.72	-1.76	0.00	1.00	0.00	1.75	-1.82	1.00	0.00	0.00
0.1	2.54	-1.75	0.10	0.99	-0.25	1.57	-1.72	1.00	-0.01	-0.16
0.2	2.37	-1.74	0.20	0.95	-0.47	1.41	-1.62	1.00	-0.03	-0.28
0.3	2.20	-1.71	0.29	0.89	-0.66	1.25	-1.52	0.99	-0.06	-0.38
0.4	2.03	-1.68	0.38	0.82	-0.81	1.10	-1.42	0.98	-0.11	-0.44
0.5	1.86	-1.64	0.45	0.73	-0.93	0.97	-1.32	0.97	-0.15	-0.48
0.6	1.70	-1.59	0.52	0.63	-1.02	0.84	-1.22	0.95	-0.20	-0.50
0.7	1.54	-1.53	0.58	0.53	-1.08	0.72	-1.13	0.93	-0.25	-0.51
0.8	1.39	-1.47	0.63	0.42	-1.11	0.61	-1.04	0.90	-0.30	-0.49
0.9	1.25	-1.41	0.66	0.30	-1.12	0.52	-0.95	0.87	-0.35	-0.46
1.0	1.11	-1.34	0.69	0.19	-1.11	0.42	-0.86	0.83	-0.40	-0.42
1.1	0.98	-1.27	0.70	0.08	-1.08	0.34	-0.78	0.79	-0.44	-0.38
1.2	0.86	-1.20	0.70	-0.03	-1.03	0.27	-0.70	0.75	-0.47	-0.32
1.3	0.74	-1.13	0.70	-0.13	-0.96	0.20	-0.63	0.70	-0.50	-0.26
1.4	0.63	-1.06	0.68	-0.22	-0.88	0.14	-0.56	0.65	-0.52	-0.20
1.5	0.53	-0.99	0.65	-0.30	-0.79	0.09	-0.50	0.59	-0.54	-0.13
1.6	0.43	-0.93	0.62	-0.38	-0.69	0.04	-0.45	0.54	-0.55	-0.07
1.7	0.34	-0.87	0.58	-0.44	-0.58	0.00	-0.40	0.48	-0.55	0.00
1.8	0.26	-0.81	0.53	-0.49	-0.47	-0.04	-0.35	0.43	-0.55	0.07
1.9	0.18	-0.76	0.48	-0.53	-0.34	-0.07	-0.31	0.37	-0.54	0.13
2.0	0.11	-0.72	0.42	-0.56	-0.21	-0.10	-0.28	0.32	-0.52	0.20
2.2	-0.03	-0.65	0.31	-0.58	0.07	-0.15	-0.22	0.22	-0.47	0.33
2.4	-0.15	-0.60	0.20	-0.54	0.37	-0.19	-0.19	0.13	-0.39	0.46
2.6	-0.27	-0.57	0.10	-0.43	0.70	-0.23	-0.17	0.06	-0.29	0.59
2.8	-0.38	-0.56	0.03	-0.25	1.07	-0.26	-0.16	0.02	-0.16	0.72
3.0	-0.49	-0.55	0.00	0.00	1.48	-0.29	-0.16	0.00	0.00	0.87

Table 5.6: $Z_{max} = 3.5$

Coefficients A & B for a pile in a Winkler medium :									
Z	A_y	A_s	A_m	A_v	A_r	B_y	B_s	B_m	B_v	B_r
0.0	2.50	-1.64	0.00	1.00	0.00	1.63	-1.76	1.00	0.00	0.00
0.1	2.33	-1.64	0.10	0.99	-0.23	1.46	-1.66	1.00	-0.01	-0.15
0.2	2.17	-1.62	0.20	0.95	-0.43	1.30	-1.56	1.00	-0.03	-0.26
0.3	2.01	-1.60	0.29	0.90	-0.60	1.15	-1.46	0.99	-0.06	-0.35
0.4	1.85	-1.56	0.38	0.83	-0.74	1.01	-1.36	0.99	-0.10	-0.41
0.5	1.70	-1.52	0.46	0.75	-0.85	0.88	-1.26	0.97	-0.14	-0.44
0.6	1.55	-1.47	0.53	0.66	-0.93	0.76	-1.16	0.96	-0.19	-0.46
0.7	1.40	-1.42	0.59	0.57	-0.98	0.65	-1.07	0.94	-0.23	-0.45
0.8	1.26	-1.35	0.64	0.47	-1.01	0.55	-0.97	0.91	-0.28	-0.44
0.9	1.13	-1.29	0.68	0.36	-1.02	0.45	-0.88	0.88	-0.32	-0.41
1.0	1.01	-1.22	0.71	0.26	-1.01	0.37	-0.80	0.85	-0.36	-0.37
1.1	0.89	-1.14	0.74	0.16	-0.98	0.30	-0.72	0.81	-0.39	-0.32
1.2	0.78	-1.07	0.75	0.07	-0.93	0.23	-0.64	0.77	-0.42	-0.27
1.3	0.67	-0.99	0.75	-0.02	-0.88	0.17	-0.56	0.72	-0.45	-0.22
1.4	0.58	-0.92	0.74	-0.11	-0.81	0.16	-0.49	0.68	-0.47	-0.16
1.5	0.49	-0.85	0.73	-0.19	-0.74	0.07	-0.43	0.63	-0.48	-0.10
1.6	0.41	-0.77	0.71	-0.26	-0.67	0.03	-0.36	0.58	-0.49	-0.05
1.7	0.34	-0.70	0.68	-0.32	-0.57	0.00	-0.31	0.53	-0.49	0.01
1.8	0.27	-0.64	0.64	-0.37	-0.48	-0.03	-0.26	0.48	-0.49	0.06
1.9	0.21	-0.58	0.60	-0.41	-0.40	-0.05	-0.21	0.44	-0.48	0.10
2.0	0.15	-0.52	0.56	-0.45	-0.31	-0.07	-0.17	0.39	-0.47	0.15
2.2	0.06	-0.42	0.46	-0.49	-0.13	-0.10	-0.10	0.30	-0.43	0.22
2.4	-0.01	-0.33	0.36	-0.50	0.03	-0.12	-0.05	0.22	-0.38	0.28
2.6	-0.07	-0.27	0.26	-0.48	0.19	-0.12	-0.02	0.15	-0.32	0.32
2.8	-0.12	-0.23	0.17	-0.43	0.34	-0.12	0.01	0.09	-0.25	0.34
3.0	-0.16	-0.20	0.10	-0.34	0.49	-0.12	0.02	0.05	-0.18	0.36
3.5	-0.26	-0.18	0.00	0.00	0.90	-0.11	0.03	0.00	0.00	0.37

DESIGN OF LATERALLY LOADED PILES

Table 5.7: $Z_{max} = 4.0$

Z	A_y	A_s	A_m	A_v	A_r	B_y	B_s	B_m	B_v	B_r
\multicolumn{11}{l}{Coefficients A & B for a pile in a Winkler medium :}
0.0	2.44	-1.62	0.00	1.00	0.00	1.62	-1.75	1.00	0.00	0.00
0.1	2.28	-1.62	0.10	0.99	-0.23	1.45	-1.65	1.00	-0.01	-0.15
0.2	2.11	-1.60	0.20	0.95	-0.42	1.29	-1.55	1.00	-0.03	-0.26
0.3	1.96	-1.58	0.29	0.90	-0.59	1.14	-1.45	0.99	-0.06	-0.34
0.4	1.80	-1.54	0.38	0.84	-0.72	1.00	-1.35	0.99	-0.10	-0.40
0.5	1.65	-1.50	0.46	0.76	-0.82	0.87	-1.25	0.97	-0.14	-0.43
0.6	1.50	-1.45	0.53	0.67	-0.90	0.75	-1.15	0.96	-0.18	-0.45
0.7	1.36	-1.40	0.59	0.58	-0.95	0.64	-1.06	0.94	-0.23	-0.44
0.8	1.22	-1.33	0.65	0.48	-0.98	0.53	-0.97	0.91	-0.27	-0.43
0.9	1.09	-1.27	0.69	0.38	-0.98	0.44	-0.88	0.88	-0.31	-0.40
1.0	0.97	-1.19	0.72	0.29	-0.97	0.36	-0.79	0.85	-0.35	-0.36
1.1	0.85	-1.12	0.75	0.19	-0.94	0.28	-0.71	0.81	-0.39	-0.31
1.2	0.74	-1.05	0.76	0.10	-0.89	0.22	-0.63	0.77	-0.41	-0.26
1.3	0.64	-0.97	0.77	0.01	-0.83	0.16	-0.55	0.73	-0.44	-0.20
1.4	0.55	-0.89	0.76	-0.07	-0.77	0.11	-0.48	0.69	-0.46	-0.15
1.5	0.46	-0.82	0.75	-0.14	-0.69	0.06	-0.42	0.64	-0.47	-0.09
1.6	0.39	-0.74	0.74	-0.21	-0.62	0.02	-0.35	0.59	-0.47	-0.04
1.7	0.32	-0.67	0.71	-0.26	-0.54	-0.01	-0.30	0.54	-0.47	0.02
1.8	0.25	-0.60	0.68	-0.31	-0.45	-0.04	-0.25	0.50	-0.47	0.07
1.9	0.20	-0.53	0.65	-0.35	-0.37	-0.06	-0.20	0.45	-0.46	0.11
2.0	0.15	-0.47	0.61	-0.39	-0.29	-0.08	-0.15	0.41	-0.45	0.15
2.2	0.06	-0.35	0.53	-0.43	-0.14	-0.10	-0.08	0.32	-0.41	0.22
2.4	0.00	-0.26	0.44	-0.44	-0.01	-0.11	-0.03	0.24	-0.36	0.26
2.6	-0.04	-0.18	0.35	-0.43	0.10	-0.11	0.01	0.17	-0.31	0.29
2.8	-0.07	-0.12	0.27	-0.40	0.19	-0.10	0.04	0.12	-0.25	0.29
3.0	-0.09	-0.07	0.19	-0.36	0.26	-0.09	0.06	0.08	-0.19	0.28
3.2	-010	-0.04	0.13	-0.30	0.31	-0.08	0.07	0.04	-0.14	0.26
3.4	-0.10	-0.02	0.07	-0.23	0.35	-0.06	0.08	0.02	-0.09	0.22
3.6	-0.11	-0.01	0.03	-0.16	0.38	-0.05	0.08	0.01	-0.05	0.17
3.8	-0.11	0.00	0.01	-0.08	0.40	-0.03	0.08	0.00	-0.02	0.12
4.0	-0.11	0.00	0.00	0.00	0.43	-0.01	0.08	0.00	0.00	0.06

Table 5.8: $Z_{max} = 5.0$

Coefficients A & B for a pile in a Winkler medium :										
Z	A_y	A_s	A_m	A_v	A_r	B_y	B_s	B_m	B_v	B_r
0.0	2.43	-1.62	0.00	1.00	0.00	1.62	-1.75	1.00	0.00	0.00
0.1	2.27	-1.62	0.10	0.99	-0.23	1.45	-1.65	1.00	-0.01	-0.15
0.2	2.10	-1.60	0.20	0.96	-0.42	1.29	-1.55	1.00	-0.03	-0.26
0.3	1.95	-1.58	0.29	0.90	-0.58	1.14	-1.45	0.99	-0.06	-0.34
0.4	1.79	-1.54	0.38	0.84	-0.72	1.00	-1.35	0.99	-0.10	-0.40
0.5	1.64	-1.50	0.46	0.76	-0.82	0.87	-1.25	0.98	-0.14	-0.43
0.6	1.49	-1.45	0.53	0.67	-0.89	0.75	-1.15	0.96	-0.18	-0.45
0.7	1.35	-1.39	0.59	0.58	-0.94	0.64	-1.06	0.94	-0.23	-0.45
0.8	1.21	-1.33	0.65	0.49	-0.97	0.54	-0.97	0.91	-0.27	-0.43
0.9	1.08	-1.27	0.69	0.39	-0.97	0.44	-0.88	0.88	-0.32	-0.40
1.0	0.96	-1.19	0.72	0.29	-0.96	0.36	-0.79	0.85	-0.35	-0.36
1.1	0.84	-1.12	0.75	0.20	-0.93	0.29	-0.71	0.81	-0.39	-0.31
1.2	0.73	-1.04	0.76	0.11	-0.88	0.22	-0.63	0.77	-0.42	-0.26
1.3	0.63	-0.97	0.77	0.02	-0.82	0.16	-0.55	0.73	-0.44	-0.21
1.4	0.54	-0.89	0.77	-0.06	-0.76	0.11	-0.48	0.68	-0.48	-0.15
1.5	0.45	-0.81	0.76	-0.13	-0.68	0.06	-0.41	0.64	-0.47	-0.10
1.6	0.38	-0.74	0.74	-0.19	-0.60	0.03	-0.35	0.59	-0.48	-0.04
1.7	0.31	-0.67	0.72	-0.25	-0.52	-0.01	-0.30	0.54	-0.48	0.01
1.8	0.24	-0.59	0.69	-0.30	-0.44	-0.03	-0.24	0.50	-0.47	0.06
1.9	0.19	-0.53	0.66	-0.34	-0.36	-0.06	-0.20	0.45	-0.47	0.10
2.0	0.14	-0.46	0.63	-0.37	-0.28	-0.07	-0.15	0.40	-0.45	0.15
2.2	0.06	-0.35	0.55	-0.41	-0.13	-0.10	-0.08	0.32	-0.42	0.21
2.4	0.00	-0.24	0.46	-0.42	0.00	-0.11	-0.03	0.24	-0.37	0.26
2.6	-0.04	-0.16	0.38	-0.41	0.11	-0.11	0.01	0.17	-0.32	0.28
2.8	-0.07	-0.09	0.30	-0.38	0.18	-0.10	0.04	0.11	-0.26	0.29
3.0	-0.08	-0.04	0.23	-0.34	0.24	-0.09	0.06	0.06	-0.20	0.28
3.5	-008	0.04	0.09	-0.21	0.27	-0.06	0.07	0.00	-0.08	0.21
4.0	-0.05	0.06	0.02	-0.08	0.20	-0.03	0.06	-0.02	0.00	0.11
4.5	-0.02	0.06	0.00	-0.01	0.09	0.00	0.05	-0.01	0.03	0.00
5.0	0.01	0.06	0.00	0.00	-0.06	0.03	0.05	0.00	0.00	-0.13

Table 5.9: $Z_{max} = 10.0$

	Coefficients A & B for a pile in a Winkler medium :									
Z	A_y	A_s	A_m	A_v	A_r	B_y	B_s	B_m	B_v	B_r
0.0	2.43	-1.62	0.00	1.00	0.00	1.61	-1.75	1.00	0.00	0.00
0.1	2.26	-1.61	0.10	0.99	-0.23	1.44	-1.65	1.00	-0.01	-0.14
0.2	2.10	-1.60	0.20	0.96	-0.42	1.28	-1.55	1.00	-0.03	-0.28
0.3	1.94	-1.58	0.29	0.90	-0.58	1.14	-1.45	0.99	-0.06	-0.34
0.4	1.79	-1.54	0.38	0.84	-0.72	1.00	-1.35	0.99	-0.10	-0.40
0.5	1.64	-1.50	0.46	0.76	-0.82	0.87	-1.25	0.98	-0.14	-0.43
0.6	1.49	-1.45	0.53	0.68	-0.89	0.75	-1.15	0.96	-0.18	-0.45
0.7	1.35	-1.39	0.59	0.58	-0.94	0.64	-1.06	0.94	-0.23	-0.45
0.8	1.21	-1.33	0.65	0.49	-0.97	0.54	-0.96	0.91	-0.27	-0.43
0.9	1.08	-1.26	0.69	0.39	-0.97	0.44	-0.87	0.88	-0.31	-0.40
1.0	0.96	-1.19	0.73	0.29	-0.96	0.36	-0.79	0.85	-0.35	-0.36
1.1	0.84	-1.12	0.75	0.20	-0.93	0.29	-0.70	0.81	-0.39	-0.31
1.2	0.73	-1.04	0.76	0.11	-0.88	0.22	-0.62	0.77	-0.42	-0.26
1.3	0.63	-0.97	0.77	0.02	-0.82	0.16	-0.55	0.73	-0.44	-0.21
1.4	0.54	-0.89	0.77	-0.06	-0.76	0.11	-0.48	0.69	-0.46	-0.15
1.5	0.46	-0.81	0.76	-0.13	-0.68	0.07	-0.41	0.64	-0.47	-0.10
1.6	0.38	-0.74	0.74	-0.19	-0.60	0.03	-0.35	0.59	-0.48	-0.04
1.7	0.31	-0.66	0.72	-0.25	-0.52	0.00	-0.29	0.54	-0.48	0.01
1.8	0.25	-0.59	0.69	-0.30	-0.44	-0.03	-0.24	0.50	-0.48	0.06
1.9	0.19	-0.52	0.66	-0.34	-0.36	-0.06	-0.19	0.45	-0.47	0.10
2.0	0.14	-0.46	0.63	-0.37	-0.28	-0.07	-0.15	0.40	-0.45	0.14
2.2	0.06	-0.34	0.55	-0.41	-0.13	-0.09	-0.08	0.31	-0.42	0.21
2.4	0.00	-0.24	0.46	-0.42	-0.01	-0.10	-0.03	0.23	-0.37	0.25
2.6	-0.04	-0.16	0.38	-0.42	0.10	-0.10	0.01	0.17	-0.32	0.27
2.8	-0.06	-0.09	0.30	-0.39	0.17	-0.10	0.04	0.11	-0.27	0.28
3.0	-0.07	-0.04	0.22	-0.35	0.22	-0.09	0.06	0.06	-0.21	0.27
3.5	-007	0.03	0.08	-0.22	0.26	-0.06	0.06	-0.02	-0.09	0.20
4.0	-0.05	0.05	0.00	-0.11	0.20	-0.03	0.05	-0.04	-0.02	0.11
4.5	-0.03	0.04	-0.03	-0.03	0.12	-0.01	0.03	-0.04	0.02	0.04
5.0	-0.01	0.02	-0.03	0.01	0.05	0.00	0.01	-0.03	0.03	0.00
5.5	0.00	0.01	0.02	0.02	0.00	0.00	0.00	-0.01	0.02	-0.02
6.0	0.00	0.00	-0.01	0.02	-0.01	0.00	0.00	0.00	0.01	-0.02
6.5	0.00	0.01	0.00	0.01	-0.02	0.00	0.00	0.00	0.00	-0.01
7.0	0.00	0.00	0.00	0.00	-0.01	0.00	0.00	0.00	0.00	-0.01
8.0	0.00	0.00	0.00	0.00	0.00	0.00	0.00	0.00	0.00	0.01
9.0	0.00	0.00	0.00	0.00	0.00	0.00	0.00	0.00	0.00	0.00
10.0	0.00	0.00	0.00	0.00	0.00	0.00	0.00	0.00	0.00	0.00

Example 5.13

A steel tube pile with a diameter *0.61m* and a flexural stiffness $E_p I_p = 56.4\,MNm^2$ is driven in a dry dense sand characterised by a subgrade reaction modulus varying linearly with depth $K = n_h z$ with $n_h = 14\,MN/m^3$. The depth of embedment is *6.5m* and the pile is subject to a horizontal force applied *1m* above the ground surface (see figure 5.55).

Calculate the maximum horizontal force H_o that can be applied to the pile if the lateral displacement at ground level is not to exceed *65 mm*. Also, estimate the depth at which the maximum bending moment generated by H_o occurs.

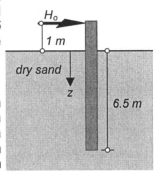

Figure 5.55. Pile dimensions and soil conditions.

Since the subgrade reaction modulus varies with depth, the coefficients *A* & *B* used in conjunction with equations 5.60 cannot be calculated from equations 5.62, but are rather determined from tables 5.1 to 5. 9. First, the characteristic length of the pile is evaluated from equation 5.67 :

$$T^* = \left[\frac{E_p I_p}{n_h}\right]^{0.2} = \left[\frac{56.4 \times 10^3}{14 \times 10^3}\right]^{0.2} = 1.321 m$$

Whence a length factor calculated from to equation 5.69:

$$Z_{max} = \frac{L}{T^*} = \frac{6.5}{1.321} = 4.92.$$

Accordingly, table 5.8 (corresponding to $Z_{max} = 5$) is used to estimate the relevant coefficients *A* and *B*. At ground level, $z = 0$ and the depth factor is : $Z = \frac{z}{T^*} = 0$ (equation 5.68), so that table 5.8 yields :

$$A_y = 2.43, \quad B_y = 1.62$$

The deflection is calculated from equation 5.60a :

$$y = \frac{T^{*2}}{E_p I_p}[A_y T^* H_o + B_y M_o].$$

Because the bending moment at ground level is $M_o = 1 \times H_o$ (refer to figure 5.55), the latter deflection equation can be rearranged as follows :

$$H_o = y\frac{E_p I_p}{T^{*2}(T^*A_y + B_y)}$$

For a maximum deflection at ground level of 65 mm, the corresponding horizontal force must therefore be :

$$H_o = 65 \times 10^{-3} \times \frac{56.4 \times 10^3}{1.321^2 \times (1.321 \times 2.43 + 1.62)} \approx 435 \, kN.$$

The location of the maximum bending moment requires the bending moment profile with depth to be determined. The calculations are undertaken in a way similar to that used previously for deflection. For instance, the bending moment at a depth $z = 2.5m$ is evaluated as follows:

- the depth factor is $Z = \frac{z}{T^*} = \frac{2.5}{1.321} = 1.89$. According to table 5.8, the bending moment coefficients are such that :

    - for a depth factor $Z = 1.8$ $\Rightarrow$ $A_m = 0.69$, $B_m = 0.50$,
    - for a depth factor $Z = 1.9$ $\Rightarrow$ $A_m = 0.66$, $B_m = 0.45$.

Thus, a straightforward linear interpolation yields the coefficients relative to a depth $z = 2.5m$:

$$A_m = 0.69 - \tfrac{9}{10} \times (0.69 - 0.66) = 0.663$$
$$B_m = 0.50 - \tfrac{9}{10} \times (0.50 - 0.45) = 0.455.$$

These coefficients are thence used to evaluate the bending moment according to equation 5.60c :

$$M_{(z=2.5)} = H_o T^* A_m + M_o B_m$$

$$= 435 \times 1.321 \times 0.663 + 1 \times 435 \times 0.455 = 578.9 \, kNm.$$

Similar calculations along the depth of embedment yield the graph of figure 5.56, in which the maximum bending moment $M_{max} = 785 \, kN.m$ occurs at an estimated depth of $z = 1.3m$.

The results illustrated in figure 5.56 show that for a pile loaded horizontally, it is imperative to have the bending moment profile with depth, *if only approximately,* so that the pile can be designed to withstand the maximum bending moment which occurs beneath the ground surface.

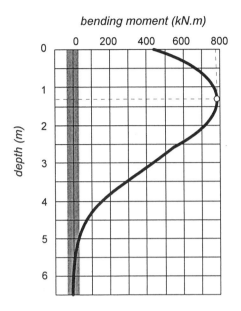

Figure 5.56. Bending moment profile.

Problems

5.1   An open end steel tube pile (figure *p5*.1) having an external
diameter $B = 0.85\,m$ and a wall thickness of $7.5\,mm$ is embedded in
a layer of stiff overconsolidated clay with an $OCR = 2$, an
undrained shear strength varying with depth :
$c_u = (120 + 2z)\,kN/m^2$ a bulk unit weight $\gamma = 18.7\,kN/m^3$ and a
saturated unit weight $\gamma_{sat} = 19.8\,kN/m^3$.

Estimate the pile length required
to carry an ultimate load
$Q_u = 3.8\,MN$. Assume that an
adhesion factor $\alpha = 0.35$ applies.
In the long term, the clay
behaviour is characterised by
$c' = 0$, $\phi' = 22°$. For steel, use
$\gamma = 77\,kN/m^3$

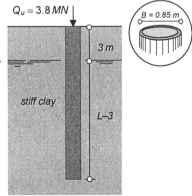

Ans : L ≈ 24.1 m

Figure p5.1

5.2   A 15 m long H-section steel pile, with the dimensions indicated in figure p5.2, has a steel cross-sectional area $S = 22 \times 10^{-3} m^2$. The pile is embedded in a normally consolidated clay characterised by an *average* shear strength $c_u = 30\,kN/m^2$ along the pile shaft, increasing to $c_u = 40\,kN/m^2$ at the pile tip. A unique unit weight $\gamma = 19\,kN/m^3$ can be assumed to apply throughout the clay layer, which is characterised in the long term by $c' = 0,\ \phi' = 23°$. Estimate the ultimate loading capacity of the pile.

Ans: $Q_u \approx 615\,kN$

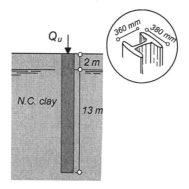

Figure p5.2

5.3   A circular concrete pile with a diameter $B = 0.5\,m$ is embedded in the soil conditions depicted in figure p5.3. The soft clay is characterised by a bulk unit weight $\gamma = 18.6\,kN/m^3$, assumed to apply throughout the layer, and an effective angle of friction $\phi' = 24°$. The stiff clay has a saturated unit weight $\gamma_{sat} = 19.8\,kN/m^3$ and an angle $\phi' = 22°$. Assume that for both layers, the coefficient of earth pressure is $K = 1 - \sin\phi'$, and for concrete, use $\gamma_c = 24\,kN/m^3$.

The upper layer of soft clay is undergoing a process of consolidation due to the load q applied at its surface, and the neutral depth is estimated at 5 m below the ground surface. Calculate the length of pile required to carry an allowable (safe) load $Q_a = 500\,kN$ corresponding to an overall factor of safety $F = 3$.

Ans: $L = 27.3\,m$

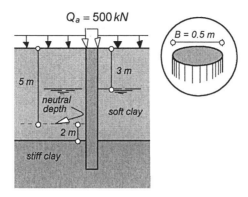

Figure p5.3

5.4 A circular concrete pile, driven in the soil conditions illustrated in figure $p5.4$, has a diameter $B = 0.52\,m$. It is assumed that a negative skin friction will develop along the pile shaft down to a depth $z_f = 15\,m$ below the ground surface. The parameters related to different layers are as follows:

- clay fill: $\gamma = 19.6\,kN/m^3$, $\phi' = 21°$, $K = (1 - \sin\phi')$

- soft clay: $\gamma = 18.5\,kN/m^3$, $\gamma_{sat} = 19.5\,kN/m^3$, $\phi' = 22°$, $K = (1 - \sin\phi')$

- dense sand: $\gamma_{sat} = 19.5\,kN/m^3$, $\phi' = 38°$, $K = 1.5(1 - \sin\phi')$

For concrete, use $\gamma_c = 24k\,N/m^3$. Estimate the allowable loading capacity Q_a that can be carried safely by the pile with an overall factor of safety $F = 3.5$.

Ans : $Q_a \approx 2077\,kN$

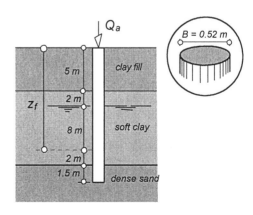

Figure p5.4

5.5 A concrete pile with a diameter $B = 0.45\,m$ is driven through two sand layers as shown in figure p5-5. The upper loose sand layer has a bulk unit weight $\gamma = 16.5\,kN/m^3$ and an effective angle of friction $\phi' = 32°$. The saturated dense sand layer is characterised by $\gamma_{sat} = 21\,kN/m^3$ and $\phi' = 41°$. Estimate the length of the pile needed to carry an ultimate load $Q_u = 1.5\,MN$. Assume for both layers a coefficient of earth pressure $K = 1.6\,(1 - \sin\phi')$.

Ans : $L = 5.64\,m$

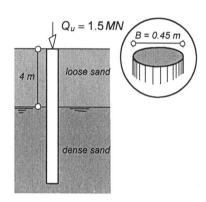

Figure p5.5

5.6 The foundation of a very tall building consists of 12 caissons, each with a diameter $B = 4\,m$, extending 45 m into a boulder clay having a saturated unit weight $\gamma_s = 22\,kN/m^3$ and an average undrained shear strength $c_u = 400\,kN/m^2$. The saturated clay layer is overlain by a 5 m thick layer of sand fill with a bulk unit weight $\gamma = 20\,kN/m^3$. The caissons are related by a 5 m thick pile cap as depicted in figure p5.6. The average skin friction along the caissons shafts is estimated at $f_s = 175\,kN/m^2$, and the bearing capacity factor $N_c = 6$ can be assumed to apply. For concrete, use $\gamma_c = 24\,kN/m^3$.

• (a) Because large (unacceptable) settlements have to occur before the caissons end bearing can be mobilised, it is suggested that the working load $Q_a = 500\,MN$ should be carried entirely through skin friction. Calculate in this case the factor of safety on skin friction.
• (b) Discarding the contribution of the pilecap to the loading capacity of the group, and assuming that at a depth of 45 m, the undrained shear strength of the clay is $c_u = 1000\,kN/m^2$ and N_c value is still 6, determine the factor of safety if the end bearing of the caissons is taken into account.

Ans :   (a) $F = 1.9$, (b) $F = 3.7$

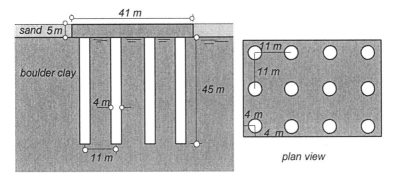

Figure p5.6

5.7   A group of 4×4 circular concrete piles are related through a square pilecap (refer to figure *p5.7*) having a total weight $W_c = 720\,kN$. The dimensions of each individual pile (*i.e.* length $L = 5.64\,m$,   diameter $B = 0.45\,m$), as well as the soil conditions in which the piles are driven, are identical to those used in problem 5.5 :
- loose sand: $\gamma = 16.5\,kN/m^3$, $\phi' = 32°$
- dense sand: $\gamma_{sat} = 21\,kN/m^3$, $\phi' = 41°$
- for both sand layers: $K = 1.6(1 - \sin\phi')$

Assuming that only a proportion of the loading capacity of the pilecap is mobilised through the use of a factor $N_\gamma = 3$ at ground level, estimate the allowable loading capacity of the group corresponding to an overall factor of safety $F = 3$.

Ans: $Q_{ag} = 8021\,kN$

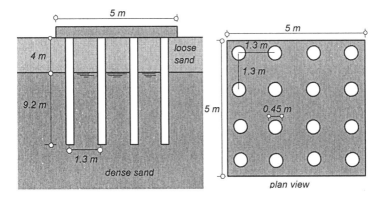

Figure p5.7

5.8   Assume that the pilecap in problem 5.7 is above the ground
surface, all other things being equal. Estimate under the same
circumstances (*i.e.* $F = 3$) the allowable loading of the free
standing group.

Ans: $Q_{ag} = 7280 \, kN$

5.9   Refer to the pile in example 5.11, then expand the calculations
along the entire depth of embedment and plot the variation with
depth of:
- the bending moment
- the shear load along the pile shaft
- the soil reaction per unit length

5.10   A flexible steel tube pile, with an external diameter $d_e = 0.45 \, m$ and
a modulus of elasticity $E = 200 \, kN/mm^2$ is driven 7 m in a dry sand
characterised by a subgrade reaction modulus varying linearly with
depth at a rate $n_h = 14 \, MN/m^3$ per metre. The pile is subjected at its
head to a horizontal force $H_o = 435 \, kN$, applied 1m above the
ground surface, under which a maximum soil reaction
$p_{max} = -430 \, kN/m$ was measured at a depth corresponding to a
ratio $z/T^* \approx 0.75$.

    a • Calculate the thickness of the pile wall (*i.e.* the internal
diameter).
    b • Plot the bending moment diagram and estimate the depth at
which the maximum bending moment occurs.
    c • Plot the soil reaction diagram and suggest a suitable depth of
embedment for the pile. Justify your answer.

Ans: *a-* $d_i = 0.434 \, m$;   wall thickness of 8 *mm.*

References

Azizi, F. (2007). Physical Behaviour in Geotechnics. Published by F. Azizi.

Berezantzev, V. C., Kristoforov, V. and Golubkov, V. (1961) *Load Bearing
Capacity and Deformation of Piled Foundations.* Proceedings of the 5th
International Conference on Soil Mechanics and Foundation Engineering.
Vol. 2, pp. 11–15.

Burland, J. B., Butler, F. G. and Dunican, P. (1966) *The behaviour and design of
large diameter bored piles in stiff clay.* Proceedings of the Symposium on
Large Bored Piles. Institution of Civil Engineers, Reinforced Concrete
Association, London, pp. 51–71.

Bustamente, M. and Gianeselli, L. (1995) *Portance d'un pieu vissé moulé dans une marne infragypseuse.* Bulletin des Laboratoires des Ponts et Chaussées, 199, pp. 19–25.

Bustamente, M. and Gianeselli, L. (1997) *Portance d'un pieu de Waal vissé moulé dans un sable sous nappe.* Bulletin des Laboratoires des Ponts et Chaussées, 208, pp. 107–115.

Chin, F. K. (1970) *Estimation of the ultimate load of piles from tests not carried to failure.* Proceedings of the 2nd S.E. Asian Conference on Soil Engineering, Singapore, pp. 81–92.

Chin, F. K. (1972) *The inverse slope as a prediction of ultimate bearing capacity of piles.* Proceedings of the 3rd S.E. Asian Conference on Soil Engineering, Hong Kong, pp. 83–91.

Chin, F. K. (1983) *Bilateral plate bearing tests.* Proceedings of International Symposium on In Situ Testing, Paris, pp. 29–33.

England, M. and Fleming, W. G. K. (1994) *Review of foundation testing methods and procedures.* Proceedings of the Institution of Civil Engineers, Geotechnical Engineering. 107, pp. 135-142.

Fellenius, B. H., Altaee, A. A. (1995). *Critical depth: how it came into being and why it does not exist.* Proceedings of the Institution of Civil Engineers, Geotechnical Engineering, 113, pp. 107–111.

Fleming, W. G. K (1992) *A new method for single pile settlement prediction and analysis.* Géotechnique, 42 (3), pp. 411–425.

Fleming, W. G. K., Weltman, A. J., Randolf, M. F. and Elson, W. K. (1992) *Piling Engineering,* 2nd edn. Wiley, New York.

Frank, R. (1995) *Fondations profondes.* Collection Technique de l'Ingénieur, C248.

Frank, R. and Zhao, S. R. (1982) *Estimation par les paramètres pressiométriques de l'enfoncement sous charge axiale de pieux forés dans des sols fins.* Bulletin des Laboratoires des Ponts et Chaussées, 119, pp. 17–24.

Imbo, R. P (1984) *The Atlas screw pile : an improved foundation technique for the vibration free execution of piles with larger bearing capacity.* Proceedings of the 6th C. S.M.F.E, Vol. 5, Budapest, pp. 363–372.

Kishida, H. (1967)*Ultimate bearing capacity of piles driven into loose sand.* Soil and Foundations, 7 (3), pp. 20–29.

Kulhawy, F. H. (1984) *Limiting tip and side resistance, fact or fallacy.* Symposium on Analysis and Design of Pile Foundations. A.S.C.E, San Francisco, pp. 80–98.

LCPC-SETRA (1985) *Règles Provisoires de Justification des Fondations sur Pieux à Partir des Résultats des Essais Pressiométriques.*

Meyer, P. L, Holmquist, D. V. and Matlock, H. (1975) *Computer predictions for axially-loaded piles with non-linear supports.* Proceedings of the 7th Offshore Technology Conference, Houston, Texas.

Meyerhof, G. G. (1976) *Bearing capacity and settlement of pile foundations.* Journal of the Geotechnical Engineering Division. A.S.C.E, 102, pp. 197–228.

Poulos, H. G. and Davis, E. H. (1980) *Pile Foundation Analysis and Design.* John Wiley & Sons, New York.

Skempton, A. W. (1951) *The bearing capacity of clays.* Proceedings of the Building Research Congress, London.

Terzaghi, K. (1943) *Theoretical Soil Mechanics.* John Wiley & Sons, New York.

Terzaghi, K. and Peck, R. B. (1967) *Soil Mechanics in Engineering Practice.* Wiley, New York.

Tomlinson, M. J. (1995) *Foundation Design and Construction.* 6th edn. Longman, London.

Vesic, A. S. (1969) *Experiments with Instrumented Pile Groups in Sand.* American Society for Testing and Materials, Special Technical Publication 444, pp. 177–222.

Vesic, A. S. (1970) *Tests on Instrumented piles, Ogeechee River site.* Proceedings of the A.S.C.E, 96 (SM-2), pp. 561–584.

Vijayvergiya, V. N. (1977) *Load-movement characteristics of piles.* Proceedings of the Ports'77 Conference, Long Beach, California.

Weltman, A. J. and Healy, P. R. (1978) *Piling in boulder clay and other glacial tills.* Construction Industry Research and Information Association, Report PG5.

CHAPTER 6

Lateral earth pressure exerted on retaining structures

6.1 Coefficient of earth pressure

The analysis of the stability of a retaining structure, such as the one depicted in figure 6.1, indicates that apart from its self weight, the structure is subjected to lateral thrusts whose intensity and direction depend on the movement (or the lack of it) of the structure itself. These thrusts are best examined using the *coefficient of earth pressure* defined as:

$$K = \frac{\sigma'_h}{\sigma'_v} \qquad (6.1)$$

where σ'_h and σ'_v are respectively the effective horizontal and vertical stresses at any given depth below the ground surface. The ratio K in equation 6.1 depends on the wall movement, its value being characterised by the following three quantities.

- (1) If the wall, subjected to lateral pressures at its back, does not move *at all*, then K is referred to as *the coefficient of earth pressure at rest K_o*, and at rest stress conditions prevail as indicated in figure 6.1a.

- (2) If the wall is pushed into the soil then, at the advent of failure, the coefficient K reaches its maximum value known as *the coefficient of passive earth pressure K_p*, hence the passive mode of failure of the block of soil behind the wall (figure 6.1b).

- (3) If the wall is moved away from the soil it supports, then at failure (figure 6.1c) the ratio K reaches its minimum value, referred to as *the coefficient of active earth pressure K_a*.

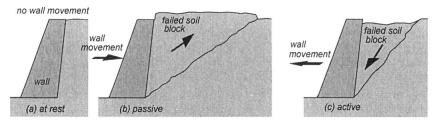

Figure 6.1: Coefficients of earth pressure.

The coefficients of active and passive earth pressure represent respectively the lower and upper limits of the coefficient of earth pressure at rest:

$$K_a < K_o < K_p \tag{6.2}$$

Moreover, the actual wall displacement that causes active or passive failure conditions to develop depends on the type of retained soil and on the mode of failure (*i.e.* active or passive). For soils without cohesion, figure 6.2 shows that the displacement prior to failure in the passive mode (y_p) is much larger than that corresponding to the active mode (y_a).

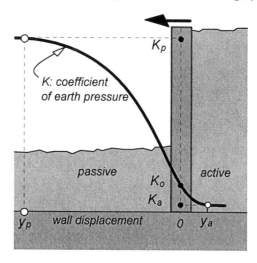

Figure 6.2: Displacement at failure related to active and passive stress conditions for cohesionless soils.

On the other hand, if the retained soil were a clay, experimental evidence shows that the displacements y_p and y_a are comparatively similar in magnitude, and the following values can be considered as *typical* (*H* represents the height of the wall):

type of soil	y_a	y_p
dense sand	0.001H	0.005H
loose sand	0.005H	0.01H
stiff clay	0.01H	0.01H
soft clay	0.05H	0.05H

6.2 At rest stress conditions: coefficient K_o

At its natural state, an element of soil located at a depth z beneath the ground surface, such as the one depicted in figure 6.3, is subject to the *in situ principal effective stresses*:

$$\sigma'_{vo} = \gamma\, z_w + (\gamma_{sat} - \gamma_w)(z - z_w) = \gamma\, z_w + \gamma'(z - z_w) \qquad (6.3a)$$

$$\sigma'_{ho} = K_o\, \sigma'_{vo} \qquad (6.3b)$$

where γ and γ_{sat} represent the bulk and saturated unit weights of soil respectively, and γ_w is the unit weight of water. For any given soil, the coefficient K_o in equation 6.3b is one of the most difficult parameters to measure, its value being linked to the *type* and *state* of soil.

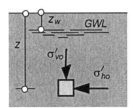

Figure 6.3: At rest stress conditions.

For *loose sands* as well as for *normally consolidated clays*, K_o can be thought of as an intrinsic soil parameter, and its value can be estimated from the relationship derived by Jaky (1944):

$$K_o = \left(1 + \frac{2}{3}\sin\phi'\right)\tan^2\left(\frac{\pi}{4} + \frac{\phi'}{2}\right)$$
$$\approx 1 - \sin\phi' \qquad (6.4)$$

For *dense sands*, experimental evidence indicates that K_o is intricately linked to the density. Sherif *et al.* (1984) suggested the following empirical relationship, which can be used with caution:

$$K_o = (1 - \sin\phi') + 5.5\left(\frac{\gamma_d}{\gamma_{dmin}} - 1\right) \qquad (6.5)$$

where γ_d is the *in situ* dry unit weight of sand, and γ_{dmin} represents the minimum dry unit weight of sand corresponding to its loosest state.

As far as *overconsolidated clays and sands* are concerned, the coefficient K_o is no longer an intrinsic soil characteristic, but is rather closely linked to the stress history of the soil. Many investigators have examined the link between the overconsolidation ratio (OCR) of a clay and the coefficient K_o. In particular, Brooker and Ireland (1965) produced very useful charts, reproduced in figure 6.4, relating K_o to the plasticity index I_P of a clay for different values of OCR. Notice that the points corresponding to $I_P = 0$ on the six curves are data corresponding to overconsolidated sands, obtained by Hendren (1963).

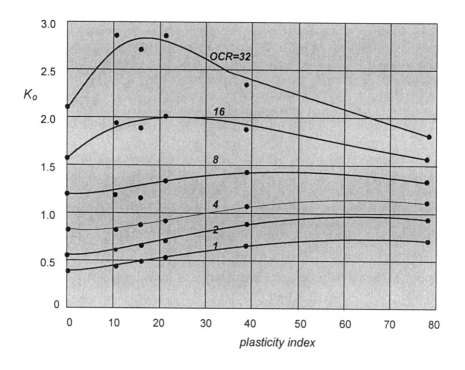

Figure 6.4 : Relationship between plasticity index, overconsolidation ratio (OCR) and coefficient of earth pressure at rest. (Reproduced by permission of the National Research Council of Canada.)

The coefficient K_o for an *overconsolidated clay* can also be estimated from the empirical relationship established by Mayne and Kulhawy (1982):

$$K_o = (1 - \sin\phi')(OCR)^{\sin\phi'} \tag{6.6}$$

ϕ' being the effective angle of shearing resistance of the clay.

6.3 Active and passive stress conditions: Rankine theory

6.3.1 Case of a smooth wall with a vertical back, retaining a horizontal cohesive backfill: drained analysis

Rankine theory, established as early as 1857, considers the limit equilibrium of an isotropic and homogeneous soil mass, subject at its *horizontal* surface to a uniform pressure *q*. The retaining wall with a *vertical back* is assumed to be *smooth* (*i.e.* there is no friction at the soil/wall interface).
For stiff, highly plastic and heavily overconsolidated clays, the corresponding failure envelope is characterised by an angle of shearing resistance ϕ' and a cohesion intercept c' as illustrated in figure 6.5.

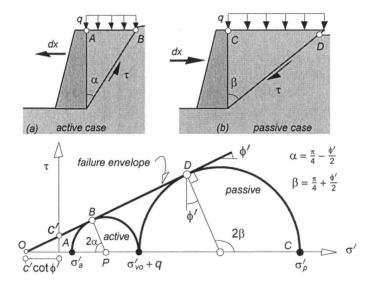

Figure 6.5: Active and passive stress conditions in relation to a smooth wall.

Let us assume that the smooth wall with a vertical back is *moved away* from the soil it retains in the active case (figure 6.5*a*) and *pushed into* the soil in the passive case (figure 6.5*b*) a distance *dx*, large enough to cause the soil to be in a state of plastic equilibrium. Consider, under these circumstances, the *limit equilibrium* of the two failing soil blocks behind the wall. Starting with the *active* case, it is seen from the corresponding Mohr's circle that:

$$\sin\phi' = \frac{PB}{OP} = \frac{(\sigma'_{vo}+q)-\sigma'_a}{(\sigma'_{vo}+q)+\sigma'_a+2c'\cot\phi'} \tag{6.7}$$

This equation can be reorganised thus:

$$(\sigma'_{vo} + q)(1 - \sin\phi') = \sigma'_a(1 + \sin\phi') + 2c'\cos\phi' \qquad (5.8)$$

But

$$\cos\phi' = \sqrt{(1 + \sin\phi')(1 - \sin\phi')} \quad \text{and} \quad \frac{1 - \sin\phi'}{1 + \sin\phi'} = \tan^2\left(\frac{\pi}{4} - \frac{\phi'}{2}\right)$$

Substituting for these quantities into equation 6.8, then rearranging, yields the *effective active pressure*:

$$\sigma'_a = (\sigma'_{vo} + q)\tan^2\left(\frac{\pi}{4} - \frac{\phi'}{2}\right) - 2c'\tan\left(\frac{\pi}{4} - \frac{\phi'}{2}\right) \qquad (6.9)$$

It is straightforward to show that a similar analysis undertaken using Mohr's circle corresponding to the passive case leads to the following *effective passive pressure*:

$$\sigma'_p = (\sigma'_{vo} + q)\tan^2\left(\frac{\pi}{4} + \frac{\phi'}{2}\right) + 2c'\tan\left(\frac{\pi}{4} + \frac{\phi'}{2}\right) \qquad (6.10)$$

Equations 6.9 and 6.10 are usually presented in the following way:

$$\sigma'_a = (\sigma'_{vo} + q)K_a - 2c'\sqrt{K_a} \qquad (6.11)$$

$$\sigma'_p = (\sigma'_{vo} + q)K_p + 2c'\sqrt{K_p} \qquad (6.12)$$

with the *coefficient of active pressure*:

$$K_a = \tan^2\left(\frac{\pi}{4} - \frac{\phi'}{2}\right) \qquad (6.13)$$

and the *coefficient of passive pressure*:

$$K_p = \frac{1}{K_a} = \tan^2\left(\frac{\pi}{4} + \frac{\phi'}{2}\right) \qquad (6.14)$$

Knowing that the overburden effective stress at a given depth z corresponds to $\sigma'_{vo} = \gamma'z$, with γ' being the appropriate effective unit weight of soil, it is seen from equation 6.11 that the active pressure σ'_a has a *negative value* (*i.e.* becomes tensile) down to a depth:

$$z = \frac{1}{\gamma'}\left(\frac{2c'}{\sqrt{K_a}} - q\right)$$

Accordingly, for a 5 m high wall retaining an overconsolidated stiff clay characterised by $c' = 10\,kN/m^2$, $\gamma = 20\,kN/m^3$ and $\phi' = 24°$, assuming the clay is totally submerged as a result of a prolonged period of heavy rainfall and considering a uniform pressure $q = 10\,kN/m^2$ applied on the horizontal surface behind the wall:

$$z = \frac{1}{(20-10)}\left(\frac{2 \times 10}{\tan(45-12)} - 10\right) = 2.08\,m$$

meaning, practically, a tensile active effective stress along the top 40% of the height of wall. This simple example implies that caution must be exercised when choosing an appropriate value for c' which is, alas, quite difficult to evaluate (refer to the discussion on this parameter in chapter 2). *In all cases, it seems logical to avoid using clay fills in conjunction with retaining walls. In the absence of an alternative, it is advisable to adopt a conservative design by assuming $c' = 0$.*

6.3.2 Case of a smooth wall with a vertical back, retaining a horizontal frictional backfill

For sands as well as for normally consolidated clays, the failure envelope is characterised by a zero intercept, as illustrated in figure 6.6, and the strength of such soils is independent of cohesion.

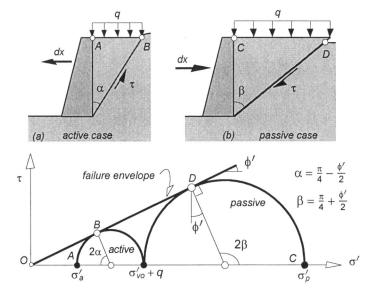

Figure 6.6: Active and passive pressures related to a smooth wall retaining a cohesionless soil.

In terms of effective stresses, the same analysis used earlier for cohesive soils applies except that, this time, no cohesion is involved. Accordingly, the *active* and *passive pressures* exerted at the *vertical back* of the *smooth* wall are determined from equations 6.11 and 6.12 in which $c' = 0$:

$$\sigma'_a = (\sigma'_{vo} + q)\,K_a \qquad\qquad\qquad (6.15)$$

$$\sigma'_p = (\sigma'_{vo} + q)\,K_p \qquad\qquad\qquad (6.16)$$

where the coefficients of active and passive earth pressure, K_a and K_p respectively, are calculated from equations 6.13 and 6.14.

Figure 6.7 indicates that, in the long term, a state of equilibrium of stresses is achieved as long as the horizontal effective stress σ'_h is within the range represented by the shaded area and corresponding to the condition:

$$\sigma'_a < \sigma'_h < \sigma'_p$$

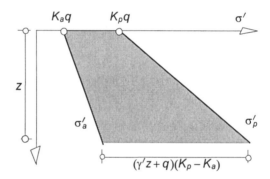

Figure 6.7: Variation with depth of σ'_h at equilibrium.

The effects due to changes in the horizontal stress level in the case of a frictional soil ($c' = 0$), without any surcharge ($q = 0$), are illustrated in the 3-D graphics of figure 6.10.

6.3.3 Rankine theory: undrained analysis

This type of analysis applies to the short term behaviour of clays where the stresses induced by an externally applied load are transmitted to the porewater, leaving the effective stresses practically unchanged. Prior to any significant consolidation (*i.e.* dissipation of excess porewater pressure) taking place, the clay's behaviour is characterised by an angle of shearing resistance $\phi = 0$ and an undrained shear strength c_u as shown in figure 6.8. Under these circumstances, both coefficients of active and passive pressure of equations 6.13 and 6.14 reduce to:

$$K_a = K_p = \tan^2 45 = 1 \qquad (6.17)$$

Substituting for $c' = c_u$ into equations 6.11 and 6.12 yields the expressions of active and passive *total* stresses:

- *active total stress*:

$$\sigma_a = \sigma_{vo} + q - 2c_u \qquad (6.18)$$

- *passive total stress*:

$$\sigma_p = \sigma_{vo} + q + 2c_u \qquad (6.19)$$

It follows that, in the short term, a state of equilibrium of stresses is achieved as long as the total horizontal stress σ_h is within the range:

$$\sigma_a < \sigma_h < \sigma_p$$

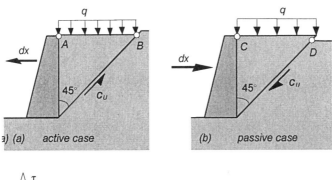

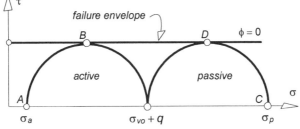

Figure 6.8: Active and passive stresses under undrained (short term) behaviour.

Notice that equation 6.18 indicates that the active pressure has a negative value down to a depth $z_c = (2c_u - q)/\gamma$. However, because a soil cannot withstand tensile stresses, *tension cracks* are very likely to appear down to the depth z_c. This, in turn, will have a restricting effect on the stress equilibrium, in that the range of stresses established earlier is now limited to:

$$\sigma_a = 0, \qquad\qquad z \le (2c_u - q)/\gamma$$

$$\sigma_a = \gamma z + q - 2c_u, \quad z > (2c_u - q)/\gamma \qquad\qquad (6.20)$$

$$\sigma_a < \sigma_h < \sigma_p$$

These conditions are represented by the shaded area in figure 6.9.

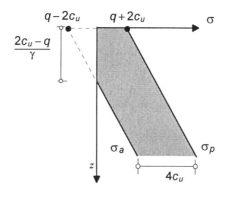

Figure 6.9: Effect of short term tensile stresses on σ_a.

The long and short term variations of active and passive pressures as represented by equations 6.15, 6.16, 6.18 and 6.19 are shown in figures 6.10 and 6.11. The third dimension representing σ'_h (σ_h in the short term) is used to illustrate the effects relative to any change in the horizontal stress (increase or decrease) with respect to the *in situ* vertical stress σ'_{vo} (σ_v in the short term). Notice that both figures correspond to a surcharge $q = 0$, and that the value of the horizontal *in situ* stress σ'_{ho} (σ_{ho} in figure 6.11) represented in figure 6.10 corresponds to a normally consolidated or a lightly overconsolidated clay.

$$K_a = \frac{1 - \sin\phi'}{1 + \sin\phi'} = \tan^2\left(\frac{\pi}{4} - \frac{\phi'}{2}\right), \qquad K_p = \frac{1}{K_a} = \tan^2\left(\frac{\pi}{4} + \frac{\phi'}{2}\right)$$

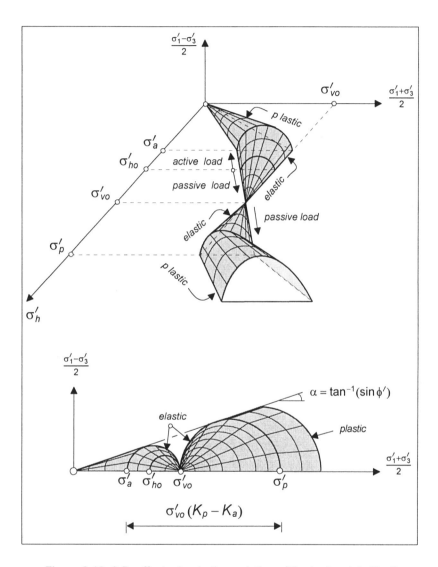

Figure 6.10: 3-D effects due to the variation of the horizontal effective stress in the case of a cohesionless drained soil.

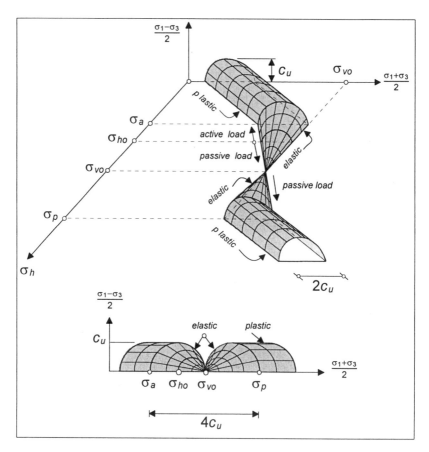

Figure 6.11: 3-D effects due to the variation of the horizontal stress in the case of an undrained clay.

6.3.4 Rankine theory: case of a sloping frictional backfill

The analysis undertaken previously related to a *smooth wall*, with a *vertical back*, retaining a *horizontal* backfill, so that no shear stresses are developed at the soil/wall interface. Although such ideal structures do not exist, this analysis can sometimes be justified, especially when little or no soil movement occurs relative to the structure. Apart from these cases, *wall friction* can significantly affect both the magnitude and the direction of the lateral thrust.

Rankine analysed these effects by considering the limit equilibrium of an element of an *isotropic homogeneous* soil in the case of an *inclined ground surface* as illustrated in figure 6.12. In order to simulate *friction* at the *vertical* back of wall, Rankine considered the forces acting on the sides of the element to be parallel to the ground surface and, in so doing, he assigned the same value of the angle of inclination of the ground surface to the angle of wall friction. Under these circumstances, the coefficient of active pressure can be written as:

$$K_a = \frac{X_a}{\sigma_v} = \frac{X_a}{\gamma' z} \qquad\qquad (6.21)$$

where the *active stress* is $X_a = \left(\sigma_h^2 + \tau_a^2\right)^{1/2}$

Referring to figure 6.12, the *normal stress* at the base of the element is:

$$\sigma = W \cos\beta = \gamma' z \cos^2\beta \qquad\qquad (6.22)$$

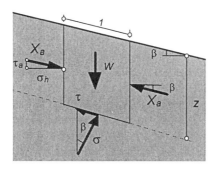

Figure 6.12: Limit equilibrium of an element of soil inclined at the surface.

The different quantities in equation 6.21 can easily be determined using Mohr's circle representation of stresses illustrated in figure 6.13. It is seen that:

$$DA = DB = OD \sin\phi'$$

$$DC = OD \sin\beta$$

hence:

$$AC = (AD^2 - DC^2)^{1/2} = OD\left(\sin^2\phi' - \sin^2\beta\right)^{1/2}$$

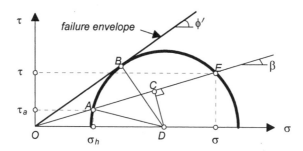

Figure 6.13: Mohr's circles related to figure 6.12.

Also, according to the same figure:

$$OC = OD\cos\beta$$

$$OA = OC - AC = OD\left[\cos\beta - \left(\sin^2\phi' - \sin^2\beta\right)^{1/2}\right]$$

$$OE = OC + CE = OC + AC = OD\left[\cos\beta + \left(\sin^2\phi' - \sin^2\beta\right)^{1/2}\right]$$

From the geometry of the figure, the following quantities are established in a straightforward manner:

$$X_a = OA \qquad \text{and} \qquad \frac{\sigma}{\cos\beta} = OE$$

Now, substituting for σ from equation 6.22 and rearranging:

$$\gamma'z = \frac{OD}{\cos\beta}\left[\cos\beta + \left(\sin^2\phi' - \sin^2\beta\right)^{1/2}\right]$$

finally, substituting for the quantities X_a and $\gamma'z$ in equation 6.21 yields the expression of the *coefficient of active pressure*:

$$K_a = \cos\beta\,\frac{\cos\beta - \sqrt{\cos^2\beta - \cos^2\phi'}}{\cos\beta + \sqrt{\cos^2\beta - \cos^2\phi'}} \tag{6.23}$$

A similar analysis using the passive stress on the element sides yields the coefficient of *passive earth pressure*:

$$K_p = \cos\beta\,\frac{\cos\beta + \sqrt{\cos^2\beta - \cos^2\phi'}}{\cos\beta - \sqrt{\cos^2\beta - \cos^2\phi'}} \tag{6.24}$$

Hence the respective resultant *active* and *passive thrusts*, acting on a *vertical wall* of height H, parallel to the slope:

$$P_a = \tfrac{1}{2}\gamma H^2 K_a, \quad P_p = \tfrac{1}{2}\gamma H^2 K_p$$

Note that for $\beta = 0$ (horizontal soil surface), equations 6.23 and 6.24 reduce to equations 6.13 and 6.14, because Rankine theory does not take into account any *wall friction* in conjunction with a *vertical wall* retaining a *horizontal ground surface*.

6.4 Coulomb theory

The pioneering work of Coulomb presented to the *Académie Royale des Sciences* in 1773, and published three years later marked a turning point in the analysis and evaluation of soil behaviour in general and of the lateral earth pressure exerted on a retaining structure in particular. Coulomb developed the theoretical basis for the analysis of the stability of retaining walls through the use of slip plane collapse mechanisms such as the two illustrated in figure 6.14. He showed that by assuming a planar failure surface, originating at the heel of the wall, the algebraic expressions of both active and passive thrusts can be established, and the ensuing *critical failure surface* can be determined by differentiating these expressions with respect to the angle a in figure 6.14.

It is essential to bear in mind that Coulomb's method of analysis, in contrast with Rankine's, yields an upper bound solution (i.e. it overestimates the passive thrust while underestimating the active one). As such, it can potentially be unsafe to use, and therefore its limitations, which are explained below, must be well understood.

With reference to figure 6.14, the analysis of forces is relatively straightforward in relation to a smooth wall. In either case (active or passive), the weight W of the failing block is known, and so are the directions of the reaction force R and the lateral thrust P. Hence for a *cohesionless soil* (*i.e.* $c' = 0$) having a unit weight γ and an angle of shearing resistance ϕ':

$$W = \tfrac{1}{2}\gamma H^2 \tan\alpha \tag{6.25}$$

Also, from the geometry of the figure, it can be seen that:
- on the active side:

$$P_a \sin(\alpha + \phi') = W\cos(\alpha + \phi')$$

- on the passive side:

$$P_p \sin(\alpha - \phi') = W\cos(\alpha - \phi')$$

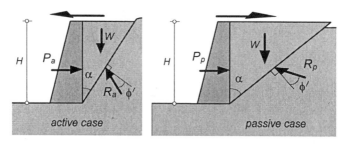

Figure 6.14: Active and passive pressures, case of a smooth wall.

Alternatively, using equation 6.25, the active and passive thrusts are respectively:

$$P_a = \frac{1}{2}\gamma H^2 \frac{\tan\alpha}{\tan(\alpha+\phi')} \qquad (6.26a)$$

$$P_p = \frac{1}{2}\gamma H^2 \frac{\tan\alpha}{\tan(\alpha-\phi')} \qquad (6.26b)$$

To find the *maximum active thrust*, the two following conditions must be fulfilled:

$$\frac{\partial P_a}{\partial\alpha} = 0 \qquad \text{and} \qquad \frac{\partial^2 P_a}{\partial\alpha^2} < 0$$

$$\frac{\partial P_a}{\partial\alpha} = \frac{1}{2}\gamma H^2 \frac{1}{\tan^2(\alpha+\phi')}\left[\frac{\tan(\alpha+\phi')}{\cos^2\alpha} - \frac{\tan\alpha}{\cos^2(\alpha+\phi')}\right]$$

writing $\partial P_a/\partial\alpha = 0$ yields:

$$\cos^2(\alpha+\phi')\tan(\alpha+\phi') = \cos^2\alpha \tan\alpha$$

or

$$\sin 2(\alpha+\phi') = \sin 2\alpha$$

leading to the solution: $\alpha = \left(\dfrac{\pi}{4} - \dfrac{\phi'}{2}\right)$

Using this value, it can be shown that $\partial^2 P_a/\partial\alpha^2 < 0$.

A back-substitution for α into equation 6.26a then yields the expression of *active thrust*:

$$P_a = \frac{1}{2}\gamma H^2 \tan\left(\frac{\pi}{4} - \frac{\phi'}{2}\right)\cot\left(\frac{\pi}{4} + \frac{\phi'}{2}\right)$$

$$= \frac{1}{2}\gamma H^2 \tan^2\left(\frac{\pi}{4} - \frac{\phi'}{2}\right) \qquad (6.27)$$

For the passive thrust, the aim is to find the *minimum* force and this can be achieved if the following conditions are met:

$$\partial P_p / \partial \alpha = 0 \quad\quad \text{and} \quad\quad \partial^2 P_p / \partial \alpha^2 > 0$$

Applying the same procedure used in the active case, it is easy to establish that:

$$\alpha = \frac{\pi}{4} + \frac{\phi'}{2}$$

Once substituted into equation 6.26b, the *passive thrust* expression is thus established:

$$P_p = \frac{1}{2}\gamma H^2 \tan^2\left(\frac{\pi}{4} + \frac{\phi'}{2}\right) \tag{6.28}$$

Several investigators used Coulomb theory to explore more complex problems pertaining to lateral pressures such as accounting for wall friction. Figure 6.15 depicts the case of a vertical *rough* wall with a *given* angle of friction d retaining a *cohesionless* horizontal backfill.

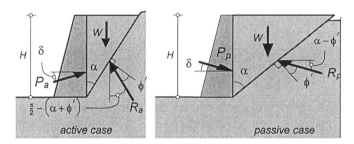

Figure 6.15: Active and passive pressures, case of a rough wall.

Using Coulomb theory, and solving perpendicular to the soil reactions *R*, it follows that:

• on the active side:

$$P_a \sin(\delta + \alpha + \phi') = W \cos(\alpha + \phi')$$

• on the passive side:

$$P_p \sin(\alpha - \phi' - \delta) = W \cos(\alpha - \phi')$$

So that when equation 6.25 is used, the active and passive thrusts become respectively:

$$P_a = \frac{1}{2}\gamma H^2 \frac{\tan\alpha \, \cos(\alpha + \phi')}{\sin(\delta + \alpha - \phi')}$$

$$P_p = \frac{1}{2}\gamma H^2 \frac{\tan\alpha \, \cos(\alpha - \phi')}{\sin(\alpha - \phi' - \delta)}$$

These two expressions can then be optimised to find the *maximum active* and the *minimum passive* thrusts; this is achieved by writing:

$$\partial P_a/\partial\alpha = 0, \quad \partial^2 P_a/\partial\alpha^2 < 0 \quad \text{and} \quad \partial P_p/\partial\alpha = 0, \quad \partial^2 P_p/\partial\alpha^2 > 0.$$

Notwithstanding the cumbersome nature of the derivations, the solution established by Mayniel in 1808 leads to:

• the active thrust:

$$P_a = \frac{1}{2}\gamma H^2 \frac{\cos^2\phi'}{\cos\delta \left[1 + \sqrt{\frac{\sin(\delta+\phi')\sin\phi'}{\cos\delta}} \right]^2} \tag{6.29}$$

• the passive thrust:

$$P_p = \frac{1}{2}\gamma H^2 \frac{\cos^2\phi'}{\cos\delta \left[1 - \sqrt{\frac{\sin(\delta+\phi')\sin\phi'}{\cos\delta}} \right]^2} \tag{6.30}$$

This solution was further refined in 1906 by Müller-Breslau who investigated the general case of a rough inclined wall retaining an inclined *cohesionless* backfill as depicted in figure 6.16. By adopting Coulomb analysis, the following expressions of active and passive thrusts were established:

• the active thrust:

$$P_a = \frac{1}{2}\gamma H^2 \frac{\sin^2(\eta + \phi')}{\sin^2\eta \, \sin(\eta - \delta) \left[1 + \sqrt{\frac{\sin(\phi'+\delta)\sin(\phi'-\beta)}{\sin(\eta-\delta)\sin(\beta+\eta)}} \right]^2} \tag{6.31}$$

• the passive thrust:

$$P_p = \frac{1}{2}\gamma H^2 \frac{\sin^2(\eta - \phi')}{\sin^2\eta \, \sin(\eta + \delta) \left[1 - \sqrt{\frac{\sin(\phi'+\delta)\sin(\phi'+\beta)}{\sin(\eta+\delta)\sin(\beta+\eta)}} \right]^2} \tag{6.32}$$

Clearly, both equations 6.31 and 6.32 encompass all previous cases derived from Coulomb theory and represent, as such, the general relationship for a *dry granular backfill*. For instance when $\eta = \pi/2$ (*i.e.* vertical wall) and $\beta = 0$ (horizontal backfill), equations 6.31 and 6.32 reduce to equations 6.29 and 6.30 (Mayniel solution). If, in addition, the wall were frictionless ($\delta = 0$), then the equations are further reduced to equations 6.27 and 6.28 (Coulomb solution). Notice that for a homogeneous dry backfill, the active thrust is assumed to be acting at the third of the wall height, measured from the base of the wall. The same applies to the passive thrust where the height refers to the embedment depth of the wall.

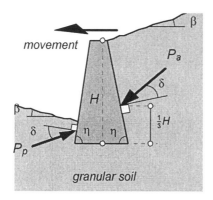

Figure 6.16: General case of a rough inclined wall retaining an inclined soil.

Experimental evidence shows that Coulomb theory yields reasonable estimates of lateral thrusts on the active side of wall. However, the passive thrusts calculated from equations 6.28, 6.30 and 6.32 are well in excess of the actual passive thrusts. This is due to the nature of slip surface assumed by Coulomb theory on the passive side, which is markedly different from the actual slip surface as depicted in figure 6.17. Accordingly, Coulomb theory is inherently (and dangerously) unsafe when used in conjunction with the calculation of passive thrusts.

6.5 Boussinesq theory

6.5.1 Introduction

Experimental evidence shows that, while the assumed shape of the failure surface for both Rankine and Coulomb theories corresponds by and large with the actual failure surface on the active side, the shape of the block failing in the passive mode differs markedly from that observed in practice as illustrated in figure 6.17. Moreover, Rankine theory leads to a *lower bound solution* whereas Coulomb analysis yields an *upper bound solution*, hence the substantial difference between Rankine and Coulomb lateral thrusts on the passive side.

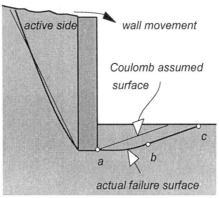

Figure 6.17: Actual and theoretical failure surfaces.

In 1882, Joseph Boussinesq correctly argued that by considering a linear failure surface, Coulomb analysis is being restrictive, whereas Rankine theory is even more so since it only takes into account a wall friction angle corresponding to the slope of the retained material. In order to offset these shortcomings, Boussinesq developed his theory by considering that the soil wedge *OAB* shown in figure 6.18 is in a state of *limit equilibrium*. The analysis hinges on the fact that, while Rankine equilibrium applies to the zone immediately to the right-hand side of the slip surface *OB*, it can no longer be used in the zone *OAB* since it violates the boundary conditions along the back of the wall where the friction developed depends only on the relative soil/wall movement.

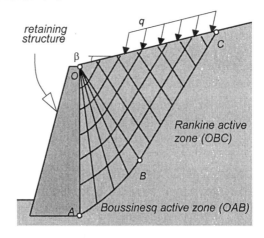

Figure 6.18: Boussinesq failure surface.

Boussinesq based his theory on the assumption that, for the general case of a structure retaining an *isotropic homogeneous* soil with a unit weight g, a cohesion c′ and a friction angle φ′, sloping at an angle b and subject to a surcharge q as depicted in figure 6.18, the active (or passive) pressure exerted on the wall can be considered as a *combination* of the three following components, that can be evaluated independently:

- (a) the pressure due to the weight of the soil, deprived of its cohesion (*i.e.* c′ = 0, γ ≠ 0, φ′ ≠ 0);
- (b) the pressure due to the surcharge q applied to a weightless, cohesionless soil (*i.e.* γ = 0, c′ = 0, φ′ ≠ 0);
- (c) the pressure due to a weightless cohesive soil (*i.e.* γ = 0, c′ ≠ 0, φ′ ≠ 0).

6.5.2 Pressure due to the weight of a frictional cohesionless soil

Consider the general case of a wall retaining a dry *isotropic homogeneous* frictional material with a unit weight g as depicted in figure 6.19. Let us isolate the radial element OCD, whose base is at a distance r from point O. The element has a weight:

$$W = \frac{r^2}{2}\gamma \, d\lambda$$

Along OD, both normal and shear stresses vary linearly with depth from zero at O to the respective values of σ and τ at the base of the element; hence the triangular distribution shown in figure 6.19. Similarly, the stresses along OC vary from zero at O to σ + dσ and τ + dτ at the base of the element. The equivalent forces per unit length exerted on OD and OC, as well as their lines of action can now be established as shown on the right-hand side of figure 6.19 in the case of normal forces. Obviously, a similar analysis applies to the shear forces, whence the complete set of normal and shear forces to which the element is subjected, represented in the figure.

Notice that for the normal force at the base of the element, the coefficient K is dependent on the ratio τ/σ. With reference to figure 6.20, it is seen that under *active* stress conditions, the mean stress at the centre of Mohr's circle (point G) is as follows:

$$p = \frac{1}{2}(\sigma + K\sigma) \qquad\qquad (6.33)$$

Also, the radius of the circle is: $FG = p \sin\phi′$.

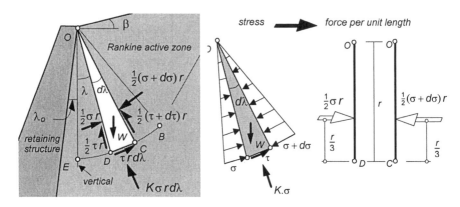

Figure 6.19: Boundary conditions related to Boussinesq theory.

Thence the normal stresses:

$$K\sigma = p + p\sin\phi'\cos(\alpha - \delta) \qquad (6.34a)$$

$$\sigma = p - p\sin\phi'\cos(\alpha - \delta) \qquad (6.34b)$$

It follows that for the *active* case:

$$K = \frac{1 + \sin\phi'\cos(\alpha - \delta)}{1 - \sin\phi'\cos(\alpha - \delta)} \qquad (6.35a)$$

It is straightforward to establish that under *passive* stress conditions:

$$K = \frac{1 - \sin\phi'\cos(\alpha - \delta)}{1 + \sin\phi'\cos(\alpha - \delta)} \qquad (6.35b)$$

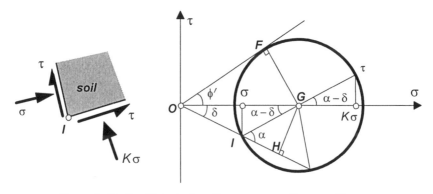

Figure 6.20: Coefficient of earth pressure; active conditions.

The angle α in equations 6.35 is such that $\sin\alpha = GH/GI$, and according to figure 6.20: $GH = p\sin\delta$, and $GI = FG = p\sin\phi'$. Whence:

$$\alpha = \sin^{-1}\left(\frac{\sin\delta}{\sin\phi'}\right) \tag{6.36}$$

the angle δ in equation 6.36 being the *known* value of the wall friction angle. Solving for the moments, with respect to O in figure 6.19, it follows that:

$$\sigma\frac{r}{2}\times\frac{2r}{3} - (\sigma+d\sigma)\frac{r}{2}\times\frac{2r}{3} + \tau r^2 d\lambda - \frac{2}{3}\gamma\frac{r^2}{2}\,d\lambda\sin\lambda = 0$$

or

$$\frac{d\sigma}{d\lambda} = 3\tau - r\gamma\sin\lambda \tag{6.37}$$

Now, resolving parallel to the surface OD:

$$\frac{(\sigma+d\sigma)r}{2}\sin d\lambda - K\sigma r d\lambda\cos\frac{d\lambda}{2} - \tau\frac{r}{2} + \frac{(\tau+d\tau)r}{2}\frac{1}{\cos d\lambda} + \frac{\gamma}{2}r^2\,d\lambda\cos\lambda = 0$$

but

$$\sin d\lambda \approx d\lambda, \quad \cos d\lambda \approx \cos\frac{d\lambda}{2} \approx 1, \quad d\lambda\,d\sigma \approx 0$$

hence:

$$\frac{d\tau}{d\lambda} = (2K-1)\sigma - \gamma r\cos\lambda \tag{6.38}$$

The ensuing set of first order differential equations, together with the boundary conditions are thus:

$$\frac{d\sigma}{d\lambda} = 3\tau - \gamma r\sin\lambda$$

$$\frac{d\tau}{d\lambda} = \sigma(2K-1) - \gamma r\cos\lambda$$

with

$$K = \frac{1+\sin\phi'\cos(\alpha-\delta)}{1-\sin\phi'\cos(\alpha-\delta)} \qquad \text{(active case)}$$

$$K = \frac{1-\sin\phi'\cos(\alpha-\delta)}{1+\sin\phi'\cos(\alpha-\delta)} \qquad \text{(passive case)}$$

$$\alpha = \sin^{-1}\left(\frac{\sin\delta}{\sin\phi'}\right)$$

where δ is the *known* value of the wall friction angle. The sign conventions are represented in figure 6.21. With reference to both figures 6.19 and 6.21, the boundary conditions for the above set of differential equations are such that:

$$\lambda = \lambda_o, \qquad \delta = \delta_a \ (or \ \delta_p)$$

A closed form solution to the above system of equations is not available. However, in 1948, Caquot and Kerisel published the numerical solution to this system in the form of tables giving both active and passive pressure coefficients for different combinations of the wall inclination λ, the slope β of the retained soil, its angle of shearing resistance ϕ' and the wall friction angle δ. Very few of these results corresponding to the case of a vertical back of wall (*i.e.* $\lambda = 0$) are reproduced in the following table and reference should be made to the complete set of results in the useful book of Kerisel and Absi (1990). Notice that the table contains the values of the coefficients K_a and K_p, *and not their horizontal components* $K_a \cos \delta$ *and* $K_p \cos \delta$.

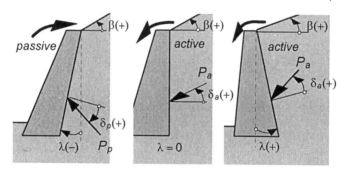

Figure 6.21: Sign conventions used in conjunction with
the boundary conditions related to figure 6.20.

N.B. According to the sign conventions used in Kerisel and Absi's book, the angle of wall friction δ is positive in the active case and negative in relation to the passive case. Therefore, all the values K_p listed in table 6.1 are easily found in the book by assigning a negative sign to the angle δ shown at the top of the table. For instance, if

$$\lambda = 0, \qquad \delta = 2\phi/3, \qquad \beta/\phi = 0.0 \ 0 \qquad and \ \phi = 35°$$

table 6.1 yields the coefficients: $K_a = 0.247$ and $K_p = 8.0$.
Using Kerisel and Absi's book, the same K_a value is read from the table on page 78 corresponding to:

$$\beta/\phi = 0, \qquad \delta/\phi = 0.66, \qquad \lambda = 0, \qquad and \ \phi = 35°.$$

As for K_p, its value is read from the table on page 14 in conjunction with:
$$\beta/\phi = 0, \qquad \delta/\phi = -0.66, \qquad \lambda = 0 \qquad and \ \phi = 35°.$$

Table 6.1: Coefficients of active and passive pressure corresponding to $\delta = \frac{2}{3}\phi'$.
(Reproduced by permission from Kerisel and Absi (1990).)

Coefficients of active and passive earth pressure K_a and K_p : $\lambda = 0$, $\delta = 2\phi'/3$									
ϕ (°)		10	15	20	25	30	35	40	45
$\frac{\beta}{\phi} = 1$	K_a	0.990	0.964	0.927	0.879	0.822	0.756	0.683	0.603
	K_p	1.910	2.800	4.300	7.000	12.50	25.00	58.00	163.0
0.8	K_a	0.806	0.715	0.628	0.546	0.469	0.397	0.330	0.269
	K_p	1.860	2.650	4.000	6.300	10.90	20.50	45.00	115.0
0.6	K_a	0.748	0.644	0.551	0.468	0.395	0.329	0.271	0.219
	K_p	1.790	2.500	3.700	5.700	9.300	16.60	34.00	78.00
0.4	K_a	0.710	0.598	0.503	0.422	0.352	0.291	0.239	0.193
	K_p	1.730	2.350	3.400	5.000	7.800	13.00	24.50	52.00
0.2	K_a	0.680	0.564	0.469	0.389	0.322	0.266	0.218	0.176
	K_p	1.660	2.200	3.100	4.300	6.500	10.00	17.50	33.00
0.0	K_a	0.656	0.537	0.442	0.364	0.300	0.247	0.202	0.163
	K_p	1.590	2.050	2.750	3.700	5.300	8.000	12.00	20.00
−0.2	K_a	0.636	0.515	0.420	0.343	0.282	0.231	0.189	0.153
	K_p	1.520	1.900	2.400	3.100	4.200	5.700	8.200	12.50
−0.4	K_a	0.619	0.496	0.401	0.326	0.266	0.218	0.177	0.144
	K_p	1.430	1.720	2.100	2.550	3.200	4.100	5.400	7.100
−0.6	K_a	0.603	0.479	0.384	0.311	0.253	0.206	0.167	0.135
	K_p	1.330	1.520	1.760	2.050	2.400	2.800	3.400	4.000
−0.8	K_a	0.590	0.464	0.370	0.298	0.241	0.195	0.158	0.127
	K_p	1.200	1.300	1.400	1.530	1.580	1.650	1.800	1.700

6.5.3 Pressure due to a uniform surcharge on a weightless cohesionless soil

Boussinesq theory makes due allowance for the effects of an inclined uniform load of infinite extent applied at the surface of a weightless cohesionless soil (*i.e.* $c' = 0$, $\gamma = 0$, $\phi' \neq 0$). With reference to the sign convention used in Kerisel and Absi's book depicted in figure 6.22, it is seen that:

$$\Omega = \frac{\pi}{2} + \beta - \lambda \tag{6.39}$$

The resulting lateral pressure exerted on the wall in the active case is:

$$\sigma_a = K'_a q \tag{6.40}$$

On the passive side, the pressure can be calculated in a similar way:

$$\sigma_p = K'_p q \tag{6.41}$$

Notice that, for the passive case, the coefficient K_p' is obtained in a very unconventional way from Kerisel and Absi's tables, in that the values of the angles α and δ (figure 6.22) are interchanged, thus yielding K_a' from which K_p' is then calculated as follows:

$$K_p' = \frac{1}{K_a'} \qquad\qquad (6.42)$$

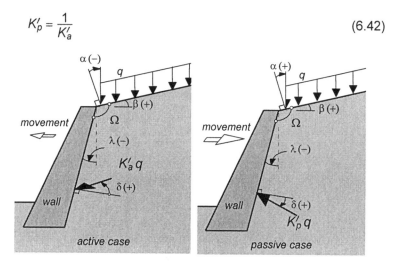

Figure 6.22: Sign convention used by Kerisel and Absi (1990).

For example, consider the case of a wall retaining a silty sand with an angle $\phi' = 30°$ as depicted in figure 6.23. Assuming an angle of wall friction $\delta = 2\phi'/3$, both coefficients of active and passive pressure, related to the uniform load q applied on either side of the wall, are found from Kerisel and Absi's book as follows.

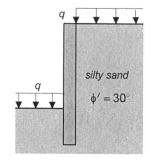

Figure 6.23: Retaining wall

- With reference to figure 6.22, it is seen that, on the active side, figure 6.23 corresponds to $\alpha = 0$, $\Omega = 90°$.

Thus, the coefficient K_a' is read from the table on page 132 for $\phi' = 30°$, $\Omega = 90°$, $\alpha = 0$ and $\delta = 20° \quad \Rightarrow \quad K_a' = 0.304$.

- On the passive side, the values of α and δ are now interchanged, so that $\alpha = 2\phi'/3 = 20°$ and $\delta = 0$. The corresponding K_a' value is read from the same table for $\phi' = 30°$, $\Omega = 90°$, $\alpha = 20°$ and $\delta = 0$: $K_a' = 0.203$, and the coefficient of passive pressure is thereafter calculated from equation 6.42:

$$K_p' = \frac{1}{0.203} = 4.926$$

Very few of the K_p' values have been *calculated* from Kerisel and Absi's book according to the procedure described above. These values, together with the coefficients K_a' corresponding to the active case, are presented in table 6.2.

Table 6.2: Coefficients of active and passive pressure applicable to a
uniform surcharge. (Reproduced by permission from Kerisel and Absi (1990).)

Coefficients K_a' and K_p': $\alpha = 0$, $\delta = 0.66\phi'$								
$\phi(°)$		15	20	25	30	35	40	45
$\Omega = 90°$	K_a'	0.542	0.447	0.369	0.304	0.249	0.206	0.165
	K_p'	2.024	2.645	3.554	4.926	7.075	10.64	17.24
95	K_a'	0.517	0.420	0.340	0.274	0.221	0.177	0.139
	K_p'	2.123	2.822	3.861	5.464	8.000	12.40	20.41
100	K_a'	0.494	0.394	0.314	0.248	0.196	0.153	0.116
	K_p'	2.222	3.006	4.178	6.024	9.063	14.28	24.39
105	K_a'	0.471	0.370	0.289	0.224	0.173	0.132	0.098
	K_p'	2.331	3.202	4.545	6.667	10.20	16.57	29.41
110	K_a'	0.450	0.347	0.266	0.203	0.153	0.114	0.082
	K_p'	2.445	3.417	4.918	7.353	11.54	19.23	34.48
115	K_a'	0.429	0.326	0.246	0.183	0.135	0.098	0.069
	K_p'	2.557	3.636	5.346	8.130	12.99	22.22	41.67
120	K_a'	0.409	0.305	0.226	0.166	0.120	0.085	0.058
	K_p'	2.681	3.876	5.803	9.010	14.78	25.42	50.00
125	K_a'	0.391	0.286	0.209	0.150	0.106	0.073	0.049
	K_p'	2.809	4.126	6.263	10.00	16.57	29.70	58.82
130	K_a'	0.373	0.269	0.192	0.136	0.094	0.063	0.041
	K_p'	2.941	4.405	6.802	10.99	18.87	34.48	71.43
135	K_a'	0.356	0.252	0.177	0.123	0.083	0.054	0.034
	K_p'	3.086	4.687	7.389	12.19	21.28	40.00	83.33

6.5.4 Pressure due to the cohesion of a weightless soil

For cohesive soils, Boussinesq considered the behaviour of such materials to be similar to that of purely frictional soils subject throughout their surface areas to an extra normal stress of a magnitude $c'\cot\phi'$. This effect can easily be established from the failure criterion of a cohesive soil, written as follows:

$$\tau = c' + \sigma'\tan\phi'$$

so that after rearranging:

$$\tau = (c'\cot\phi' + \sigma')\tan\phi' = \sigma^{*'}\tan\phi' \tag{6.43}$$

Equation 6.43 is that of a frictional soil in which part of the normal stress $\sigma^{*\prime}$ is due to cohesion. Consequently, the cohesion effect on the lateral thrust induced by a cohesive weightless soil can be evaluated by considering that the soil in question is frictional ($c' = 0$), but subject throughout to an external normal stress $c'\cot\phi'$ as depicted in figure 6.24.

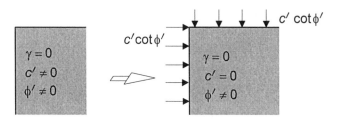

Figure 6.24: Effect of cohesion in Boussinesq theory.

In the general case of a *rough wall* with an inclined back, retaining a sloping cohesive soil, the active pressure due to cohesion is as depicted in figure 6.25. Whence the ensuing value of the component of the active pressure, *normal to the wall*:

$$\sigma_{an} = -c'\cot\phi'\,(1 - K'_a\cos\delta) \tag{6.44}$$

the corresponding shear stress along the back of the wall being:

$$\tau = c'\cot\phi'K'_a\sin\delta \tag{6.45}$$

It is straightforward to show that, for the passive case, the component of passive pressure due to cohesion, *normal to the wall* is given by:

$$\sigma_{pn} = c'\cot\phi'\left(K'_p\cos\delta - 1\right) \tag{6.46}$$

the corresponding shear stress due to wall friction being:

$$\tau = c'\cot\phi'\,K'_p\sin\delta \tag{6.47}$$

The angle δ in equations 6.44 to 6.47 is the *angle of wall friction,* the coefficient of active pressure K'_a being the same as in the case of a uniformly loaded weightless cohesionless soil. The coefficient K'_p is related to K'_a through equation 6.42.

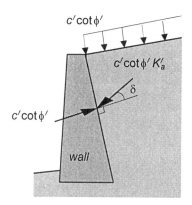

Figure 6.25: Coefficient of active pressure due to cohesion in the case of a sloping rough wall.

As can be seen from equations 6.44 and 6.46, the cohesion causes the overall active pressure at the back of a retaining wall to *decrease* (notice the negative sign of the quantity σ_{an}, since $K'_a \cos \delta < 1$), and the overall passive pressure in front of the wall to *increase*. However, these variations depend to a large extent on the value of cohesion and, as mentioned earlier, caution must be exercised when choosing a value for c'; it is even advisable to ignore the cohesion effects in the absence of representative reliable measurements of this parameter.

6.6 Lateral thrust due to different types of ground loading

6.6.1 Uniform load of infinite extent

As seen in figure 6.22, the analysis of the general case of an inclined uniform ground pressure q of infinite extent led to equations 6.40 and 6.41 of the active and passive effective pressure. These stresses propagate constantly throughout the appropriate height of wall, so that the induced lateral thrusts are found by simple integration of both equations. For instance, the lateral active thrust in the case of figure 6.26, is calculated as follows:

$$P'_a = \int_0^H q\,K'_a\,dz = qK'_aH \tag{6.48}$$

where K'_a refers to the coefficient of active earth pressure. The lateral passive thrust is calculated in a similar way if a surcharge is applied in front of the wall.

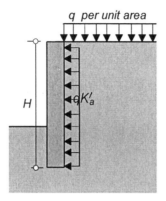

*Figure 6.26: Lateral thrust due to
a uniform load of infinite extent.*

6.6.2 Strip load

The increase in horizontal pressure σ'_h due to a strip load can be calculated using Boussinesq's elastic solution. However, the value of σ'_h is doubled to make allowance for the effects of rigidity of the wall. Hence, with reference to figure 6.27:

$$\sigma'_h = 2\frac{q}{\pi}[\beta - \sin\beta\,\cos(\beta + 2\alpha)] \qquad (6.49)$$

where α and β are expressed in radians.

The lateral thrust due to such a stress distribution as well as the location of its line of action can be found numerically.

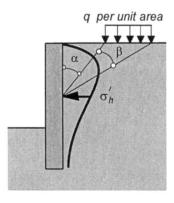

Figure 6.27: Lateral thrust due to a strip loading.

6.6.3 Line load

The increase in horizontal pressure is calculated, in this case, according to the following relationships suggested by Terzaghi (1954) (refer to figure 6.28 for m and n):

- for $m \leq 0.4$:
$$\sigma'_h = q \frac{n}{5H(0.16+n^2)^2} \qquad (6.50)$$

- for $m > 0.4$:
$$\sigma'_h = q \frac{4m^2 n}{\pi H(m^2+n^2)^2} \qquad (6.51)$$

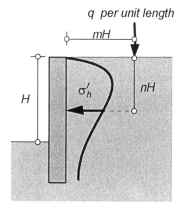

Figure 6.28: Lateral thrust due to a line load.

6.6.4 Point load

Terzaghi suggested using the following relationships for the calculation of the lateral pressure caused by a point load as depicted in figure 6.29:

- for $m \leq 0.4$:
$$\sigma'_h = 0.28 \frac{q}{H^2} \frac{n^2}{(0.16+n^2)^3} \qquad (6.52)$$

- for $m > 0.4$:
$$\sigma'_h = 1.77 \frac{q}{H^2} \frac{m^2 n^2}{(m^2+n^2)^3} \qquad (6.53)$$

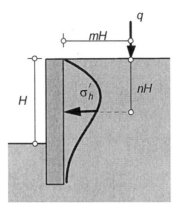

Figure 6.29: Lateral thrust due to a point load.

6.7 Effect of water pressure on the lateral thrust exerted on retaining structures

The *total* lateral thrust per metre length exerted on a retaining structure is the sum of the *effective* lateral thrust *augmented* by the hydrostatic force due to *water pressure* when applicable. It can easily be calculated from the integration of lateral pressures (including water pressure) throughout the relevant height of the structure.   Consider the wall with the dimensions shown in figure 6.30, retaining a totally submerged *isotropic homogeneous* soil characterised by a saturated unit weight γ_{sat}, a cohesion c' and an angle of shearing resistance ϕ'. The back of the wall is inclined at an angle λ with respect to the vertical (positive anticlockwise as in figure 6.21) and the backfill is horizontal.

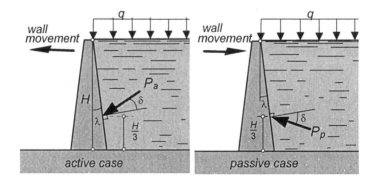

Figure 6.30: Effect of water pressure on lateral thrust.

Assuming that there is little or no seepage around the wall so that there is a *static* water table, then for a given wall friction angle δ and a uniform pressure q, the *total* lateral active thrust P_{an}, *normal* to the wall is the sum of the *effective normal thrust* P'_{an} calculated using Boussinesq theory, for instance, and the hydrostatic force per linear metre P_w due to water pressure. Thus, with reference to figure 6.31:

$$P_{an} = P'_{an} + P_w \qquad\qquad (6.54)$$

$$P'_{an} = A_1 + \int_0^{H/\cos\lambda} \left[K'_a q \cos\delta - \frac{c'}{\tan\phi}(1 - K'_a \cos\delta) \right] dz \qquad (6.55)$$

where A_1 represents the *effective thrust, normal to the wall* due to the effective weight of soil, and the integral quantity corresponds to the contribution to the *effective normal thrust* of both the soil cohesion c' and the uniform load q. Accordingly, the quantity A_1 is obtained by multiplying the *average* effective active pressure (*i.e.* one half of the effective active pressure at point O in figure 6.31) by the length $oa = H/\cos\lambda$:

$$A_1 = \frac{H^2}{2} K_a (\gamma_{sat} - \gamma_w) \frac{\cos\delta}{\cos\lambda}$$

γ_w being the unit weight of water.

Substituting for A_1 in equation 6.55 yields the expression for the *effective normal active thrust*:

$$P'_{an} = \frac{H^2}{2} K_a (\gamma_{sat} - \gamma_w) \frac{\cos\delta}{\cos\lambda} + \frac{H}{\cos\lambda}\left[K'_a q \cos\delta - \frac{c'}{\tan\phi}(1 - K'_a \cos\delta) \right]$$

The lateral thrust due to the water pressure is calculated in a way similar to that used to calculate A_1:

$$P_w = A_2 = \frac{\gamma_w}{2\cos\lambda} H^2$$

so that the *total normal active thrust* exerted on the wall is:

$$P_{an} = \frac{H^2}{2\cos\lambda}[\gamma_w + K_a \cos\delta (\gamma_{sat} - \gamma_w)]$$

$$+ \frac{H}{\cos\lambda}\left[K'_a q \cos\delta - \frac{c'}{\tan\phi}(1 - K'_a \cos\delta) \right] \qquad (6.56a)$$

For the passive case, the *total normal passive thrust* is calculated in precisely the same way using the passive pressures. Consequently:

$$P_{pn} = \frac{H^2}{2\cos\lambda}[\gamma_w + K_p \cos\delta\,(\gamma_{sat} - \gamma_w)]$$

$$+ \frac{H}{\cos\lambda}\left[K_p' q \cos\delta + \frac{c'}{\tan\phi}\left(K_p' \cos\delta - 1\right)\right] \qquad (6.56b)$$

Notice that, with respect to equations 6.56, K_a, K_a', K_p and K_p' represent the coefficients of earth pressure obtained from the Boussinesq theory (Kerisel and Absi's tables).

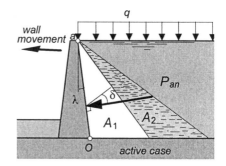

Figure 6.31: Evaluation of the effect of water pressure on the total lateral thrust.

Let us now appraise the effect of water pressure on the magnitude of the *total normal lateral thrust* by considering that the soil behind the wall is *totally dry*, in which case the thrust due to water becomes zero. Assuming the dry soil has a bulk unit weight γ, it is easy to see that both equations 6.56 reduce to:

$$P_{an} = K_a \gamma H^2 \frac{\cos\delta}{2\cos\lambda} + \frac{H}{\cos\lambda}\left[K_a' q \cos\delta - \frac{c'}{\tan\phi}(1 - K_a' \cos\delta)\right] \qquad (6.57a)$$

$$P_{pn} = K_p \gamma H^2 \frac{\cos\delta}{2\cos\lambda} + \frac{H}{\cos\lambda}\left[K_p' q \cos\delta + \frac{c'}{\tan\phi}\left(K_p' \cos\delta - 1\right)\right] \qquad (6.57b)$$

It is always useful to have a feel for these effects by using simple examples. Take the wall depicted in figure 6.30: for a height $H = 7\,m$ and a vertical back (*i.e.* $\lambda = 0$), consider first the case of a clayey backfill with the following characteristics: $c' = 0$, $\phi' = 20°$, $\gamma = 19\,kN/m^3$ and $\gamma_{sat} = 20\,kN/m^3$. Assume a wall friction angle $\delta = 2\phi/3$, a uniform pressure $q = 20\,kN/m^2$, and a unit weight of water $\gamma_w = 10\,kN/m^3$. Prior to any calculation of lateral thrusts, the values of the coefficients of active and passive earth pressure must be found from different tables. Hence:

- from table 6.1: ($\lambda = 0$, $\delta = 2\phi/3$, $\beta/\phi = 0$, $\phi = 20°$):
  $$K_a = 0.442, \quad K_p = 2.75$$

- using table 6.2: ($\alpha = 0$, $\delta = 2\phi'/3$, $\Omega = 90°$, $\phi = 20°$):
  $$K_a' = 0.447, \quad K_p' = 2.645$$

For a *totally submerged* backfill, the *total lateral thrust* is calculated using equation 6.56. Thus, using the superscript w for wet:
- the active normal thrust:

$$P_{an}^w = \frac{7^2}{2}[10 + 0.442 \times (20 - 10) \cos 13.3]$$

$$+ 7 \times 0.447 \times 20 \cos 13.3 = 411 \, kN/m$$

- the passive normal thrust:

$$P_{pn}^w = \frac{7^2}{2}[10 + 2.75 \times (20 - 10) \cos 13.3]$$

$$+ 7 \times 2.645 \times 20 \cos 13.3 = 1261 \, kN/m$$

For a *dry* backfill, equation 6.57 applies for the calculation of *total normal* active and passive thrusts. Using the superscript d for dry:
- the active normal thrust:

$$P_{an}^d = 19 \times \frac{7^2}{2} \times 0.442 \cos 13.3$$

$$+ 7 \times 0.447 \times 20 \cos 13.3 = 261 \, kN/m$$

- the passive normal thrust:

$$P_{pn}^d = 19 \times \frac{7^2}{2} \times 2.75. \cos 13.3 + 7 \times 2.645 \times 20 \cos 13.3 = 1606 \, kN/m$$

Comparing these values, it follows that:

$$P_{an}^w \approx 1.57 \, P_{an}^d \quad \text{and} \quad P_{pn}^w \approx 0.78 \, P_{pn}^d$$

These simple findings indicate that, in this particular instance, if the backfill were to be totally submerged, the active thrust, normal to the wall will *increase* by more than 50%, whereas the passive thrust will *decrease* by more than 20%.

Now what about the effect of the nature of backfill? Consider a granular backfill in conjunction with the same wall with a vertical back, and assume that the soil has the following parameters:

$$\gamma = 18 \, kN/m^3, \; \gamma_{sat} = 20 \, kN/m^3, \; c' = 0, \; \phi' = 35°.$$

Also, assume a uniform load and a wall friction angle identical to those used previously (*i.e.* $q = 20 \, kN/m^2$, $\delta = 2\phi'/3$). Prior to calculating the active and passive lateral thrusts for the limiting cases of totally dry and totally submerged backfill, the coefficients of earth pressure need to be determined:

- using table 6.1: ($\lambda = 0$, $\delta = 2\phi'/3$, $\beta/\phi' = 0$, $\phi' = 35°$):
  $K_a = 0.247$, $K_p = 8.00$

- from table 10.2: ($\alpha = 0$, $\delta = 2\phi'/3$, $\Omega = 90°$, $\phi' = 35°$):
  $K'_a = 0.249$, $K'_p = 7.08$

Starting with a *totally submerged* backfill, equations 6.56 yield the following:

- active normal thrust:

$$P^w_{an} = \frac{7^2}{2}[10 + 0.247 \times (20 - 10) \cos 23.3]$$

$$+ 7 \times 0.249 \times 20 \cos 23.3 = 333 \, kN/m$$

- passive normal thrust:

$$P^w_{pn} = \frac{7^2}{2}[10 + 8 \times (20 - 10) \cos 23.3]$$

$$+ 7 \times 7.08 \times 20 \cos 23.3 = 2955 \, kN/m$$

For a *dry* backfill, use equations 6.57:

- active normal thrust:

$$P^d_{an} = \frac{7^2}{2} \times 18 \times 0.247 \cos 23.3$$

$$+ 7 \times 0.249 \times 20 \cos 23.3 = 132 \, kN/m$$

- passive normal thrust:

$$P^d_{pn} = \frac{7^2}{2} \times 18 \times 8 \cos 23.3$$

$$+ 7 \times 7.08 \times 20 \cos 23.3 = 4151 \, kN/m$$

Whence:

$$P^w_{an} \approx 2.52 \, P^d_{an} \quad \text{and} \quad P^w_{pn} \approx 0.71 \, P^d_{pn}$$

It is clear that the water pressure has a more marked effect in the case of a granular backfill as opposed to a cohesive (clayey) backfill. It is seen that in conjunction with a granular backfill, in this instance, if the soil conditions were to change from totally dry to fully saturated, the *total active normal thrust* would more than double, while the *total passive normal thrust (i.e.* the resistance offered by the soil) would reduce by about one third. These simple examples show how crucial it is for the drainage behind the wall to take place, as the structural stability might be compromised due to the build-up of excessive water pressure.

6.8 Relevance of analytical solutions

The analyses undertaken thus far in relation to active and passive stresses point to the fact that, *when applicable*, the Boussinesq theory yields the most realistic predictions for either active or passive lateral thrusts exerted on retaining structures. The Rankine and Coulomb theories, on the other hand, lead to lower and upper bound solutions respectively. Moreover, the restrictive nature of Rankine's theory makes it the least advisable for use in practice. Specifically, the assumption of a wall friction angle equal to the slope of the ground surface for vertical walls (refer to equations 6.23 and 6.24) is at best arguable and at worst unrealistic (see for example Terzaghi (1936)). There is, however, a particular case in which Rankine analysis might be useful, namely the design of cantilever walls as depicted in figure 6.32. In this case, failure of the backfill occurs along the shear planes *ad* and *de* and it can be seen from the Mohr's circle in figure 6.33 that, for a wall friction d (equal to the slope of the ground surface in figure 6.32), the shear surface *Fl* is inclined at an angle h with respect to the horizontal. The relationships relating different angles can be established in a straightforward manner. Thus:

$$\xi = \frac{\pi}{2} + \phi' - \alpha + \delta \qquad \text{and} \qquad \xi + 2(\eta + \alpha - \delta) = \pi$$

hence:

$$\eta = \frac{\pi}{4} - \frac{\phi'}{2} + \frac{1}{2}(\delta - \alpha) \qquad\qquad (6.58)$$

where the angle a is given by equation 6.36:

$$\alpha = \sin^{-1}(\sin \delta / \sin \phi')$$

Checking on equation 6.58, it can be seen that for no wall friction (*i.e.* $\delta = \alpha = 0$), the shear surface corresponds to *FC* (figure 6.33) and the angle h becomes:

$$\eta = \frac{\pi}{4} - \frac{\phi'}{2}$$

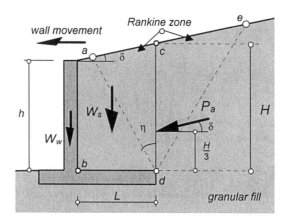

Figure 6.32: Lateral thrust exerted on cantilever walls.

On the opposite side when $\delta = \phi'$, then $\alpha = \pi/2$ and $\eta = 0$. Consequently, with reference to figure 6.32, provided that:

$$\tan^{-1}\left(\frac{L}{h}\right) \geq \eta \qquad (6.59)$$

then the magnitude of the lateral thrust P_a is almost unaffected by wall friction along *ab,* and Rankine analysis can be applied. Notice that, in this particular instance, the lateral thrust is assumed to be acting on the *virtual* back of wall *cd*, so that the weight W_s of the volume of soil above the base of the wall *abdc* is added to the actual weight of the wall W_w for stability calculations. Also, the active pressure is assumed to be increasing linearly with depth and, consequently, the line of action of the lateral thrust is situated at a height $H/3$ as depicted in figure 6.32.

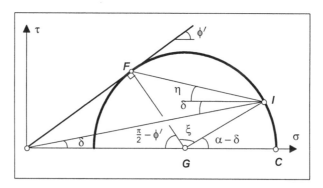

Figure 6.33: Effect of wall friction on the magnitude of total lateral thrust.

By considering the assumptions used in each of the three theories presented earlier, it quickly emerges that they can only be applied under very specific conditions relating to the type of soil (*i.e.* isotropic and homogenous) and to the geometry of the problem (*i.e.* backfill either horizontal or sloping at a constant gradient). In particular, the long term analytical solutions derived from both Rankine and Coulomb theories do not allow for any cohesion effect to be considered. When the retained soil is *cohesive, partially* or *totally submerged* and *non- homogeneous (i.e.* multi-layered), with *uneven sloping surface* and subject to a given loading as depicted in figure 6.34, the limitations of the previous theories become apparent. Faced with such a problem, the designer has to resort to other techniques and, in this regard, finite element modelling can be a very useful tool for calculating the distribution of the effective horizontal stresses along the wall. Bear in mind that the method requires the input of several soil parameters such as elastic modulii, Poisson's ratios, elastic–plastic stress–strain relationships, and water pressures. The implications are that the output of a finite element analysis is as accurate (or inaccurate!) as the soil parameters are representative of the soil behaviour, and it is therefore advisable to assess the input and appraise the output with a critical eye. A simpler and sufficiently accurate alternative to finite element modelling consists of using either an approximate analytical solution based on Boussinesq theory or a graphical method of solution utilising the principles of Coulomb theory. Notwithstanding the approximate nature of either of these methods, they are deemed to be sufficiently accurate in engineering practice.

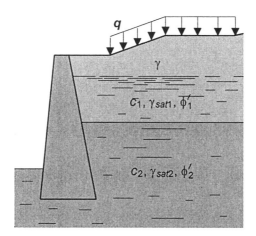

Figure 6.34: Case of non-homogeneous soils.

6.9 Boussinesq solution adapted to isotropic homogeneous backfill with uneven surface

Let us consider the two retaining walls depicted in figure 6.35, where the retained *dry, isotropic and homogeneous* soil has an uneven profile. Starting with figure 6.35(a), the magnitude of the lateral (active in this case) thrust P_a due to the weight of the soil corresponds to the shaded area $(A_1 + A_2 + A_3)$. This area is determined by *assuming* that, at the top of the wall, the lateral stress σ'_a is mainly due to a sloping backfill, hence the linear distribution of σ'_a from the depth b (corresponding to the crest of the wall) at a slope $\gamma K_a(\beta)$, where γ represents the unit weight of soil and $K_a(\beta)$ is the coefficient of active pressure corresponding to the angle β and read from Kerisel and Absi's tables. At the depth z, the slope then becomes $\gamma K_a(0)$ where $K_a(0)$ represents the coefficient of active pressure corresponding to an angle $\beta = 0$, and reflects the fact that below the depth z, the lateral stress is mainly due to a *horizontal* backfill.

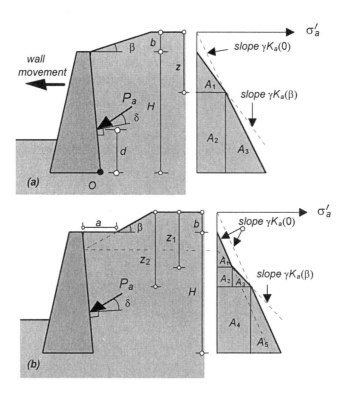

Figure 6.35: (a) Initially sloping backfill and (b) initially horizontal backfill.

Referring to figure 6.35(a), the lateral thrust as well as its line of action can be determined in a straightforward way if the depth z were known. But z is where the two slopes intersect, thence:

$$K_a(\beta)\gamma(z-b) = K_a(0)\gamma z$$

or

$$z = \frac{bK_a(\beta)}{K_a(\beta) - K_a(0)} \tag{6.60}$$

Using equation 6.60, the lateral thrust is thereafter calculated as follows :

$$P_a = A_1 + A_2 + A_3 \tag{6.61}$$

with $A_1 = (z-b)^2 \frac{\gamma}{2} K_a(\beta) = \frac{1}{2}b^2 K_a(\beta)\left[\frac{K_a(0)}{K_a(\beta) - K_a(0)}\right]^2$

$A_2 = \gamma(H+b-z)(z-b)K_a(\beta)$

$A_3 = \frac{\gamma}{2}(H+b-z)^2 K_a(0)$

The line of action of the lateral thrust is such that the distance d (refer to figure 6.35(a)) is found by taking moments about point O:

$$d = \frac{A_1 d_1 + A_2 d_2 + A_3 d_3}{A_1 + A_2 + A_3} \tag{6.62}$$

with $d_1 = H + \frac{2}{3}(b-z)$, $d_2 = \frac{1}{2}(H+b-z)$ and $d_3 = \frac{1}{3}(H+b-z)$.

With respect to the backfill profile in figure 6.35(b), the shaded area corresponding to the lateral pressure distribution has a slope $\gamma K_a(0)$ between a depth b and a depth z_1 (i.e. the coefficient of active pressure corresponds to a horizontal backfill). The slope then changes to $\gamma K_a(\beta)$ from z_1 to z_2, only to rejoin the initial slope $\gamma K_a(0)$ below the depth z_2. Both z_1 and z_2 can easily be calculated by writing:

$$\gamma K_a(0)(z_1 - b) = \gamma K_a(\beta)(z_1 - b - a\tan\beta)$$

and

$$z_2 \gamma K_a(0) = \gamma K_a(\beta)(z_2 - b - a\tan\beta)$$

Hence the ensuing values of z_1 and z_2:

$$z_1 = \frac{K_a(\beta)(b+a\tan\beta) - bK_a(0)}{K_a(\beta) - K_a(0)} \tag{6.63}$$

$$z_2 = \frac{K_a(\beta)(b+a\tan\beta)}{K_a(\beta) - K_a(0)} \tag{6.64}$$

The lateral thrust is in this case:

$$P_a = \sum_{k=1}^{5} A_k \tag{6.65}$$

with

$$A_1 = \gamma \frac{(z_1 - b)^2}{2} K_a(0)$$

$$A_2 = \gamma (z_1 - b)(z_2 - z_1) K_a(0)$$

$$A_3 = \gamma \frac{(z_2 - z_1)^2}{2} K_a(\beta)$$

$$A_4 = \gamma (H + b - z_2)[(z_1 - b) K_a(0) + (z_2 - z_1) K_a(\beta)]$$

$$A_5 = \gamma \frac{(H + b - z_2)}{2} K_a(0)$$

The line of action of the lateral thrust is then calculated in the same way used in conjunction with figure 6.35(a). If the soil were cohesive, then the lateral thrust *normal* to the wall and due to cohesion is evaluated as detailed in the Boussinesq theory, except that the appropriate coefficients of active pressure are taken as follows:

- with respect to figure 6.35(a), use $K_a'(\beta)$ from the crest of the wall to the depth z, below which $K_a'(0)$ must be used.
- in the case of a backfill profile such as in figure 6.35(b), first use $K_a'(0)$ between the top of the wall and the depth z_1, then use $K_a'(\beta)$ between z_1 and z_2, and finally revert to $K_a'(0)$ for any depth below z_2.

Example 6.1

Consider the case of the wall depicted in figure 6.36, retaining a dry clayey isotropic and homogeneous backfill with the following characteristics:

$\gamma = 18\,kN/m^3$, $\phi' = 20°$, $c' = 5\,kN/m^2$.

The wall friction angle is $\delta = 2\phi'/3$ and the dimensions of the uneven backfill surface are as depicted in the figure.

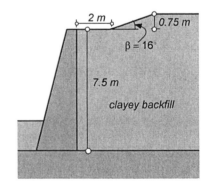

Figure 6.36: Uneven surface of backfill.

The procedure developed in conjunction with figure 6.35(*b*) applies to this problem and, accordingly, the component of the lateral thrust due to the self weight of backfill is calculated from equation 6.65 for which the following quantities need to be evaluated:

- *The coefficients of active earth pressure are read from table 6.1:*

$$\lambda = 0,\ \delta = 2\phi'/3,\ \phi' = 20°,\ \beta/\phi' = 0 \quad \Rightarrow \quad K_a(0) = 0.442$$

$$\lambda = 0,\ \delta = 2\phi'/3,\ \phi' = 20°,\ \beta/\phi' = \frac{16}{20} = 0.8 \quad \Rightarrow \quad K_a(16) = 0.628$$

- *The depths z_1 and z_2 are determined from equations 6.63 and 6.64:*

$$z_1 = \frac{0.628 \times (0.75 + 2\tan 16) - 0.75 \times 0.442}{0.628 - 0.442} = 2.69\,m$$

$$z_2 = \frac{0.628 \times (0.75 + 2\tan 16)}{0.628 - 0.442} = 4.47\,m$$

whence:

$$A_1 = \frac{18}{2}(2.69 - 0.75)^2 \times 0.442 = 15\,kN/m$$

$$A_2 = 18(2.69 - 0.75)(4.47 - 2.69) \times 0.442 = 27.5\,kN/m$$

$$A_3 = \frac{18}{2}(4.47 - 2.69)^2 \times 0.628 = 17.9\,kN/m$$

$$A_4 = 18 \times (7.5 + 0.75 - 4.47)$$

$$\times\,[(2.69 - 0.75) \times 0.442 + (4.47 - 2.69) \times 0.628] = 134.4\,kN/m$$

$$A_5 = \frac{18}{2}(7.5 + 0.75 - 4.47) \times 0.442 = 15\,kN/m$$

The lateral thrust, due to the weight of backfill is therefore:

$$P_{a1} = \sum_{k=1}^{5} A_k = (15 + 27.5 + 17.9 + 134.4 + 15) = 209.8\,kN/m$$

This component is applied at a distance d_1 (from the base of the wall) which can easily be found by taking the moments about the point O (see figure 6.37). It is straightforward to show that in this case $d_1 \approx 2.73\,m$.

The second component of the lateral thrust is due to cohesion. In this regard, prior to any calculations, the appropriate coefficients of active pressure need to be found. Referring to the table on page 111 in Kerisel and Absi's book, it is seen that:

$$\alpha = \frac{2\phi'}{3} = 13.3°, \ \delta = 0, \ \phi' = 20°, \ \Omega = 90° \ \Rightarrow \ K_a'(0) = 0.378$$

$$\alpha = \frac{2\phi'}{3}, \ \delta = 0, \ \Omega = 90 + 16 = 106° \ \Rightarrow \ K_a'(16) \approx 0.312$$

Hence the active pressure due to cohesion and *normal* to the back of the wall, calculated according to equation 6.44:

$$\sigma_{an} = -\frac{c'}{\tan\phi}(1 - K_a' \cos\delta)$$

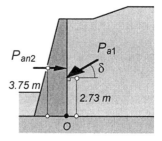

Figure 6.37: components of the lateral thrust applied to the wall.

The corresponding lateral thrust P_{an2} *normal to the wall* is found by integrating the expression of the normal active pressure throughout the height of wall. Care must be taken when choosing the appropriate value for the coefficient K_a', and with reference to figure 10.35(b), P_{an2} is calculated as follows:

$$P_{an2} = \int_0^{z_1-b} [c'\cot\phi(\cos\delta \, K_a'(0) - 1)]dz$$

$$+ \int_{z_1}^{z_2} [c\cot\phi(\cos\delta \, K_a'(16) - 1)]dz$$

$$+ \int_{z_2-b}^{H} [c\cot\phi(\cos\delta \, K_a'(0) - 1)]dz$$

$$= c'\cot\phi \, (z_1 - b)\Big(K_a'(0) \cos\delta - 1\Big)$$

$$+ c'\cot\phi \, (z_2 - z_1)\Big(K_a'(16) \cos\delta - 1\Big)$$

$$+ c'\cot\phi \, (H - z_2 + b)\Big(K_a'(0) \cos\delta - 1\Big)$$

knowing that: $c' = 5 \, kN/m^2$, $\phi = 20°$, $\delta = 2\phi/3$, $H = 7.5 \, m$, $b = 0.75 \, m$, $z_1 = 2.69 \, m$, $z_2 = 4.47 \, m$, $K_a'(0) = 0.378$, $K_a'(16) = 0.312$, the above expression yields a value:

$$P_{an2} = -66.7 \, kN/m$$

The line of action of this *normal thrust* is situated at a distance $d_2 = \frac{H}{2} = 3.75\,m$ from the base of the wall.

The *overall lateral thrust normal to the back of wall* is thus:

$$P_{an} = P_{an2} + P_{a1}\cos\delta = -66.7 + 209.8\cos\left(\tfrac{40}{3}\right) \approx 137.4\,kN/m$$

and the line of action of this total normal thrust is situated at a distance d such that:

$$d = \frac{1}{P_{an}}(d_1 P_{a1}\cos\delta + d_2 P_{an2})$$

$$= \frac{1}{137.4} \times (2.73 \times 209.8 \times \cos 13.3 - 3.75 \times 66.7) = 2.24\,m$$

6.10 Coulomb solution adapted to multi-layered soils with uneven surface

The solutions to lateral thrust problems based on any of the three theories (Boussinesq, Coulomb or Rankine) are *only* valid if the retained soil is *isotropic and homogeneous*. In practice however, there can be cases whereby a structure is needed to retain a multi-layered soil (*i.e.* non homogeneous), subjected at its surface to a complex loading as depicted in figure 6.34. Such cases *can* be solved satisfactorily using a graphical technique, based on the principles of Coulomb theory. At this stage, it must be emphasised that this technique is *only realistic* when used in conjunction with active pressure, since the actual failure surface on the passive side may differ markedly from the linear surface assumed in Coulomb theory (refer to figure 6.17).

The graphical solution to the problem corresponding to figure 6.34 is introduced in steps. First, consider a wall having a back inclined at an angle λ and retaining an *isotropic homogeneous dry cohesionless soil* ($c' = 0$) with a unit weight γ, an angle of shearing resistance ϕ' and an even sloping surface as shown in figure 6.38. The method consists first of choosing a number of slip planes such as oa_1, oa_2, a_3, ... on which the soil reactions $R_1, R_2, R_3, ...$ are drawn. At this stage, only the *directions* of the reactions are known since each one is inclined at an angle ϕ' with respect to the normal to each slip plane. Similarly, the wall reaction to the active thrust P_a, whose magnitude is not yet known, is drawn inclined at an angle δ with respect to the normal to the back of the wall, δ being the angle of wall friction. The next step consists of calculating the weight per linear metre w_1 of the block nearest to the wall oa_1a_2, then using the polygon of forces to find graphically the magnitude of the soil reaction R_1 as well as the active thrust P_{a1} in the knowledge that w_1 is *known in magnitude and in direction*, and the *directions* of both R_1 and P_{a1} are as depicted in figure 6.38.

Any appropriate scale can be used to plot the corresponding polygon of forces from which the magnitude of both R_1 and P_{a1} can be scaled. Physically, P_{a1} represents the magnitude of the active thrust that would be mobilised were the wedge oa_1a_2 to be the *actual* block that fails. Notice that, with reference to figure 6.38, the weight per linear metre w_n of any block oa_1a_n is calculated as follows:

$$w_n = \frac{dH\gamma}{2\cos\lambda} \cos(\beta - \lambda) \qquad (6.66)$$

where d represents the distance a_1a_n.

If the same procedure were repeated for the remaining blocks (*i.e.* $oa_1a_3, oa_1a_4, oa_1a_5$), then the magnitude of each corresponding active thrust can be determined. These values can thereafter be plotted at any convenient scale above the retained soil in a way that the slip planes are projected vertically as depicted in figure 6.38. A curve can then be drawn, leading to the *maximum* value of the active thrust as well as the location of the corresponding failure surface.

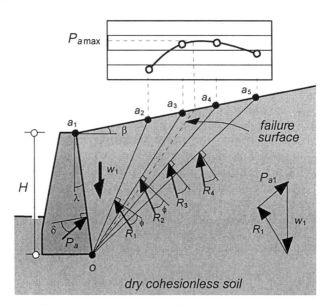

Figure 6.38: Coulomb graphical solution adapted to a backfill with uneven surface.

Let us now tackle the case of a wall retaining a *dry, homogeneous, isotropic cohesive soil* ($c' \neq 0$). The graphical solution drawn in figure 6.39, is determined in precisely the same way as the one depicted in figure 6.38 *except* that in this case, the polygon of forces includes the *shear forces per linear metre* T_1 and T_2 developed along the shear planes oa_1 and oa_2

respectively. If d_1 represents the distance oa_1, then the shear force per linear metre developed along the back of wall is evaluated as follows:

$$T_1 = c_w d_1 \tag{6.67}$$

with c_w representing the cohesion at the soil/wall interface. In practice, its value can be taken as:

$$c_w \approx \frac{1}{2} c' \tag{6.68}$$

Similarly, the force T_2 is calculated using the following:

$$T_2 = c' d_2 \tag{6.69}$$

where d_2 represents the length of the shear plane (*i.e.* the distance oa_2).

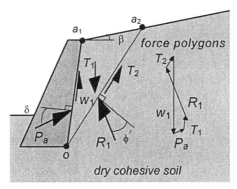

Figure 6.39: Case of a sloping cohesive backfill.

The next instance corresponds to the general case of a wall retaining a *totally submerged cohesive soil* (figure 6.40). The groundwater level is assumed to be *static* and the soil is *isotropic* and *homogeneous*. Once more, the same principles as in the graphical method used previously apply. However, care must be taken as regards the following.

- The *total* weight w_1 is calculated using the soil saturated unit weight. Any surface loading q applied between a_1 and a_2 must be *added* to w_1. Notice that q has a unit of a *force per linear metre*.
- The *average* water pressure is the same along oa_1 and oa_2 and has a value $u = h_w \gamma_w / 2$, with γ_w being the unit weight of water.

  Accordingly, the thrust due to the water pressure along these planes (see figure 6.40) are such that:

$$U_1 = u d_1 = \frac{1}{2} h_w d_1 \gamma_w \tag{6.70}$$

$$U_2 = ud_2 = \frac{1}{2}h_w d_2 \gamma_w \qquad\qquad (6.71)$$

where d_1 and d_2 represent the distances oa_1 and oa_2 respectively.

- The cohesion force per linear metre T_2 is calculated according to equation 6.69, however, when calculating the quantity T_1, equation 6.68 is in all probability no longer realistic because the *lubricating* effect of water would result in a substantial reduction in the value of c_w. Since the estimation of the *actual* value of soil cohesion c' is often fraught with difficulties, it is advisable in this case to discard the thrust T_1.
- The thrust P'_a and the force R'_1 determined from the force polygons are *effective forces per linear metre*.
- The porewater pressures being *identical* along the planes oa_1 and oa_2, the *horizontal components* of the thrusts U_1 and U_2 are equal and opposite.
- The *total active thrust* applied to the wall is the (vectorial) sum of the quantities P'_a and U_1.

Note that all previous remarks and calculations regarding the thrust due to water pressure are no longer applicable under steady state seepage conditions. In such a case, the porewater pressure profile can be evaluated either analytically (using Mandel theory presented in Azizi (2007) for instance) or graphically (from a flownet), then integrated along the slip planes thus leading to the appropriate thrusts. The details of such calculations will be presented in the following chapter 7.

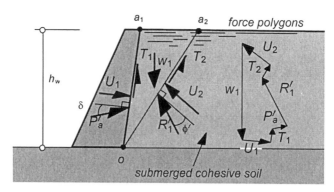

Figure 6.40: Case of a totally submerged cohesive backfill.

Let us now make use of the knowledge accumulated from the previous cases to attempt a graphical solution to the more complex problem of figure 6.34. Since we know how to take into account both cohesion and water pressure (refer to figure 6.40), the graphical solution sought can be made clearer if we assumed that both c_1 and c_2 are zero, and that both soil layers are dry (no water pressure) as illustrated in figure 6.41. The wall is characterised by the friction angles δ_1 across the top layer and δ_2 throughout the bottom layer. For the sake of clarity, the procedure will be introduced in steps as follows.

• *Step 1*

The first step of the graphical method is to consider the top layer *on its own* and find the maximum thrust P_{a1} using precisely the same technique as that developed in conjunction with figure 6.34, bearing in mind that the portion of the external load q applied at the surface of the block (*i.e.* between a_2 and a_3) in figure 6.41 should be added to the weight w_1 as a force per linear metre.

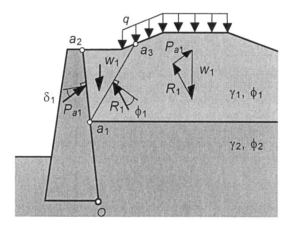

Figure 6.41: Lateral thrust due to the top layer.

• *Step 2*

A failure plane is assumed across the bottom layer, originating at the toe of the wall (point O) as illustrated in figure 6.42. This plane meets the top layer at point a_4 and is then projected vertically, intersecting the surface at point a_5. At this stage, the block $a_4 a_5 a_6$ is considered on its own and the same technique as that used in step 1 is applied to determine the *maximum* thrust F_a that would develop along $a_4 a_5$ if the block were to fail on its own. Once more, remember to include the external load as a force per linear meter when calculating the weight w_2 of the block.

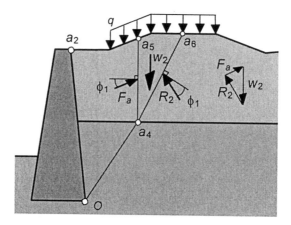

Figure 6.42: Selection of a failure plane across the bottom layer.

• *Step 3*

Now that the magnitude, as well as the direction, of both thrusts P_{a1} and F_a are known, the next phase consists of finding the contribution to the active thrust exerted on the wall by the bottom layer of soil. In this respect, the force polygons depicted in figure 6.43 yield the component P_{a2}. Notice that the *total* weight W used in conjunction with the force polygons corresponds to the weight of the block $oa_2a_5a_4$, augmented by the appropriate external load applied at the surface of the block. Naturally, the different unit weights γ_1 and γ_2 of the two layers must be used accordingly.

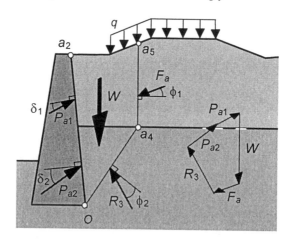

Figure 6.43: Contribution of the bottom layer to the total lateral thrust.

• *Step 4*

The procedure is then repeated from step 2 by assuming different failure planes oa_6, oa_8, oa_{10} across the bottom layer as depicted in figure 6.44, and calculating the magnitude of the respective thrusts P_{a2} as detailed in step 3. These values are thereafter plotted at any convenient scale above the retained soil as illustrated in the figure, and a curve is plotted across the different points leading to the *maximum* value of the thrust $P_{a2\,max}$ as well as to the location of the critical failure plane in the bottom layer. The point of intersection of this failure plane with the top layer is projected vertically and step 2 is thenceforth used to determine the location of the critical failure plane in the top layer. The *total active thrust* P_a exerted on the wall can now be calculated and corresponds to the vectorial sum of P_{a1} and $P_{a2\,max}$, so that the total thrust *normal to the wall* is:

$$P_{an} = P_{a1} \cos \delta_1 + P_{a2\,max} \cos \delta_2 \qquad (6.72)$$

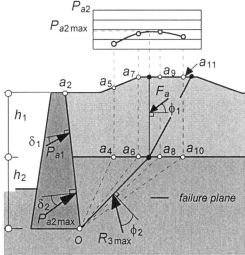

Figure 6.44: Determination of the optimum failure plane across both layers.

The line of action of the total thrust is difficult to determine with certainty. However, its position can be *approximated* by assuming that the thrusts P_{a1} and $P_{a2\,max}$ act at a distance $h_2 + \dfrac{h_1}{3}$ and $\dfrac{h_2}{3}$ respectively from the base of the wall. Whence, the total thrust acts at a distance d from the base of the wall such that:

$$d = \frac{(h_2 + \frac{h_1}{3}) P_{a1} \cos \delta_1 + \frac{h_2}{3} P_{a2\,max}}{P_{an}}$$
(6.73)

Note that, with regard to figure 6.44, the external load q was omitted for sake of clarity. In addition, the thrusts P_{a1} and $P_{a2\,max}$ represent the reaction of the wall and therefore the *actual* thrusts are equal and opposite to P_{a1} and $P_{a2\,max}$ respectively.

The graphical solution in relation to multi-layered soils appears to be arduous and time consuming, especially when cohesion and water pressures are to be included. However the method can be programmed reasonably well.

6.11 Critical appraisal of engineering practice

There seems to be a certain degree of confusion (lack of critical analysis perhaps?) when it comes to choosing the appropriate method of calculation related to lateral pressures. Most of the examples presented so far were tackled with the view to simulating the real problems an engineer would most likely face in practice. Yet, any practising geotechnical engineer will recognise that making a decision with regard to the level of the water table and the nature of flow, for example, is far from being a straightforward matter. Similarly, the nature of the retained soil with respect to isotropy can be difficult to determine with sufficient accuracy.

However, assuming that these points of detail (important though they may be!) are solved, there is a problem specific to soil homogeneity, which appears to be ignored (even trivialised). This problem is depicted in figure 6.45 which shows a wall retaining a partially submerged layer of an otherwise *isotropic homogeneous* soil. The temptation to apply an analysis of the Boussinesq type is somewhat irresistible. However, the error engendered by a mechanical decision in terms of the evaluation of the *actual* lateral thrust can be substantial. The reason for this is that Boussinesq analysis can only be applied in conjunction with *isotropic homogenous* soils, and a partially submerged soil is *no longer homogeneous* since the effective lateral pressures are calculated using a bulk unit weight γ above the water table and an effective unit weight $(\gamma_{sat} - \gamma_w)$ below the water table. This amounts *precisely* to having two different layers of soil, thus making the problem become one of a muti-layer nature that can be solved using, for instance, the graphical technique developed earlier.

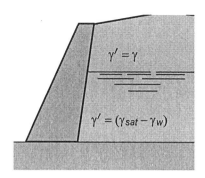

*Figure 6.45: Effect of non-homogeneity
on the method of analysis of lateral thrusts.*

Consider the wall depicted in figure 6.46 with a rough back inclined at an angle λ, retaining an *à priori homogeneous isotropic* granular fill having an angle of shearing resistance ϕ', a bulk unit weight γ (which applies above water level) and a saturated unit weight γ_{sat}. The fill material is sloping at an angle β and the water table (assumed to be static) is situated at a depth z_w from the crest of the wall whose height is H.

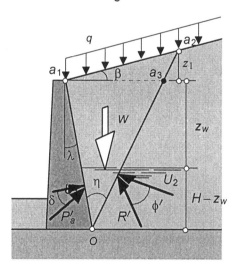

*Figure 6.46: Effect of water pressure on the total
lateral thrust in the case of a rough inclined wall.*

Let us now examine the effects that a *partially submerged* backfill has on the procedure of analysis, starting with a Coulomb type method. Since Coulomb analysis can be applied either analytically or graphically, let us first attempt to establish the analytical solution. The analytical procedure described in section 6.4 yields the *maximum* active lateral effective thrust $P'_{a\,max}$ exerted on the back of the wall (the angle of soil/wall friction being δ).

This is achieved analytically by, first, establishing the expression of the active lateral effective thrust P'_a with respect to the angle η (refer to figure 6.46), then optimising it by writing $\partial P'_a/\partial \eta = 0$. The corresponding polygon of forces, and the angles between the different components are as shown in figure 6.47.

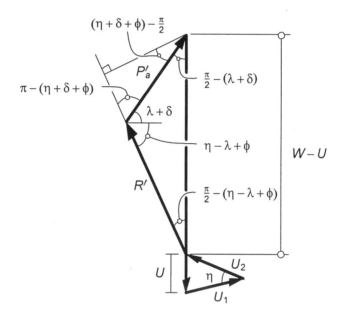

Figure 6.47: Polygon of forces corresponding to figure 6.46.

Thus, solving perpendicular to the soil reaction R', it follows that:

$$P'_a \cos\left((\eta + \phi + \delta) - \frac{\pi}{2}\right) = (W - U)\sin\left[\frac{\pi}{2} - (\eta - \lambda + \phi)\right]$$

or

$$P'_a \sin(\eta + \delta + \phi) = (W - U)\cos(\eta - \lambda + \phi)$$

Whence the effective active thrust:

$$P'_a = (W - U)\frac{\cos(\eta - \lambda + \phi)}{\sin(\eta + \delta + \phi)} \tag{6.74}$$

the quantity W in equation 6.74 corresponds to the *total weight* of the block oa_1a_2 (figure 6.46), and is calculated as follows:

$$W = q\frac{(H+z_1)\tan(\eta-\lambda) + H\tan\lambda}{\cos\beta} \tag{6.75}$$

$$+ \frac{\tan(\eta-\lambda) + \tan\lambda}{2}\left[\gamma\, z_w(2H-z_w) + \gamma H z_1 + \gamma_{sat}(H-z_w)^2\right]$$

As for the quantity U, it represents the vertical component of the resultant of the water thrust as can be seen from figure 6.47, and is calculated from the following expression:

$$U = \left(U_1^2 + U_2^2 - 2U_1U_2\cos\eta\right)^{1/2} \tag{6.76}$$

Once these two quantities are substituted into equation 6.74, the ensuing equation can then be optimised by writing $\partial P_a'/\partial\eta = 0$, from which the value of the angle η corresponding to the *maximum* active lateral effective thrust $P_{a\,max}'$ can be determined. This value is then substituted into equation 6.74, yielding thus the quantity $P_{a\,max}'$. Obviously, establishing the first derivative of equation 6.74 with respect to η by hand, after having substituted for W and U from equations 6.75 and 6.76 is a tedious task in this case. In practice, such derivations can be undertaken numerically. However, if the back of wall were vertical (*i.e.* $\lambda = 0$) as illustrated in figure 6.48, then the problem can readily be handled analytically. The corresponding polygon of forces is, in this case, identical to the one represented in figure 6.47 except for two minor changes: (*a*) the angle λ is now *zero*, and (*b*) the water thrust U_1 becomes *horizontal*. Under these circumstances, equations 6.75 and 6.76 reduce to:

$$W = \tan\eta\left[q\frac{(H+z_1)}{\cos\beta} + \gamma\frac{z_w(2H-z_w) + Hz_1}{2} + \gamma_{sat}\frac{(H-z_w)^2}{2}\right] \tag{6.77}$$

$$U = U_1\tan\eta = \gamma_w\frac{(H-z_w)^2}{2}\tan\eta \tag{6.78}$$

Substituting for these two quantities in equation 6.74, then rearranging, it follows that:

$$P_a' = C.\tan\eta\,\frac{\cos(\eta+\phi)}{\sin(\eta+\phi+\delta)} \tag{6.79}$$

where the quantity C is expressed as follows:

$$C = \frac{q}{\cos \beta}(H + z_1) + \frac{\gamma}{2}[z_1 H + z_w(2H - z_w)]$$

$$+ \frac{1}{2}(\gamma_{sat} - \gamma_w)(H - z_w)^2 \qquad (6.80)$$

At this stage, a straightforward derivation of equation 6.79 yields the condition related to the optimum angle at failure η, and it can readily be shown that:

$$\partial P_a'/\partial \eta = 0 \quad \Rightarrow \quad \tan(\eta + \delta + \phi)\left[\frac{1}{\cos \eta \, \sin \eta} - \tan(\eta + \phi)\right] = 1 \qquad (6.81)$$

Once the angle η is found from equation 6.81, its value is substituted into equation 6.79 which then yields the *maximum* effective lateral thrust exerted on the wall.

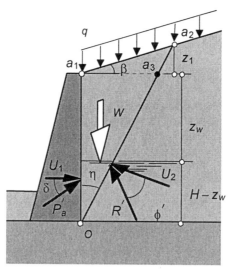

Figure 6.48: Effect of water pressure; case of a vertical wall.

N.B. According to figure 6.48, the quantity z_1 can be expressed as follows:

$$z_1 = H \frac{\tan \beta \, \tan \eta}{(1 - \tan \beta \, \tan \eta)}$$

However, because the effects of any variation of the angle η on z_1 are minimal, and to avoid any unnecessary complication of equation 6.79, z_1 is assumed to be independent of η. Accordingly, equation 6.79 yields an effective active thrust estimated to be less than 2% in excess of the actual thrust (i.e. the error is on the safe side). Therefore, for all practical purposes, the assumption made as regards z_1 does not, in any way, affect the accuracy of the results obtained from equations 6.77 to 6.81.

Example 6.2

Consider the wall depicted in figure 6.49, in conjunction with the following characteristics: a height $H = 6\,m$, a granular backfill sloping at an angle $\beta = 15°$ and having $\phi' = 35°$, $\gamma = 19\,kN/m^3$, $\gamma_{sat} = 21\,kN/m^3$, a uniform pressure $q = 15\,kN/m^2$ applied at the surface, and an angle of wall friction $\delta = 24°$. Assuming that the drainage behind the wall is not functional up to a height of 3 m above the base of the wall (*i.e.* $z_w = 3\,m$), find the potential plane of failure and the corresponding maximum total active thrust applied to the wall.

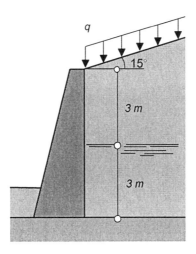

Figure 6.49: Wall dimensions and soil conditions.

First, let us apply the graphical technique to find the maximum effective active thrust as well as the plan of failure (*i.e.* the angle η). The graphical procedure is illustrated in figure 6.50 and is of a straightforward nature. To apply the method, first *choose* different slip planes such as oa_3, oa_4,... , then, starting from the slip plane nearest to the wall (oa_3 in this case), proceed as detailed in section 6.10.

- (a) Calculate the *total weight* w_1 of the wedge oa_1a_3 using equation 6.77.
- (b) Compute the magnitude of the thrust U_1 due to the water pressure from equation 6.70.
- (c) Because the horizontal components of the thrusts U_1 and U_2 are equal and opposite, the magnitude of U_2 can now be determined using the relationship $U_2 = \dfrac{U_1}{\cos \eta}$.

- (d) Use the polygon of forces to determine the magnitude of the soil reaction R' and the lateral effective active thrust P'_a, their direction being as depicted in figure 6.50.
- (e) Select the next slip plane oa_4, then repeat the procedure from step (a).

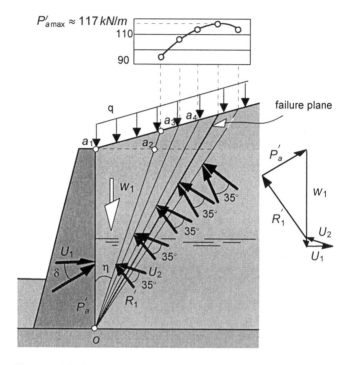

Figure 6.50: Graphical solution to example 6.2.

The computed values of P'_a are then plotted as illustrated in figure 6.50, and a curve is constructed, the peak of which represents the *maximum effective active thrust*, which in this case has a value $P'_{a\,max} \approx 117\,kN/m$. The *maximum total active thrust, normal to the wall* corresponds to the (vectorial) sum of $P'_{a\,max}$ and U_1, whence:

$$P_{a\,max} = U_1 + P'_{a\,max} \cos \delta = 45 + 117 \times \cos 24 = 151.9\,kN/m$$

the corresponding *failure plane* being at angle $\eta \approx 30°$ with respect to the vertical.

If the analytical procedure were applied instead of the graphical method, then the solution will consist of:

- finding the optimum angle of failure η from equation 6.81:

$$\tan(\eta + 24 + 35)\left[\frac{1}{\cos\eta\,\sin\eta} - \tan(\eta + 35)\right] = 1 \quad \Rightarrow \quad \eta \approx 31.147°$$

N.B. The solution to the above equation is very sensitive to small changes in η.

- estimating the height z_1 from the following relationship (refer to figure 6.48):

$$z_1 = H\frac{\tan\beta\,\tan\eta}{1 - \tan\beta\,\tan\eta} = 6 \times \frac{\tan 15\,\tan 31.1}{1 - \tan 15\,\tan 31.1} \approx 1.157\,m$$

- calculating the constant C from equation 6.80:

$$C = \frac{15}{\cos 15}(6 + 1.157) + \frac{19}{2}[1.157 \times 6 + 3(12 - 3)]$$

$$+ \frac{1}{2}(21 - 10)(6 - 3)^2 = 483.1\,kN/m$$

- computing the *maximum effective active thrust* exerted on the wall from equation 6.79:

$$P'_a = 483.1 \times \tan 31.1 \times \frac{\cos(31.1 + 35)}{\sin(31.1 + 35 + 24)} \approx 118\,kN/m$$

- finally, calculating the *total thrust normal to the wall* as follows:

$$P_{an} = U_1 + P'_a \cos\delta = 45 + 118\cos 24 = 152.8\,kN/m$$

Obviously the solutions, in terms of the active thrust P_{an} and the angle of failure η are, for all practical purposes, very similar to the ones determined from the graphical method.

Let us now apply a Boussinesq type analysis to the problem of figure 6.49, and calculate both *effective* and *total thrusts* applied to the wall. Prior to any calculations, the relevant coefficients of active pressure are determined as follows:

- from table 6.1:

$$\lambda = 0,\ \phi = 35°,\ \delta = 24° \approx \frac{2}{3}\phi,\ \beta = 15° \approx 0.43\phi \quad \Rightarrow \quad K_a \approx 0.297$$

- from Kerisel and Absi (1990), page152:

$$\alpha = -15°,\ \phi = 35°,\ \delta = \frac{2}{3}\phi,\ \Omega = 105° \quad \Rightarrow \quad K'_a \approx 0.308$$

The effective active thrust applied to the wall can now be estimated:

$$P'_a = 15 \times 6 \times 0.308 + \frac{1}{2} \times 3 \times 3 \times 19 \times 0.297$$

$$+ \frac{3}{2}(11 \times 3 + 19 \times 6) \times 0.297 = 118.6 \, kN/m$$

so that the *total thrust, normal to the wall* is in this case:

$$P_{an} = U_1 + P'_a \cos \delta$$

$$= 45 + 118.6 \cos 24 = 153.3 \, kN/m$$

Compared with the value of total thrust determined previously using Coulomb's procedure, it is seen that both Boussinesq and Coulomb analyses yield similar results on the active side of the wall.

Now consider the passive case depicted in figure 6.51 where a rough wall, with a back inclined at an angle λ, is retaining a *homogeneous isotropic granular fill* having an angle of shearing resistance ϕ', a bulk unit weight γ (which applies above water level) and a saturated unit weight γ_{sat}. The fill material is horizontal and the water table (*assumed to be static*) is situated at a depth z_w from the crest of the wall whose height is H.

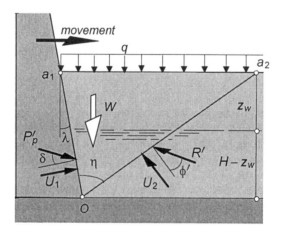

Figure 6.51: Effect of water pressure; passive case.

The corresponding polygon of forces, and the angles between the different components are as shown in figure 6.52. Thus, solving perpendicular to the soil reaction R' then rearranging, it follows that:

$$P'_p \sin(\eta - \delta - \phi') = (W - U)\cos(\eta - \lambda - \phi')$$

Whence the *effective passive thrust*:

$$P'_p = (W - U)\frac{\cos(\eta - \lambda - \phi)}{\sin(\eta - \delta - \phi)} \qquad (6.82)$$

the quantity W in equation 6.82 corresponds to the *total weight* of the block oa_1a_2 (figure 6.51), and is calculated as follows:

$$W = [\tan(\eta - \lambda) + \tan\lambda]\left[qH + \tfrac{\gamma}{2}z_w(2H - z_w) + \tfrac{\gamma_{sat}}{2}(H - z_w)^2\right] \qquad (6.83)$$

As in the previous case, the quantity U represents the vertical component of the resultant of the water thrust, and is calculated from equation 6.76. Once these two quantities are substituted into equation 6.74, the ensuing expression can then be optimised by writing $\partial P'_p / \partial \eta = 0$, from which the value of the angle η corresponding to the *maximum* passive lateral effective thrust $P'_{p\,max}$ can be determined. This value is thereafter substituted into equation 6.74, yielding the quantity $P'_{p\,max}$.

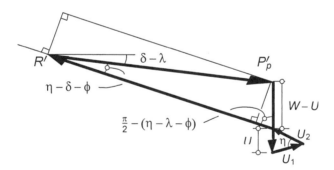

Figure 6.52: Polygon of forces corresponding to figure 6.51.

If the back of wall were vertical (*i.e.* $\lambda = 0$) as illustrated in figure 6.53, then the water thrust U_1 in figure 6.52 becomes *horizontal*. Under these circumstances, both equations 10.83 and 10.76 reduce to:

$$W = \tan\eta\left[qH + \tfrac{\gamma}{2}z_w(2H - z_w) + \tfrac{\gamma_{sat}}{2}(H - z_w)^2\right] \qquad (6.84)$$

$$U = U_1\tan\eta = \tfrac{\gamma_w}{2}(H - z_w)^2\tan\eta \qquad (6.85)$$

Substituting for these two quantities into equation 10.82, then rearranging, it follows that:

$$P'_p = C \tan \eta \, \frac{\cos (\eta - \lambda - \phi)}{\sin (\eta - \delta - \phi)} \tag{6.86}$$

where the *constant C* represents the following quantity:

$$C = qH + \tfrac{\gamma}{2} z_w (2H - z_w) + \tfrac{1}{2}(\gamma_{sat} - \gamma_w)(H - z_w)^2 \tag{6.87}$$

At this stage, a straightforward derivation of equation 6.86 yields the condition related to the optimum angle of failure η, and it can readily be shown that:

$$\partial P'_p / \partial \eta = 0 \quad \Rightarrow \quad \tan (\eta - \delta - \phi) \left[\frac{1}{\cos \eta \, \sin \eta} - \tan (\eta - \phi) \right] = 1 \tag{6.88}$$

Once the angle η is found from equation 6.88, its value is substituted into equation 6.86 which then yields the *maximum effective passive thrust* exerted on the wall.

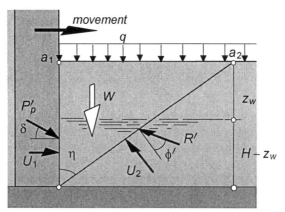

Figure 6.53: Case of a vertical wall.

Example 6.3

Consider the wall depicted in figure 6.54, retaining a partially submerged sand similar to the one used in the previous example 6.2, that is:
$\phi' = 35°$, $\gamma = 19 \, kN/m^3$, $\gamma_{sat} = 21 \, kN/m^3$. The angle of wall friction is $\delta = 24°$, and a uniform pressure $q = 15 \, kN/m^2$ is applied at the ground surface. Let us apply both Coulomb and Boussinesq analyses to estimate the *passive thrust* resisting the wall movement.
First, the analytical solution based on Coulomb theory consists of solving the transcendental equation 10.88 to find the optimum angle η, whence:

$$\tan (\eta - 35 - 24) \left[\frac{1}{\sin \eta \, \cos \eta} - \tan (\eta - 35) \right] = 1 \quad \Rightarrow \quad \eta \approx 76°$$

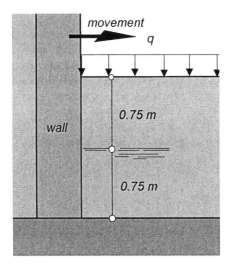

Figure 6.54: Wall dimensions and soil conditions.

Next, the constant C is estimated from equation 6.87:

$$C = 15 \times 1.5 + \frac{19}{2} \times 0.75 \times (3 - 0.75)$$

$$+ \frac{1}{2} \times (21 - 10) \times (1.5 - 0.75)^2 = 41.6 \, kN/m$$

Equation 6.86 can now be used to estimate the *effective passive thrust* developed by the soil:

$$P'_p = 41.6 \times \tan 76 \times \frac{\cos(76 - 35)}{\sin(76 - 35 - 24)} = 431 \, kN/m$$

so that the *total passive thrust normal to the wall* is calculated as follows:

$$P_{pn} = 2.8 + 431 \cos 24 = 396.8 \, kN/m$$

N.B. the porewater pressure thrust is $U = 10 \times 0.75^2/2 = 2.8 \, kN/m$

An alternative solution to the above analytical method consists of applying the graphical technique used in conjunction with the previous active case example depicted in figure 6.50. The outcome in terms of the magnitude of the total passive thrust would be similar.

As regards Boussinesq analysis, the relevant coefficients of passive pressure related to our problem are as follows:

- using table 6.1:

$$\lambda = 0, \ \phi' = 35°, \ \delta = 24° \approx \frac{2}{3}\phi', \ \beta = 0 \quad \Rightarrow \quad K_p = 8$$

- from table 10.2:

  $\alpha = 0$, $\phi' = 35°$, $\delta = \frac{2}{3}\phi'$, $\Omega = 90°$ $\Rightarrow$ $K_p' = 7.09$.

Whence the *effective passive thrust*:

$$P_p' = 15 \times 1.5 \times 7.09 + \frac{1}{2} \times (0.75 \times 0.75 \times 19 \times 8)$$

$$+ \frac{0.75}{2} \times 8 \times (11 \times 0.75 + 11 \times 1.5) = 276.5\, kN/m$$

and the *total passive thrust normal to the wall*:

$$P_{pn} = 2.8 + 276.5 \cos 24 = 255.4\, kN/m$$

A quick comparison of these results reinforces the point made earlier; that is Coulomb analysis yields an unrealistic and *unsafe passive thrust*. It is therefore essential to bear in mind that, while Coulomb analysis is deemed acceptable on the active side, its use in conjunction with passive thrusts can be dangerously optimistic and therefore ineffectual. This is illustrated in figure 6.55 where the coefficient of passive pressure is calculated from both Coulomb and Boussinesq analyses for an angle of wall friction $\delta = 2\phi'/3$.

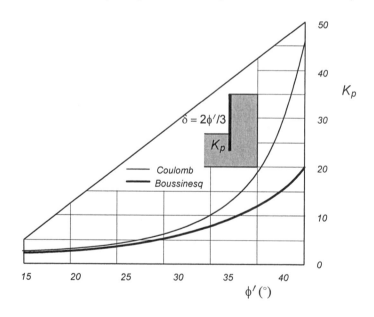

Figure 6.55: Comparison between Coulomb and Boussinesq theories for passive stress conditions.

It is clear that, as the angle ϕ' increases, both analyses yield increasingly different K_p values. Accordingly, it is strongly advisable to use a Boussinesq type analysis on the passive side in conjunction with any type of retaining structures. On the active side, either Boussinesq or Coulomb analyses can be applied. In particular, the Coulomb graphical solution can be very handy in the case of multi-layered soils subjected to complex loading conditions applied on uneven surfaces. As far as Rankine theory is concerned, its use should be restricted to the case of cantilever retaining walls for which the effects of wall friction are very limited.

6.12 Practical aspects of the design of retaining walls

Considering that, in essence, an earth retaining structure is used to provide support for steep, often vertical, cuts in different types of soils, the nature and shape of the structure can vary to suit the site conditions. Figure 6.56 depicts *some* of the wall types used in practice. Their height can vary up to a maximum of about 8 *m*, and they include:

- gravity (or semi-gravity) walls;
- cantilever walls;
- counterfort (or buttress) walls.

Besides the gravitational forces due to its self weight and the weight of soil immediately above its base, a retaining wall is invariably subjected to *lateral thrusts* caused by the already detailed *active and passive pressures*. In practice, the first steps in the design process of a retaining wall consist of choosing some of the dimensions according to the *empirical relationships* shown in figure 6.57.

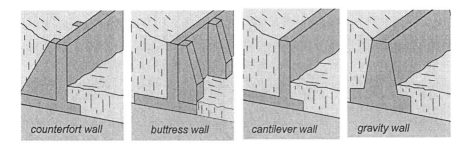

Figure 6.56: Some types of retaining walls.

This procedure, referred to as *proportioning,* allows for an iterative design process to take place whereby the dimensions are adjusted at the end of calculations if need be.

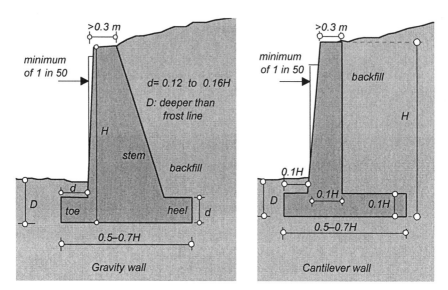

Figure 6.57: Empirical relationships related to the design of walls.

Notice that, in conjunction with figure 6.56, the counterfort or buttress slabs in the case of a cantilever wall are usually placed at a spacing of around 0.5 to 0.7H.

6.13 Stability criteria relating to the design of retaining walls

The designer must ensure that a retaining wall is stable *vis à vis* the following failure criteria.

• (a) Forward sliding

The combination of *horizontal forces* may cause the wall to slide along its base the moment the sum of horizontal *sliding forces* ΣF_s (due entirely to the horizontal component of the active thrust) equals the sum of horizontal *resisting forces* ΣF_r (due to the horizontal shear force developed at the base of the wall). In practice, any component of the resisting force due to the passive thrust is usually discarded when calculating the factor of safety against sliding, the reason being that the full mobilisation of passive thrust requires a large translational movement as can be seen from figure 6.58. Accordingly, the quantity ΣF_r is reduced to the shear force F_b mobilised at the base of the wall, which is the product of the mobilised shear stress, times the area of the base. Thus, when expressed *per unit length*, F_b is written as follows:

$$F_b = B \times 1 \times \tau_{mob} \tag{6.89}$$

where B represents the width of the wall base, and the mobilised shear stress at foundation level is:

$$\tau_{mob} = c'_{mob} + \sigma \tan \phi'_{mob} \tag{6.90}$$

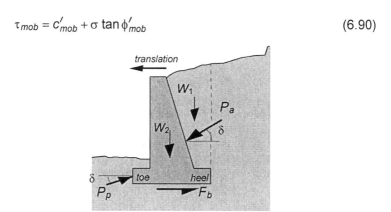

Figure 6.58: Forces resisting wall sliding.

But σ represents the stress, *normal to the base,* generated by the *sum of vertical forces* $\sigma = \Sigma F_v / B$. Moreover, the mobilised angle of shearing resistance can be taken as $\phi'_{mob} \approx 2\phi'/3$; the same applies to cohesion (if any): $c'_{mob} \approx 2c'/3$. Whence the force F_b:

$$F_b = \frac{2}{3}Bc' + \Sigma F_v \tan \frac{2}{3}\phi' \tag{6.91}$$

As seen in figure 6.58:
- the sum of vertical forces: $\Sigma F_v = W_1 + W_2 + P_a \sin \delta$ (6.92)
- the sliding force: $F_s = P_a \cos \delta$ (6.93)

Whence the factor of safety against sliding:

$$F = \frac{F_r}{F_s} = \frac{\frac{2}{3}Bc' + (W_1 + W_2 + P_a \sin \delta) \tan \frac{2}{3}\phi'}{P_a \cos \delta} \tag{6.94}$$

For all practical purposes, a minimum factor of safety of 1.5 is considered to be adequate. However, the designer must always bear in mind that, were a large factor of safety against sliding to be considered, the consequence might be to prevent the wall from moving forward at all, increasing inadvertently perhaps the possibility of generating large pressures behind the wall during compaction of backfill, which can result in structural damage. No wonder that an upper limit to the factor of safety in this case must be imposed, and in this respect, a maximum value of 2.5 is advisable. Thence for sliding:

$$1.5 \le F = \frac{\Sigma F_r}{\Sigma F_s} \le 2.5 \tag{6.95}$$

• (b) Overturning

Another mode of failure consists of the overturning of the wall about its toe (point O in figure 6.59). Failure occurs once the *overturning moment* M_o (entirely due to the active thrust) exceeds the *resisting moments* ΣM_r developed by the self weight of the wall and any soil above its base, as well as the passive thrust. However, this mode of failure is only credible when the wall is founded on a hard clay or on rocks. If this is not the case, then not only is the centre of rotation no longer at point O, but more importantly a bearing capacity failure would in all probability occur before any significant rotation takes place because of the high concentration of stresses around the toe of the wall.

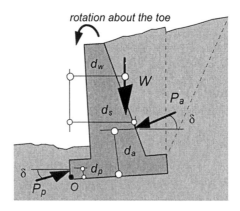

Figure 6.59: Resisting and overturning forces.

When applicable, the resisting moments can be written, according to figure 6.59, as follows:

$$\Sigma M_r = d_w W + d_p P_p \cos \delta + d_s P_a \sin \delta \tag{6.96}$$

and the overturning moment is:

$$M_o = d_a P_a \cos \delta \tag{6.97}$$

A minimum factor of safety of 2 is deemed to be adequate when dealing with this type of failure, hence:

$$F = \frac{\Sigma M_r}{M_o} \ge 2.0 \tag{6.98}$$

• (c) Bearing capacity failure

The third and perhaps most serious mode of failure relates to the bearing capacity of the soil on which the wall is built as sketched in figure 6.60. This type of failure occurs when the *mobilised shear stresses* τ_{mob} due to the vertical components of the active pressure as well as the weight of the wall and any soil above its base exceed the *shear strength* τ_{max} of the soil on which the wall is founded. Consequently, one must ensure that at no time is the bearing capacity of the soil beneath the foundation exceeded. This can be achieved by adopting an adequate factor of safety in the design.

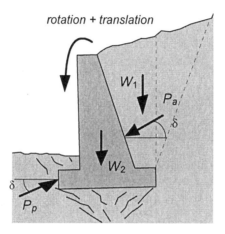

Figure 6.60: Bearing capacity failure.

Consider the retaining wall prior to the occurrence of a bearing capacity failure. The system of forces established earlier are:
 • the sum of *all* vertical forces ΣF_v given by equation (6.92);
 • the horizontal component of the active thrust: $P_a \cos \delta$.

The resultant eccentric force R will be inclined at an angle a with respect to the vertical as shown in figure 6.61. It is straightforward to establish that the *net moment* with respect to the toe of the wall (point O), generated by the resultant force R is:

$$M_{net} = \Sigma M_r - M_o \qquad (6.99)$$

where ΣM_r and M_o are given by equations 6.96 and 6.97 respectively. Using equation 6.99, the eccentricity e can then be derived:

$$e = \frac{B}{2} - \frac{M_{net}}{\Sigma F_v} \qquad (6.100)$$

Now that the eccentricity is known, the pressure distribution at the wall base can be established:

$$q = \frac{\Sigma F_v}{B \times 1} \pm \frac{My}{I} = \frac{\Sigma F_v}{B \times 1} \pm \frac{ye \Sigma F_v}{I} \qquad (6.101)$$

with I being the moment of inertia *per unit length* of the base of the wall:

$$I = \frac{LB^3}{12} = \frac{B^3}{12}$$

Substituting for $y = B/2$ in equation 6.101 and rearranging, the *maximum* (at the toe) and *minimum* (at the heel) *pressures* can be calculated as follows:

$$q_{max} = \frac{\Sigma F_v}{B \times 1}\left(1 + \frac{6e}{B}\right)$$

$$\qquad (6.102)$$

$$q_{min} = \frac{\Sigma F_v}{B \times 1}\left(1 - \frac{6e}{B}\right)$$

Equations 6.102 indicate that the pressure at the heel becomes *negative* as soon as the eccentricity e exceeds the value *B/6*. Therefore, the well-known engineering rule stating that the line of application of the resultant force must be within the middle third of the base of the wall. This criterion can be expressed as:

$$e \leq \frac{B}{6} \qquad (6.103)$$

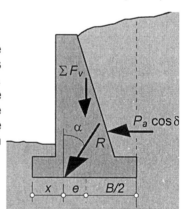

Figure 6.61: Load eccentricity at the base of wall.

At this stage, it is important to remember that the pressure distribution represented by equation 6.101 is only an *approximation* of the *actual* pressure distribution observed in the field. Once the maximum pressure q_{max} is calculated, the ultimate bearing capacity of the soil q_u can be determined by applying the procedure used in conjunction with the design of shallow foundations as per chapter 4. It is a usual practice to consider a minimum factor of safety of 3 against shear failure, and accordingly:

$$F = \frac{q_u}{q_{max}} \geq 3.0 \qquad (6.104)$$

Notice, however, that the bearing capacity criterion is affected by settlement considerations. In fact, a structure such as a retaining wall with a large base is most likely to settle by a large amount before the occurrence of a bearing capacity failure and the settlement needed to herald such a failure will be well in excess of the tolerable limit. Consequently, a much larger factor of safety might be needed to keep the settlement within an acceptable range.

- (*d*) **Deep slip failure**

This type of failure, depicted in figure 6.62, was dealt with in detail in chapter 3.

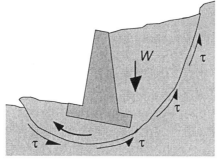

Figure 6.62: Slip failure beneath a wall.

Example 6.4

Consider once more example 6.3 and use the results obtained using the Boussinesq method to check the stability of the wall *vis à vis* sliding, overturning and bearing capacity failures. The 10 *m* long wall is founded on a stiff clay having an effective cohesion $c' = 10\,kN/m^2$, a bulk unit weight $\gamma = 21\,kN/m^3$ and an effective angle of shearing resistance $\phi' = 22°$, the water level being well below the base of wall. Assume the unit weight of concrete is $\gamma_c = 24\,kN/m^3$.

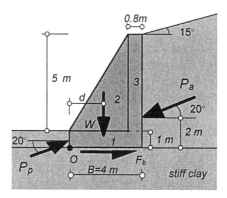

Figure 6.63: Wall dimensions.

Since the magnitude, direction and line of action of both active and passive thrusts have been already established, only the calculation of the weight *per linear metre* as well as the shear force at the base of the wall are required. The total weight W of the wall and its line of action are easily determined using the three elementary areas *1, 2* and *3* in figure 6.63:

- *area 1:* $w_1 = 1 \times 4 \times 24 = 96 \ kN/m$
  moment arm from O: $d_1 = \dfrac{4}{2} = 2 \ m$

- *area 2:* $w_2 = \dfrac{1}{2} \times 5 \times 3.2 \times 24 = 192 \ kN/m$
  moment arm from O: $d_2 = \dfrac{2}{3} \times 3.2 = 2.13 \ m$

- *area 3:* $w_3 = 0.8 \times 5 \times 24 = 96 \ kN/m$
  moment arm from O: $d_3 = 3.2 + 0.4 = 3.6 \ m$

The total weight is therefore:

$$W = w_1 + w_2 + w_3 = 384 \ kN/m$$

and the corresponding moment arm from point O is:

$$d = \frac{96 \times 2 + 192 \times 2.13 + 96 \times 3.6}{384} = 1.824 \ m$$

- **Factor of safety against forward sliding**

The sum of vertical forces is calculated from equation 6.92:

$$\Sigma F_v = W + P_a \sin 20 = 384 + 113.4 \sin 20 = 422.8 \ kN/m$$

Using equation 6.91, it follows that:

$$F_b = \frac{2}{3} \times 30 \times 4 + 422.8 \tan \frac{2 \times 22}{3} = 190.7 \ kN/m$$

Since the passive thrust is ignored in the calculation of the factor of safety against translational movements, the force resisting the sliding is:

$$F_r = F_b = 190.7 \ kN/m$$

The sliding force, on the other hand, is calculated from equation 6.93:

$$F_s = P_a \cos 20 = 113.4 \cos 20 = 106.5 \ kN/m$$

Hence the factor of safety against sliding:

$$F = \frac{F_r}{F_s} = \frac{190.7}{106.5} = 1.79$$

this value being within the limits set by the inequality 6.95.

- **Factor of safety against overturning**

The resisting as well as the overturning moments with respect to O are required to evaluate the factor of safety according to equation 6.98. As can be seen from figure 6.59, the resisting moments are exerted by the weight of the wall, the *vertical* component of the active thrust and the *horizontal* component of the passive thrust (the moment arms being respectively $d = 1.82\,m$ for the weight, $d = 4\,m$ for the vertical active thrust and $d = 0.33\,m$ for the horizontal passive thrust). Hence:

$$\Sigma M_r = 1.82W + 4P_a \sin 20 + 0.33P_p \cos 20$$
$$= 1.82 \times 384 + 4 \times 120.8 \sin 20 + 0.33 \times 47.7 \cos 20$$
$$= 878.9\,kN\,m/m$$

The overturning moment is entirely due to the *horizontal* component of the active thrust whose moment arm is $d = 2\,m$:

$$M_o = 2P_a \cos 20 = 2 \times 120.8 \cos 20 = 227\,kN\,m/m$$

Equation 6.98 then yields a factor of safety against overturning:

$$F = \frac{\Sigma M_r}{M_o} = \frac{878.9}{227} = 3.87$$

this value does not violate the criterion set by equation 6.98.

- **Factor of safety against bearing capacity failure**

In order to calculate a factor of safety, we need to determine the shear stress distribution beneath the base of the wall caused by an inclined, eccentric resultant force. The eccentricity is estimated from equation 6.100:

$$e = \frac{B}{2} - \frac{\Sigma M_r - \Sigma M_o}{\Sigma F_v} = \frac{4}{2} - \frac{878.9 - 227}{422.8} = 0.46\,m$$

the criterion of equation 6.103 is not violated since:

$$e = 0.46\,m < \frac{B}{6} = 0.67\,m$$

The shear stress can now be calculated using equation 6.101:

$$q_{max,min} = \frac{\Sigma F_v}{B}\left(1 \pm \frac{6 \cdot e}{B}\right)$$

hence:

$$q_{max} = \frac{422.8}{4}\left(1 + \frac{6 \times 0.46}{4}\right) = 178.6 \ kN/m^2$$

$$q_{min} = \frac{422.8}{4}\left(1 - \frac{6 \times 0.46}{4}\right) = 32.8 \ kN/m^2$$

The angle of inclination is found from the ratio of horizontal to vertical forces, with the horizontal forces being:

$$\Sigma F_h = (P_a - P_p)\cos 20 = (120.8 - 47.7)\cos 20 = 68.7 \ kN/m$$

therefore:

$$\alpha = \tan^{-1}\left(\frac{\Sigma F_h}{\Sigma F_v}\right) = \tan^{-1}\left(\frac{68.7}{422.8}\right) \approx 9°$$

The ultimate bearing capacity is then calculated from equation 4.57 in which $\sigma'_o = \gamma' D$ (D being the depth of embedment of the wall). Because of the load eccentricity, the foundation width will have to be reduced to:

$$B' = B - 2e = 4 - 2 \times 0.46 = 3.08 \ m$$

Thus:

$$q_u = \left(\gamma' D N_q \, s_q \, d_q \, i_q + c' N_c \, s_c \, d_c \, i_c + \gamma' \frac{B'}{2} N_\gamma \, s_\gamma \, d_\gamma \, i_\gamma\right)$$

The bearing capacity as well as the correction factors that will have to be applied in conjunction with the above equation are as follows.

• The bearing capacity factors are estimated from figure 4.26. Hence for $\phi' = 22°$, it is seen that:

$$N_c = 18.5, \quad N_q = 8, \quad N_\gamma = 6$$

• The shape factors are calculated from equations 4.55a–c using the effective width B' (section 4.8):

$$s_c = 1 + \frac{3.08}{10}\frac{8}{18.5} = 1.13$$

$$s_q = 1 + \frac{3.08}{10}\tan 22 = 1.12$$

$$s_\gamma = 1 - 0.4 \times \frac{3.08}{10} = 0.88$$

- The depth factors are determined using equations 4.55d–f , knowing that $\xi = 1/4 = 0.25$:

$$d_c = 1 + 0.4 \times 0.25 = 1.1, \quad d_q = 1 + 0.25\tan 22\,(1 - \sin 22) = 1.05$$
$$d_\gamma = 1$$

- The inclination factors calculated from equations 4.56 are as follows:

$$I_c = I_q = \left[1 - \frac{9}{90} \right]^2 = 0.81$$

$$I_\gamma = \left[1 - \frac{9}{22} \right]^2 \approx 0.35$$

The ensuing ultimate bearing capacity is thence:

$$q_u = (21 \times 1 \times 8 \times 1.12 \times 1.05 \times 0.81)$$

$$+ (10 \times 18.5 \times 1.13 \times 1.1 \times 0.81)$$

$$+ \left(\frac{21 \times 3.08}{2} \times 6 \times 0.88 \times 1 \times 0.35 \right) = 406 \; kN/m^2$$

The factor of safety against shear failure is the ratio of the ultimate capacity of the clay to the maximum shear stress caused by the loading from the wall. Hence, according to equation 6.104:

$$F = \frac{\tau_{max}}{\tau_{mob}} = \frac{q_u}{q_{max}} = \frac{406}{178.6} = 2.27$$

It is seen that the criterion set in equation 6.104 is not fulfilled, and therefore in order to improve the factor of safety against shear failure, one might either increase the base (*i.e.* the width B) of the wall, or increase its embedment.

Problems

6.1   A 15 *m* long cantilever rough wall, with the dimensions indicated in figure p6.1, is retaining a dense silty sand sloping at an angle $\delta = 16°$. The sand has an effective angle of friction $\phi' = 35°$ and a bulk unit weight $\gamma = 20 \, kN/m^3$.

(*a*) Check that the magnitude of the active lateral thrust P_a' is unaffected by the wall friction, then apply a Rankine type analysis to estimate P_a' and its line of action.

(b) If the wall were founded on a clean dense sand having an angle $\phi' = 38°$, calculate the factors of safety against sliding (F_s) and bearing capacity failure (F_c) discarding the lateral passive thrust.

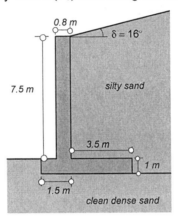

0.8 m

$\delta = 16°$

7.5 m

silty sand

3.5 m

1 m

1.5 m

clean dense sand

Figure p6.1

Ans: (a) $P'_a = 216.8$ *kN/m applied at d = 3.83 m from the base of the wall.*
(b) $F_s = 2$, $F_c \approx 7.6$

6.2   Estimate the active thrust applied to the wall of figure *p6.1* using Coulomb analysis.

Ans: $P'_a \approx 139$ *kN/m*

6.3   Assuming that the rough wall in figure *p6.1* has an angle of friction $\delta = 2\phi'/3$, with $\phi' = 35°$, all other things being equal, use Boussinesq analysis to calculate the ensuing active lateral thrust.

Ans: $P'_a \approx 170$ *kN/m*

6.4   A rough diaphragm wall is retaining a (dry) firm clay with an effective angle of friction $\phi' = 22.5°$ ($c' = 0$) and a unit weight $\gamma = 20\,kN/m^3$. The angle of wall friction is $\delta = 15°$, and on the active side, the sloping ground surface is subjected to a vertical uniform pressure $q_a = 15\,kN/m^2$, the passive side having a surcharge $q_p = 25\,kN/m^2$ (refer to figure *p6.4*).

Use Boussinesq analysis and estimate the components of active and passive lateral thrusts applied *normal* to the wall.

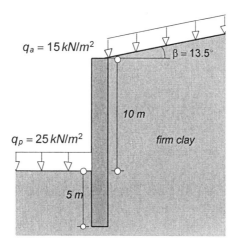

Figure p6.4

Ans: $P_{an} \approx 1182\,kN/m$, $P_{pn} \approx 1151.9\,kN/m$

6.5   A 7 *m* high concrete wall is retaining a cohesive fill material
having an effective friction angle $\phi' = 25°$, an apparent cohesion
$c' = 5\,kN/m^2$, a bulk unit weight $\gamma = 19k\,N/m^3$, and a saturated unit
weight $\gamma_{sat} = 20.5\,kN/m^3$. The wall friction angle is $\delta = 2\phi'/3$ and,
on the active side, the ground surface sloping at an angle $\beta = 13°$ as
depicted in figure *p6.5*, is subjected to a uniform pressure
$q = 40\,kN/m^2$.

(a) The fill behind the wall being fully drained, use Boussinesq
analysis to calculate the *normal* component of the total active
thrust applied to the wall, as well as its line of action.

(b) Assume now, because of faulty drainage, the soil behind the
wall is waterlogged. Estimate the new value of the *normal*
component of the total active thrust, as well as the location of
its point of application.

Ans: (a) $P_a \approx 226.7\,kN/m$ *applied at a distance* $d_1 = 2.48\,m$ *above the
wall base.*

(b) $P_{an} \approx 372.5\,kN/m$ *applied at* $d_2 = 2.42\,m$ *above the wall base.*

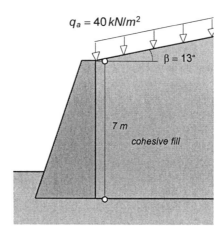

Figure p6.5

6.6   Use the Boussinesq adapted analytical solution to calculate the
normal component of the total active thrust, as well as its point of
application, in conjunction with the wall of figure *p6.6* retaining a
cohesive fill with the following properties:
$\phi' = 21°$, $c' = 5\ kN/m^2$, $\gamma = 20\ kN/m^3$.
Assume the wall friction angle is $\delta = 2\phi'/3$.

Ans: $P_{an} \approx 133.5\ kN/m$ applied at a distance $d = 1.68\ m$ above the
base of the wall.

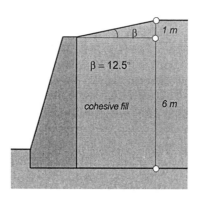

Figure p6.6

6.7   Consider the wall depicted in figure *p6.7*, retaining a normally
consolidated clay having an effective angle of friction $\phi' = 22°$,
a bulk unit weight $\gamma = 19\ kN/m^3$, and a saturated unit weight
$\gamma_{sat} = 20.5\ kN/m^3$. The retained ground, subjected to a uniform

pressure $q = 30\,kN/m^2$, is sloping at an angle $\beta = 14°$.
A faulty drain has caused the clay behind the wall to be partially
submerged. Assuming the wall friction angle is $\delta = 2\phi'/3$, use the
Coulomb analytical method to locate the potential failure surface,
then calculate the maximum total active thrust *normal* to the wall.

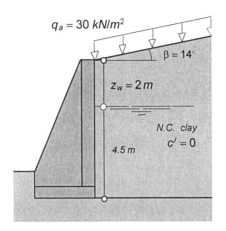

$q_a = 30\ kN/m^2$

$\beta = 14°$

$z_w = 2\,m$

N.C. clay
$c' = 0$

4.5 m

Figure p6.7

Ans: *The failure plane is situated at an angle $\eta = 38.8°$ from the heel of
the wall.*

$P_{an} \approx 363\ kN/m$

References

Brooker, E. and Ireland, H. (1965) *Earth pressure at rest related to stress
history.* Canadian Geotechnical Journal, 2 (1), pp. 1–15.
Caquot, A. and Kerisel, J. (1948) *Tables for the Calculation of Passive Pressure,
Active Pressure and Bearing Capacity of Foundations.* Gauthier-Villars,
Paris.
Caquot, A. and Kerisel, J. (1966) *Traité de Mécanique des Sols,* 4th edn.
Gauthier-Villars, Paris.
Hendren, A. J. (1963) *The behaviour of sand in one-dimensional compression.*
PhD thesis, Department of Civil Engineering, University of Illinois.
Jaky, J. (1944) *The coefficient of earth pressure at rest.* Journal of the Society of
Hungarian Architects and Engineers, 78 (22), pp. 355–358.
Kerisel, J. and Absi, E. (1990) *Active and Passive Earth Pressure Tables,* 3rd
edn. A.A. Balkema, Rotterdam.
Mayne, P. W. and Kulhawy, F. H. (1982) $K_o - OCR$ *relationships in soil.*
ASCE Journal, 108 (GT6), pp. 851–872.

Sherif, M. A., Fang, Y. S. and Sherif, R. I. (1984) K_a and K_o behind rotating and non-yielding walls. Journal of Geotechnical Engineering, ASCM, 110 (GT1), pp. 41–56.

Terzaghi, K. (1936) The shearing resistance of saturated soils. Proceedings of the 1st International Conference on Soil Mechanics, Harvard, pp. 54–56.

Terzaghi, K. (1954) Anchored bulkheads. Trans. ASCE, 119.

CHAPTER 7

Design of sheet-pile and diaphragm walls

7.1 Introduction

The retaining structures dealt with in the previous chapter related to walls of *modest height*, founded at *shallow depths* and retaining a vertical or a sloping backfill. In contrast, the execution of a deep excavation necessitates the use of a different type of retaining structure to provide support for the ensuing *high lateral thrusts* that are dependent on the depth of excavation and the type of soil in which it is executed. *Steel sheet-piles* are widely used in practice as a means of support for the sides of deep excavations. Apart from their flexibility, such structures present the advantage of being widely available in different shapes, easy to drive through a wide range of soils, and simple to weld on site if the need arises for a deeper wall. In practice, a sheet-pile can be *cantilevered*, *encastré*, or *anchored*, depending on the height of the retained soil. *Cantilever sheet-piles* are of modest height and quickly become uneconomical once the height above the dredge level exceeds the nominal value of about 5 *m* (refer to figure 7.1). If the height of the retained soil exceeds 5 *m*, then piles can be anchored in the manner depicted in the figure whereby the use of a single anchor (or a line of anchors) results in a controlled deflection and bending moments, thus allowing for a greater height of soil retention. From a design view point, a combination of the depth of embedment D and anchor size can provide support for heights up to 20 *m* as indicated in figure 7.1.

There are three ways in which sheet pile walls are installed:
- piles are first driven then backfill is placed
- the soil is first dredged then the piles are driven, followed by the placement of backfill
- the soil is excavated after the piles are driven to the required depth of embedment. In all cases, it is *assumed* that active stress conditions are developed behind the wall.

When the use of steel sheet-piles becomes either uneconomical or impractical, an alternative solution consists of using reinforced concrete *diaphragm walls*, as well as *contiguous* or *secant pile* walls. The technical progress achieved in this area is such that reinforced concrete diaphragm walls of depths in excess of 50 *m* can be constructed, though in practice, the depth usually varies up to 30 *m*. Although there are instances in which they can be anchored or propped, most diaphragm walls are designed as cantilevers, and depending on the type of soil through which they are constructed, such walls can support up to 10 m high of retained soil as depicted in figure 7.2.

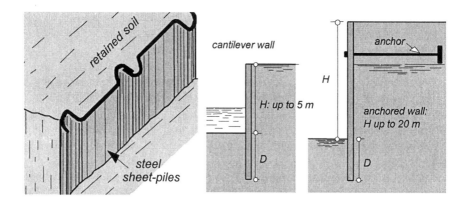

Figure 7.1: Types of sheet-pile walls.

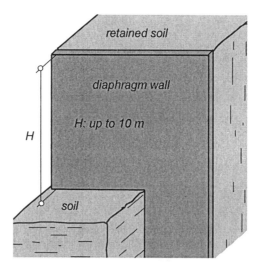

Figure 7.2: Typical diaphragm wall.

Bored pile walls, which can be constructed in any soil conditions, are of two types depending on the nature of the soil to be supported, and also on the need to control water seepage. *Contiguous pile walls* are constructed with a spacing between consecutive piles of 75 mm to 10 mm and are depicted schematically in figure 7.3. This type of wall is ideally suited for clayey soils with little or no water seepage, although, as pointed out by Fleming *et al.* (1992), there are instances in which contiguous piles can be used to support granular materials, so long as soil collapse between consecutive piles is prevented from occurring. If the structure has to be watertight, then *secant pile walls* may be used whereby the interlocking of piles can prevent water from seeping through the wall as indicated in the figure. The height of soil retained depends primarily on the size of the piles and in this regard, a cantilever contiguous pile wall, made of piles of about 500 *mm* diameter, is capable of retaining up to 5 *m* of soil.

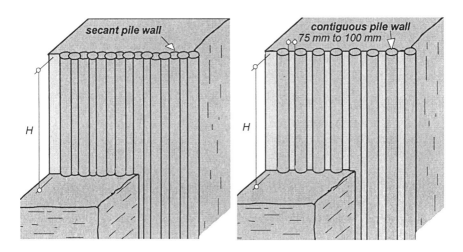

Figure 7.3: Contiguous and secant pile walls.

7.2 Methods of design

Several methods can be used to design *anchored* as well as *cantilever sheet piles*, each necessitating a specific input, yielding thus a wide range of results, some of which can be most conservative. These methods can be numerical (*i.e.* mainly based on finite element modelling), semi-empirical (such as the one based on subgrade reaction modulii), or analytical. The first two categories are outside the scope of this text and, consequently, only the two analytical methods of design, namely *the modified free earth support* and *the fixed earth support* will be presented in details in what follows. Both methods assume that active stress conditions are fully developed behind the wall, so that the actual active stress distribution at the back of the wall can be calculated fairly accurately using Coulomb or Boussinesq theories. For this to happen, the wall is supposed to have yielded sufficiently, thus leading to the active stress distribution depicted diagrammatically in figure 7.4 (Terzaghi, 1954). Only under these circumstances can a Coulomb or a Boussinesq type analysis be applied.

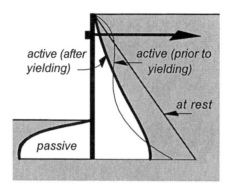

Figure 7.4: Active and passive stress profiles.

7.3 Design of anchored sheet-piles using the modified free earth support method

Anchored sheet piles are usually used when the height of the retained soil is in excess of 5 *m*. With increasing height, a series of anchors, as opposed to a single anchor, might be necessary, so as to limit the deflection and control the bending moments as depicted diagrammatically in figure 7.5.

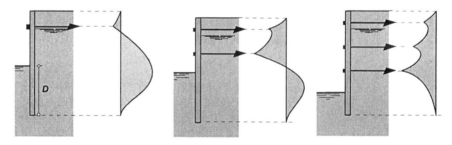

Figure 7.5: Bending moment diagrams related to different anchorage systems.

Notwithstanding (and perhaps because of) its somewhat conservative nature, the classical *free earth support method* of design is still widely used in practice. The method assumes (rather arguably) that the shear strength of the soil is mobilised throughout the depth of embedment *D* (refer to figure 7.5). In other words, the entire volume of soil below dredge level is presumed to be in limit equilibrium. Moreover, the *net lateral pressure* (that is the difference between active and passive *total* pressures) is *assumed* to cause the *rigid anchored pile* to rotate about the anchorage point *O*, yielding a distribution of displacements, shear forces, and bending moments, similar to those depicted in figure 7.6.

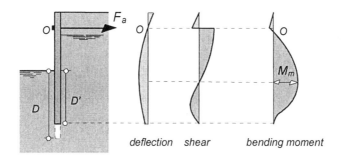

Figure 7.6: Deflection, shear force and bending moment diagrams corresponding to the free earth support method.

The *net pressure diagram* is therefore a prerequisite for the establishment of the equilibrium equations. In this respect, *either* of the two following procedures may be applied to produce the pressure diagram which is then used to determine the depth of embedment D, the anchorage force F_a, and the maximum bending moment M_m in the pile (remember that the active pressure is *assumed* to be fully mobilised at the back of the wall).

●(1)   The distribution of the effective active and passive thrusts along both sides of the pile is calculated using a factor of safety on the coefficient of passive earth pressure. It is a usual practice to reduce the actual coefficient of passive pressure K_p by a factor of safety $F = 2$. The net pressure diagram is thereafter determined by adding the total active and passive thrusts (*i.e.* the effective active and passive thrusts augmented by the net thrust due to water when applicable) on both sides of the pile. At that stage, the moment equilibrium equation can then be established with respect to the anchorage point O; the depth of embedment D being the only unknown contained in the equation. The anchor force F_a is then found from the equilibrium equation of horizontal forces, and the diagram of shear forces along the pile is determined. This diagram is then used to locate the depth corresponding to zero shear force, at which the maximum bending moment M_m is calculated. Apart from the case of stiff structures such as thick diaphragm walls, this procedure usually overestimates both the maximum bending moment and the anchorage force.

●(2)   The distribution of the effective active and passive thrusts along both sides of the pile is calculated using the limiting conditions (*i.e.* a factor of safety $F = 1$ on the coefficient of passive earth pressure). The net pressure diagram is then determined, taking care to add any net thrust due to water when applicable, and the depth of embedment D' (refer to figure 7.6) as well as the anchorage force F_a are calculated from the moment equilibrium equation and the equilibrium equation of horizontal forces respectively. The actual depth of embedment D is then obtained by multiplying the calculated depth D' by a factor of between $\sqrt{2}$ and $\sqrt{3}$ depending on the soil type [Tschebotarioff (1973) reported that a depth $D = \sqrt{2} \, D'$ is equivalent to using a factor of safety $F \approx 1.7$ on the coefficient of passive pressure in conjunction with procedure (1) above]. The diagram of shear forces can now be found, from which the maximum bending moment M_m (occurring at the depth of zero shear force) can then be calculated.

Experimental evidence tends to confirm the *conservative* nature of the design of anchored sheet piles using the *free earth support method*, and this may result, in some instances, in overdesigned uneconomical structures. These experimental findings seem to suggest that a *pressure redistribution* takes place around the pile once yielding has occurred. In 1952, Peter Rowe embarked on a series of experimental and theoretical analyses and his findings (see also Rowe (1955, 1957)), related to model laboratory tests, led to the publication of his *moment reduction factors* in relation to sheet piles stiffness, the details of which will be explained shortly.

However, there seems to be a degree of confusion surrounding the use of the otherwise excellent analysis of Rowe, since its application is sometimes advocated in a somewhat perfunctory way in conjunction with the free earth support method . What is clear though, is that the graphs in figure 7.7 were generated from *model laboratory tests*, and that a redistribution of lateral earth pressure around a yielding wall under these circumstances cannot be extrapolated mechanically to *field conditions* if only because of the *scale effects*. Accordingly, because the reduction in the maximum bending moment of a sheet pile, due to its flexibility under field conditions, may not be as high as the one implied by Rowe's method (see for example Terzaghi (1954)), the graphs in figure 7.7 (in the case of sands) should be used with great caution. In this respect, it is *advisable* to disregard any reduction in bending moments if the sheet pile is embedded in clays as suggested by Skempton (1951).

If, on the other hand, the pile is embedded in a sand or a silty sand, then the graphs in figure 7.7 are *only useful in the case of flexible piles (such as steel sheet piles) for which the net pressure diagram is calculated according to procedure* (1) (*i.e.* using a factor of safety $F = 2$ in conjunction with the coefficient of passive pressure). In which case, only a fraction of the soil passive resistance is mobilised and, for that to happen, some displacement of the toe of the pile, relative to the anchorage point, has to occur as depicted in figure 7.6, leading forcibly to a stress redistribution behind the wall. This movement at the toe is bound to cause a reduction in the value of the maximum bending moment M_{max}, which should be, therefore, corrected to allow for a *degree* of pile flexibility. Nevertheless, it is important to bear in mind that the justification of a reduction in the value of M_{max} is entirely based on the movement at the toe of the sheet pile *after* it has been driven to the required depth. However, most of the severe stress conditions are applied during driving, and therefore the question that arises is, when applicable, of by how much M_{max} should be reduced. Too large a reduction could result in a sheet pile with a steel section that is too thin for it to be driven to the required depth.   For these reasons, it is advisable to be cautious and to limit any reduction to the following.

- *For sheet piles embedded in clean sands*:

$$M_c = M_m - \frac{1}{2}(M_m - M_r) \qquad\qquad (7.1)$$

- *For sheet piles embedded in dense or medium silty sands*:

$$M_c = M_m - \frac{1}{4}(M_m - M_r) \qquad\qquad (7.2)$$

with
M_m :   maximum bending moment determined from the
           net pressure diagram
M_r :   reduced bending moment obtained from Rowe's method
M_c :   corrected bending moment used to select an appropriate
           sheet pile section.

The reduced bending moment M_r is obtained using the value M_m and the graphs in figure 7.7 according to the following *modus operandi*.
- (1) Calculate the ratio α (refer to figure 7.7) from the pile geometry, then select the appropriate curve in the figure.
- (2) Use the selected curve to read the values of $\rho = H^4/EI$ corresponding to different ratios M/M_{max}.
- (3) Multiply the different ratios M/M_{max} by the maximum bending moment M_m, then plot the curve $(M, \log\rho)$.
- (4) Use tables to select different sheet pile sections and calculate their stiffness and maximum bending moments:

$$\rho_t = \frac{H^4}{EI} \quad \text{and} \quad M_t = \sigma_a \frac{I}{y}$$

σ_a being the working (*i.e.* allowable) stress for steel (for permanent work, $\sigma_a = 180\,N/mm^2$ for mild steel (S270GP, British Steel), and $\sigma_a = 230\,N/mm^2$ for high yield steel (S355GP). For temporary work, $\sigma_a = 200\,N/mm^2$ for mild steel and $\sigma_a = 260\,N/mm^2$ for high yield steel). The steel modulus of elasticity can be taken as $E = 2.1 \times 10^5\,N/mm^2$, and y represents the distance from the neutral axis to the edge of section. In Steel sheet piling manuals, the section modulii I/y are usually provided.

- •(5) Plot the corresponding points (M_t, $\log\rho_t$) on the same curve produced in step (3) and select the sheet pile section nearest to the curve from above. Sections relating to all points situated below the curve are inadequate (*i.e.* unsafe).

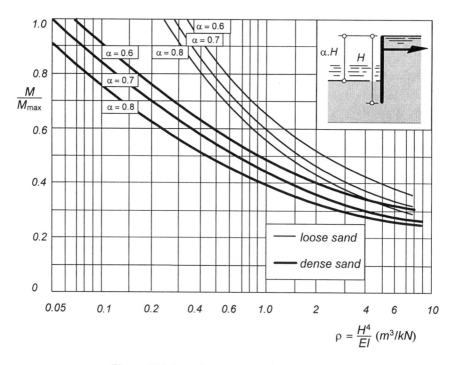

$$\rho = \frac{H^4}{EI}\ (m^3/kN)$$

Figure 7.7: Rowe's moment reduction graphs.
(Reproduced by permission of the Institution of Civil Engineers, London.)

Example 7.1

Use the *free earth support method* to check the adequacy of the depth of embedment of the anchored sheet pile cut-off wall driven in the soil conditions depicted in figure 7.8, then determine the appropriate steel section of the pile. The isotropic and homogeneous dense sand through which the pile is driven has a bulk unit weight $\gamma = 19\,kN/m^3$, a saturated unit weight $\gamma_{sat} = 21\,kN/m^3$, and an angle of shearing resistance $\phi' = 38°$; the angle of wall friction on either side of the pile being $\delta = 2\phi'/3$. The pile is assumed to have yielded sufficiently for the active stresses to be fully mobilised behind the wall.   First, the *net pressure diagram* needs to be established. The steady state seepage conditions around the pile will cause the effective stresses to increase on the active side and to decrease on the passive side. Hence, it is imperative to calculate the precise nature of water pressure distribution as well as the variation of the hydraulic gradient on each side of the pile. These calculations can easily be made using the Mandel method presented in detail in Azizi (2007).

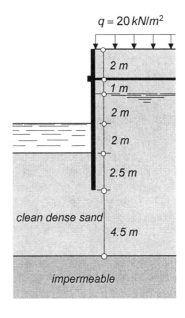

Figure 7.8: Pile dimensions and soil conditions.

Referring to figure 7.9, it can be seen that:

$$h_u = 0, \quad h_d = 2\,m, \quad H = 2\,m, \quad L = 4.5\,m, \quad T = 11\,m, \quad D = 7\,m$$

Whence the quantity ξ (equation 4.92, section 4.5.3, Azizi 2007):

$$\xi = \frac{H}{\ln\left(\frac{T}{L} + \sqrt{\frac{T^2}{L^2} - 1}\right) + \ln\left(\frac{D}{L} + \sqrt{\frac{D^2}{L^2} - 1}\right)}$$

$$= \frac{2}{\ln\left[\frac{11}{4.5} + \sqrt{\left(\frac{11}{4.5}\right)^2 - 1}\right] + \ln\left[\frac{7}{4.5} + \sqrt{\left(\frac{7}{4.5}\right)^2 - 1}\right]} = 0.783\,m$$

and the respective velocity potentials at points A, F and B (equations 4.91, Azizi 2007):

$$\Phi_A = \xi \ln\left(\frac{T}{L} + \sqrt{\left(\frac{T}{L}\right)^2 - 1}\right)$$

$$= 0.783 \ln\left[\frac{11}{4.5} + \sqrt{\left(\frac{11}{4.5}\right)^2 - 1}\right] = 1.207\,m$$

$$\Phi_F = 0$$

$$\Phi_B = -\xi \ln\left|\frac{D}{L} + \sqrt{\left(\frac{D}{L}\right)^2 - 1}\right|$$

$$= -0.783 \ln\left[\frac{7}{4.5} + \sqrt{\left(\frac{7}{4.5}\right)^2 - 1}\right] = -0.791\,m$$

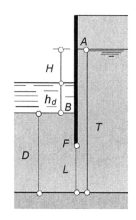

Once these three key velocity potentials are known, the variation along the pile of both the hydraulic gradient and porewater pressure can easily be calculated in the following way (refer to section 3.5.3).

Figure 7.9: Key dimensions.

• On the *active side* (behind the wall), the velocity potential at any elevation y measured from the top of the impermeable layer, and the corresponding total head are respectively:

$$\Phi_y = \xi \ln\left|\frac{y}{L} + \sqrt{\left(\frac{y}{L}\right)^2 - 1}\right| \quad \text{and} \quad h = \Phi_y - \Phi_A + h_u + T$$

The hydraulic gradient, the porewater pressure, as well as the effective unit weight of sand at any elevation y are thence calculated as follows:

$$i_y = \frac{\Phi_A - \Phi_y}{T - y}, \quad u = \gamma_w(h - y) \quad \text{and} \quad \gamma'_y = \gamma_{sat} - \gamma_w(1 - i_y)$$

The ensuing results on the active side (*i.e.* from point A for which $y = 11\,m$ to point F where $y = 4.5\,m$) are presented in the following table.

$y(m)$	$u(kN/m^2)$	i_y	$\gamma'(kN/m^3)$
11	0	0	11.0
9	18.2	0.09	11.9
7	35.8	0.10	12.0
6	44.1	0.12	12.2
5	51.6	0.14	12.4
4.5	52.9	0.19	12.9

• On the *passive side* (*i.e.* in front of the wall), the velocity potential and the total head are determined using the following (see section 4.5.3, Azizi 2007):

$$\Phi_y = -\xi \ln\left[\frac{y}{L} + \sqrt{\left(\frac{y}{L}\right)^2 - 1}\right] \quad \text{and} \quad h_y = \Phi_y - \Phi_B + h_d + D$$

and the corresponding hydraulic gradient, porewater pressure and effective unit weight of sand along the pile are then calculated as follows:

$$i_y = \frac{\Phi_y - \Phi_B}{D - y}, \qquad u = \gamma_w(h - y), \qquad \gamma_y' = \gamma_{sat} - \gamma_w(1 + i_y)$$

Once applied, these relationships yield the results in the table below on the passive side (*i.e.* between points B where $y = 7\,m$ and F corresponding to $4.5\,m$).

$y(m)$	$u\,(kN/m^2)$	i_y	$\gamma'\,(kN/m^3)$
7	20	0	11.0
6	31.7	0.17	9.3
5	44.3	0.21	8.9
4.5	52.9	0.32	7.8

Now that the variations of the porewater pressure as well as the effective unit weight of sand are known on both sides of the pile, the distribution of both *effective active* and *passive pressures* can be calculated using the appropriate *coefficients of earth pressure*. In this respect, a Boussinesq type analysis will be applied through Kerisel and Absi's tables. Accordingly, the coefficients are determined from table 6.1 (chapter 6), so that for $\beta = 0$, $\phi' = 38°$, a linear interpolation between the values corresponding to $\phi' = 35°$ and those of $\phi' = 40°$ yields:

$$K_a = 0.247 - \frac{3}{5}(0.247 - 0.202) = 0.22$$

$$K_p = 8 + \frac{3}{5} \times (12 - 8) = 10.4$$

Also, the coefficient of active pressure, applicable to the uniform load q, is found from Kerisel and Absi's tables corresponding to a weightless soil. Thus, it can be seen on page 130 of Kerisel and Absi's book that:

$$\phi' = 35°, \ \Omega = 90°, \ \alpha = 0, \ \delta = 2\phi'/3 \approx 25° \Rightarrow K_{a1}' = 0.250$$

similarly on page 173 (Kerisel and Absi, 1990):

$$\phi' = 40°, \ \Omega = 90°, \ \alpha = 0, \ \delta = 25° \Rightarrow K_{a2}' = 0.203$$

Whence the value corresponding to $\phi' = 38°$:

$$K_a' = 0.25 - \frac{3}{5} \times (0.25 - 0.203) = 0.222$$

Obviously, in this case there is little difference between the values of K_a and K'_a and, accordingly, it is reasonable to assume that, on the active side, the same coefficient $K_a = 0.22$ applies to both the self weight of soil and the uniform load q.

Both procedures (1) and (2) will be used in the following.

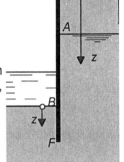

- (1) *A factor of safety F = 1 is applied to K_p*

The stress values are listed in the following tables in which z refers to the depth, on each side of the pile, from the ground surface as depicted in figure 7.10.

Figure 7.10: Reference system.

The active and passive pressures are calculated in the following way:

- *active effective normal pressure*: $\sigma'_a = K_a(\sigma'_v + q)\cos\delta$

$z(m)$	$\gamma'(kN/m^3)$	$u(kN/m^2)$	$\sigma'_v(kN/m^2)$	$\sigma'_a(kN/m^3)$
0	19	0	0	4
3	19	0	57	15.3
5	11.9	18.2	80.8	20
7	12	35.8	104.9	24.8
8	12.2	44.1	117.1	27.2
9	12.4	51.6	129.5	29.7
9.5	12.9	52.9	136	31

- *passive effective normal pressure*: $\sigma'_p = K_p \sigma'_v \cos\delta$

$z(m)$	$\gamma'(kN/m^3)$	$u(kN/m^2)$	$\sigma'_v(kN/m^2)$	$\sigma'_p(kN/m^3)$
0	11	20	0	0
1	9.32	31.7	9.3	87.6
2	8.88	44.3	18.2	171.1
2.5	7.84	52.9	22.1	207.9

The *total pressure* as well as the *net total pressure diagrams* can now be drawn as shown in figures 7.11(*a*) and (*b*).

The factor of safety on the passive side, corresponding to the ratio of available passive resistance of the sand to the mobilised one, can easily be calculated by writing that the moments about the anchorage point (point O in figure 7.11*b*) must balance:

$$\Sigma M_{(O)} = 0$$

The detailed calculations are presented in the following table, and reference should be made to the *net pressure diagram* of figure 7.11(*b*).

area (kN/m)		lever arm (m)	moment (kN m/m)
4×2	$= 8$	1	-8
$0.5 \times (11.5 - 4) \times 2$	$= 7.5$	2/3	-5
11.5×1	$= 11.5$	0.5	5.8
$(15.3 - 11.5) \times 1 \times 0.5$	$= 1.9$	2/3	1.3
15.3×2	$= 30.6$	2	61.2
$(38.2 - 15.3) \times 2 \times 0.5$	$= 22.9$	$1 + (4/3)$	53.4
38.2×2	$= 76.4$	4	305.6
$(40.6 - 38.2) \times 2 \times 0.5$	$= 2.4$	$3 + (4/3)$	10.4
$40.6 \times 0.467 \times 0.5$	$= 9.5$	$5 + (0.467/3)$	48.9
$(46.4 \times 0.533 \times 0.5)/F$	$= 12.4/F$	$5.467 + (2 \times 0.533/3)$	$-72/F$
$(46.4 \times 1.5)/F$	$= 69.6/F$	6.75	$-469.8/F$
$[0.5 \times (133.4 - 46.4) \times 1]/F$	$= 43.5/F$	$6 + (1 \times 2/3)$	$-290/F$
$[(133.4 - 46.4) \times 0.5]/F$	$= 43.5/F$	$7 + 0.25$	$-315.4/F$
$[0.5 \times (176.9 - 133.4) \times 0.5]/F$	$= 10.9/F$	$7 + (0.5 \times 2/3)$	$-79.7/F$

Whence

$$\Sigma M_{(O)} = 0 \quad \Rightarrow \quad 473.6 - \frac{1226.9}{F} = 0$$

This yields a factor of safety $F = 2.59$.

The *anchorage force* can now be found from the equilibrium equation of horizontal forces. Referring to figure 7.11(*b*), it is seen that the sum of the horizontal forces corresponds to the *area* of the net pressure diagram, *augmented* by the anchorage force F_a. Whence the following equilibrium equation:

$$-(4+11.5) \times \tfrac{2}{2} + F_a - (11.5+15.3) \times \tfrac{1}{2}$$

$$-(15.3+38.2) \times \tfrac{2}{2} - (38.2+40.6) \times \tfrac{2}{2} - 40.6 \times \tfrac{0.467}{2}$$

$$+\tfrac{1}{2.59}\left[176.9 \times \tfrac{2.03}{2} \right] = 0$$

leading to an anchorage force $F_a = 101.4 \, kN/m$.

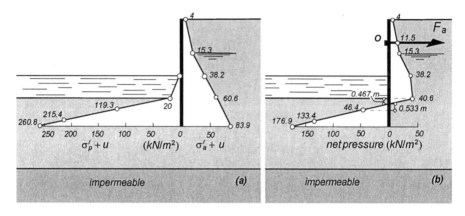

Figure 7.11: (a) Total and (b) net pressure diagrams
along both sides of the sheet-pile.

The precise distribution of shear forces along the pile length is thereafter determined in a straightforward way. The detailed calculations are presented in the following table (in which the depth z is with respect to the ground surface on the active side), and the corresponding shear force diagram is depicted in figure 7.12.

$z\,(m)$	shear force (kN/m)	
0	0	
2^-	$-(4+11.5) \times 2/2$	$= -15.5$
2^+	$-15.5 + 101.4$	$= 85.9$
3	$85.9 - (11.5 + 15.3) \times 0.5$	$= 72.5$
5	$72.5 - (15.3 + 38.2) \times 2/2$	$= 19$
7	$19 - (38.2 + 40.6) \times 2/2$	$= -59.8$
7.467	$-59.8 - (40.6 \times 0.467)/2$	$= -69.3$
8	$-69.3 + (46.4 \times 0.533)/2$	$= -56.9$
9	$-56.9 + (46.4 + 133.4) \times 0.5$	$= 33$
9.5	$33 + (133.4 + 176.9) \times 0.5/2$	$= 110.6$

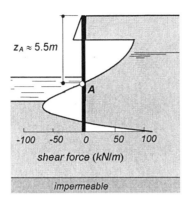

Figure 7.12: Shear force diagram.

The maximum bending moment M_m corresponds to zero shear force, the location of which can easily be obtained from the diagram of figure 7.12 (point A). With reference to figure 7.11(*b*), it is seen that the *net lateral pressure* at a depth $z_A = 5.5\,m$ is determined using a straightforward linear interpolation and corresponds to a value of $38.5\,kN/m^2$. Evaluating M_m^A at point A, it follows that:

$$M_m^A = -4 \times 2 \times (5.5 - 1) - (11.5 - 4) \times \tfrac{2}{2} \times \left(3.5 + \tfrac{2}{3}\right)$$
$$+101.2 \times 3.5 - 11.5 \times 1 \times 3 - (15.3 - 11.5) \times \tfrac{1}{2} \times \left(2.5 + \tfrac{1}{3}\right)$$
$$-15.3 \times 2 \times 1.5 - (38.2 - 15.3) \times \tfrac{2}{2} \times \left(0.5 + \tfrac{2}{3}\right)$$
$$-38.2 \times 0.5 \times 0.25 - (38.5 - 38.2) \times \tfrac{0.5}{2} \times \tfrac{0.5}{3}$$
$$= 169.7\,kN\,m/m$$

The selection of the appropriate steel section can thence be made according to the following: $M_m^A = \sigma_a\,I/y$. Hence, for $\sigma_a = 180\,N/mm^2$ (mild steel), the section modulus required is:

$$\frac{I}{y} = \frac{M_m^A}{\sigma_a} = \frac{169.7}{180} \times 10^3 = 943\,cm^3/m$$

The nearest pile section satisfying this requirement is a *Larssen LX12* with a section modulus $I/y = 1208\,cm^3/m$. Notice that, in practice, the anchorage force $F_a = 101.4\,kN/m$ calculated previously is increased by about 15% to allow for the possibility of any *horizontal arching effect* or any *stress redistribution* behind the wall. Consequently, the anchor section must be designed to support a horizontal force $F_a^* \approx 116.6\,kN/m$.

- (2) *A factor of safety F = 2 is used in conjunction with K_p*

In this case, the *active pressures* calculated previously using a factor of safety $F = 1$ on K_p still apply. However, the *passive pressures* are recalculated using the new reduced value of the coefficient of passive pressure $K_p^* = 10.4/2 = 5.2$. The *effective normal passive stresses* are then calculated using the same effective vertical stresses determined previously on the passive side:

$$\sigma_p' = \sigma_v' K_p^* \cos \delta$$

Whence the values listed in the following table:

$z(m)$	$\gamma'(kN/m^3)$	$u(kN/m^2)$	$\sigma_v'(kN/m^2)$	$\sigma_p'(kN/m^2)$
0	11	20	0	0
1	9.32	31.7	9.3	43.8
2	8.88	44.3	18.2	85.6
2.5	7.84	52.9	22.1	103.9

The corresponding net total pressure diagram is shown in figure 7.13, and the moment equilibrium equation with respect to the anchorage point can now be established. For the sake of clarity, the detailed calculations are once more tabulated as follows.

area (kN/m)		*lever arm (m)*	*moment (kN m/m)*
4×2	$= 8$	1	-8
$(11.5 - 4) \times 0.5 \times 2$	$= 7.5$	$2/3$	-5
11.5×1	$= 11.5$	0.5	5.8
$(15.3 - 11.5) \times 1 \times 0.5$	$= 1.9$	$2/3$	1.3
15.3×2	$= 30.6$	2	61.2
$(38.2 - 15.3) \times 0.5 \times 2$	$= 22.9$	$1 + 4/3$	53.4
38.2×2	$= 76.4$	4	305.6
$(40.6 - 38.2) \times 2 \times 0.5$	$= 2.4$	$3 + 4/3$	10.4
$40.6 \times 0.91 \times 0.5$	$= 18.5$	$5 + 0.91/3$	98
$(4.2 \times 0.09 \times 0.5) \times 2/F$	$= 0.38/F$	$5.91 + 0.09 \times 2/3$	$-2.27/F$
$(4.2 \times 1.5) \times 2/F$	$= 12.6/F$	$6 + 1.5/2$	$-85/F$
$(48.6 - 4.2) \times 0.5 \times 2/F$	$= 44.4/F$	$6 + 2/3$	$-296/F$
$(48.6 - 4.2) \times 0.5 \times 2/F$	$= 44.4/F$	$7 + 0.5/2$	$-321.9/F$
$(71.6 - 48.6) \times 0.25 \times 2/F = 11.5/F$		$7 + 0.5 \times 2/3$	$-84.3/F$

Accordingly: $\Sigma M_{(O)} = 0 \implies 522.7 - \dfrac{789.5}{F} = 0$

leading to a factor of safety: $F = 1.51$.

This factor of safety represents the ratio of the available passive resistance of the soil *(calculated using a factor of safety of 2 on K_p)* to the mobilised one.

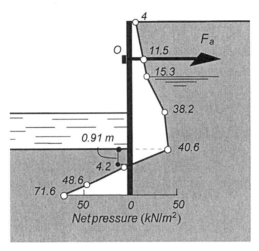

Figure 7.13: Net pressure diagram.

The *anchorage force* is calculated from the equilibrium equation of horizontal forces established with reference to figure 7.13:

$$F_a = (4 + 11.5) \times \frac{2}{2} + (11.5 + 15.3) \times \frac{1}{2}$$

$$+ (15.3 + 38.2) \times \frac{2}{2} + (38.2 + 40.6) \times \frac{2}{2} + 40.6 \times \frac{0.91}{2}$$

$$- \frac{2}{1.5} \times \left[4.2 \times \frac{0.09}{2} + (4.2 + 48.6) \times \frac{1}{2} + (48.6 + 71.6) \times \frac{0.5}{2} \right]$$

leading to a force $F_a = 104.2 \, kN/m$.

The shear force diagram, depicted in figure 7.14, is obtained in precisely the same way, used in conjunction with figure 7.12. Of particular interest, the maximum bending moment M_m^B (corresponding to zero shear force) occurs at a depth $z_B \approx 5.6 \, m$. Accordingly:

$$M_m^B = -4 \times 2 \times (1 + 3.6) - (11.5 - 4) \times \left(\frac{2}{3} + 3.6\right) + 104.2 \times 3.6$$
$$-11.5 \times (0.5 + 3.1) - (15.3 - 11.5) \times \frac{1}{2} \times \left(\frac{1}{3} + 2.6\right)$$
$$-15.3 \times 2 \times 1.6 - (38.2 - 15.3) \times \left(\frac{2}{3} + 0.6\right)$$
$$-38.2 \times \frac{0.6^2}{2} - (38.9 - 38.2) \times \frac{0.6^2}{6} = 180.2 \, kN \, m/m$$

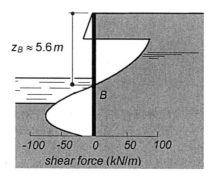

Figure 7.14: Shear force diagram.

Since the pile is embedded in a clean dense sand, the maximum bending moment must be somewhat *reduced* to allow for a degree of flexibility in accordance with equation 7.1:

$$M_c = M_m - \frac{1}{2}(M_m - M_r)$$

where M_r represents the reduced moment obtained from Rowe's method in the following manner.

- An appropriate curve in figure 7.7 corresponding to a ratio $\alpha = 7/9.5 = 0.73$ is selected. Obviously an intermediate curve needs to be pencilled, from which the points (ρ, M/M_{max}) tabulated below are read. The corresponding values of M^* are calculated by multiplying the different ratios M/M_{max} by the maximum bending moment $M_m = 180.2 \, kN \, m/m$.

$\rho \, (m^3/kN)$	M/M_{max}	$M^* \, (kNm/m)$
0.05	0.97	174.8
0.07	0.89	160.4
0.10	0.82	147.8
0.20	0.68	122.5
0.40	0.56	100.9
1.00	0.43	77.5

- The points (ρ, M^*) are thereafter plotted as depicted in figure 7.15.
- The next step consists of using a sheet piling manual to select different pile sections. In this respect, the following characteristics correspond to *Larssen* sections of mild steel with a modulus of elasticity $E = 2.1 \times 10^5\,N/mm^2$ and a working stress $\sigma_a = 180\,N/mm^2$.

Notice that in the following table, I corresponds to the combined moment of inertia of the pile, and I/y represents its section modulus (refer to the piling handbook by British Steel (1997)). Also, $M_t = \sigma_a I/y$ and $\rho_t = H^4/EI$.

pile section	$I\,(cm^4/m)$	$I/y\,(cm^3/m)$	$M_t\,(kNm/m)$	$\rho_t\,(m^3/kN)$
6W	6459	610	109.8	0.6
LX8	12861	830	149.4	0.3
GSP2	8740	874	157.3	0.44
LX12	18723	1208	217.4	0.21

- The points (ρ_t, M_t) are then plotted in figure 7.15, and the *appropriate* pile section corresponds to the point nearest to the curve in the figure, which is in this instance a *Larssen 6W*. Thus, Rowe's method leads to a reduction in the value of the maximum bending moment in the pile from $M_m = 180.2\,kNm/m$ to the value $M_r = 109.8\,kNm/m$ (refer to the table above).

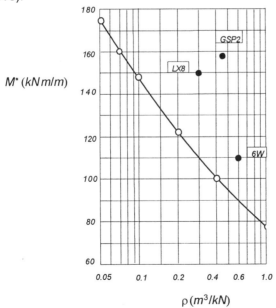

Figure 7.15: Selection of an appropriate steel section.

However, a more realistic reduction is calculated from equation 7.1, so yielding the maximum bending moment that must be used to select a pile section:

$$M_c = 180.2 - \frac{1}{2}(180.2 - 109.8) = 145\,kN\,m/m$$

Therefore, a *Larssen LX8* is, according to the table above, a more appropriate section.

A quick comparison of the outcome of both procedures (1) and (2) points to the fact that, while the depth of embedment is adequate and the calculated anchorage forces are similar in both cases, the maximum bending moment (which governs the selection of the sheet pile section) obtained from Rowe's method is 17% smaller than that corresponding to the limiting conditions.

Example 7.2

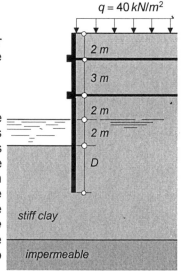

A steel sheet pile is driven into a thick layer of a stiff overconsolidated clay with the following characteristics:
$\gamma = 18.5\,kN/m^3$, $\gamma_{sat} = 19.5\,kN/m^3$,
$\phi' = 25°$ and $c' = 5\,kN/m^2$.
The (static) water is situated at the same level on each side of the pile which is supported by two lines of anchors as depicted in figure 7.16. Allowing for an angle of wall friction $\delta = 16°$ and a uniform pressure $q = 40\,kN/m^2$ applied on the ground surface on the active side, calculate the *depth of embedment*, the *anchorage forces* and the *steel section* of the pile. The active stress conditions are assumed to have been fully mobilised behind the wall.

Figure 7.16: Pile dimensions and soil characteristics.

With the use of two lines of anchors, the structure in figure 7.16 becomes statically indeterminate. Such a problem is usually solved in practice using numerical methods such as finite elements. However, an approximate but acceptable solution can be obtained by assuming that the two lines of anchors are reduced to a single fictitious line, placed midway between the two actual ones. This assumption allows for the anchorage force F corresponding to the fictive line of anchors to be calculated from the equilibrium equation of horizontal forces. The force F is thereafter spread between the two actual lines of anchors, and the ensuing calculations related to shear forces and bending moments are readily undertaken in the usual manner.

Because the water level is static, only the effective active and passive stress distributions on both sides of the pile need be calculated. Once again, Boussinesq analysis is used to evaluate the coefficients of active and passive earth pressure through the use of Kerisel and Absi's tables. Thus, for $\phi = 25°$, $\delta = 2\phi'/3$, and $\beta = 0$, table 6.1 yields: $K_a = 0.364$, $K_p = 3.7$.
Moreover, the coefficients applicable to the cohesion of the clay and to the uniform load q are found from table 6.2 for $\phi' = 25°$, $\delta = 2\phi'/3$, $\alpha = 0$ and $\Omega = 90°$: $K'_a = 0.369$, $K'_p = 3.554$.

Using the limiting conditions on the passive side (*i.e.* a factor of safety $F = 1$ in conjunction with K_p), both active and passive normal effective stresses can now be calculated in the following way (refer to section 6.5.4):

$$\sigma'_a = \cos\delta(K_a\sigma'_v + K'_a q) - c'\cot\phi(1 - K'_a\cos\delta)$$

$$\sigma'_p = \sigma'_v K_p\cos\delta + c'\cot\phi\left(K'_p\cos\delta - 1\right)$$

σ'_v being the effective vertical stress. Whence the values in the tables below:

• *Active side*

z (m)	σ'_v (kN/m^2)		σ'_a (kN/m^2)
0	0		174.8
2.0	18.5×2	$= 37$	20.3
3.5	18.5×3.5	$= 64.8$	30
5.0	18.5×5	$= 92.5$	39.7
7.0	18.5×7	$= 129.5$	52.6
9.0	$129.5 + 9.5 \times 2 = 148.$		59.3
9+D	$148.5 + 9.5D$		$59.3 + 3.325D$

• *Passive side*

z(m)	σ'_v (kN/m^2)	σ'_p (kN/m^2)
0	0	25.9
D	$9.5D$	$33.782D + 25.9$

Prior to establishing the moment equilibrium equation, the two levels of anchors are replaced by a *fictitious* single anchor, whose line of action is situated mid-distance between the two *actual* anchors as shown in figure

7.17. Thus, with reference to the *effective pressure diagram* in the figure, the equilibrium of moments with respect to the fictive anchorage point O is as follows: $\Sigma M_O = 0 \Rightarrow$

$$-7.3 \times 3.5 \times 1.75 - (30 - 7.3) \times \frac{3.5}{2} \times \frac{3.5}{3} + 30 \times 3.5 \times 1.75$$
$$+(52.6 - 30) \times \frac{3.5}{2} \times \frac{2}{3} \times 3.5 + 52.6 \times (2 + D) \times \left(3.5 + \frac{2 + D}{2}\right)$$
$$+(59.3 - 52.6 + 3.32D) \times \left(\frac{2 + D}{2}\right) \times \left[3.5 + \frac{2}{3}(2 + D)\right]$$
$$-25.9 \times D \times \left(5.5 + \frac{D}{2}\right) - 33.78D \times \frac{D}{2} \times \left(5.5 + \frac{2D}{3}\right) = 0$$

or $690.75 + 183.56D - 67.08D^2 - 10.15D^3 = 0$

Whence a depth of embedment $D \approx 3.61\,m$.

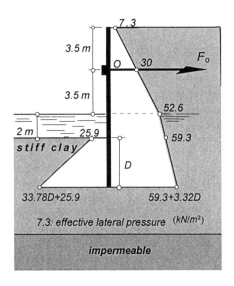

Figure 7.17: Effective lateral pressure diagram.

Next, the net pressure diagram can readily be established as depicted in figure 7.18(a), and the anchorage force F_o can be calculated from the equilibrium equation of horizontal forces. Accordingly:

$$\Sigma F_h = 0 \Rightarrow$$

$$F_o = (7.3 + 52.6) \times \frac{7}{2} + (52.6 + 59.3) \times \frac{2}{2} + 33.4 \times \frac{1.10}{2} - 76.6 \times \frac{2.51}{2}$$
$$= 243.8\,kN/m$$

The anchorage force F_o is then spread equally between the two *actual* anchors as shown in figure 7.18.(*b*) (*i.e.* $F_{a1} = F_{a2} = 121.9 \, kN/m$).

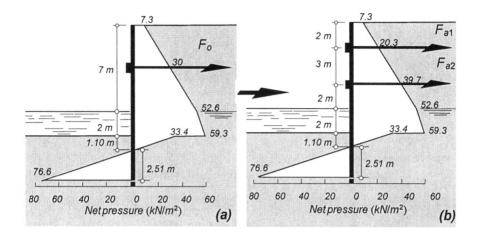

Figure 7.18: Net pressure diagram (a) fictive anchor and (b) actual anchors.

The distribution of shear forces along the pile is calculated in precisely the same way as used in the previous example:

z (m)	shear force (kN/m)	
0		0
2^-	$-(7.3 + 20.3) \times 2/2$	$= -27.6$
2^+	$-27.6 + 121.9$	$= 94.3$
5^-	$94.3 - (20.3 + 39.7) \times 3/2$	$= 4.3$
5^+	$4.3 + 121.9$	$= 126.2$
7	$126.2 - (39.7 + 52.6) \times 2/2$	$= 33.9$
9	$33.9 - (52.6 + 59.3) \times 2/2$	$= -78$
10.35	$-78 - 33.4 \times 1.1/2$	$= -96.4$
12.61	$-96.4 + 76.6 \times 2.51/2$	≈ 0

The corresponding shear force and bending moment diagrams are plotted in figure 7.19. Of particular interest are the effects that two lines of anchors have on the shape of the bending moment diagram, as well as the location of the maximum bending moment ($M_{max} = 312 \, kNm/m$).

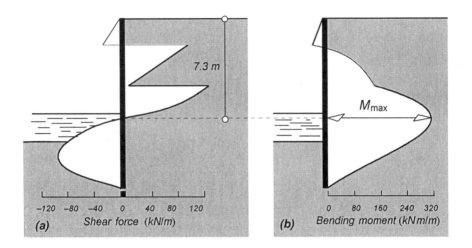

Figure 7.19: (a) Shear force and (b) bending moment diagrams.

Now that all the above quantities have been calculated using the limiting conditions (*i.e.* a factor of safety $F = 1$ on the passive side of the pile), the *actual* characteristics of the pile are such that:

- depth of embedment $D = \sqrt{2} \times 3.61 = 5.10\,m$; hence a total pile length:

$$L = 9 + 5.1 = 14.1\,m$$

- pile steel section: $M_{max} = \sigma_a \dfrac{I}{y} = 312\,kNm/m \quad \Rightarrow$

$$\frac{I}{y} = \frac{M_{max}}{\sigma_a} = \frac{312}{180} \times 10^3 = 1733\,cm^3/m$$

The appropriate steel section corresponds to a *Larssen LX20* with a section modulus $I/y = 2022\,cm^3/m$.

Notice that the calculated anchorage forces must be increased by 25% in the upper line of anchors, and by 15% in the lower one to allow for any stress redistribution behind the wall. The 25% increase in the upper level is justified by the fact that the line of anchors at that level will be subjected, if only temporarily, to a larger horizontal force prior to the installation of the second line. Accordingly, the upper line of anchors must be designed to support a horizontal force $F_{a1} = 121.9 \times 1.25 = 152.4\,kN/m$, and the lower one must withstand a horizontal force $F_{a2} = 121.9 \times 1.15 = 140\,kN/m$.

7.4 Design of anchored sheet-piles using the fixed earth support method

7.4.1 Elastic line method

When the depth of embedment D of the pile becomes substantive compared with the height h above dredge level, the *passive pressure* in front of the wall becomes such that it *can no longer be fully mobilised.* Under such circumstances, the deflection of the pile generates an amount of *active pressure* in front of the wall *and passive pressure* behind the wall, due to the anticlockwise rotation of the toe of the pile around the point of fixity C as illustrated in figure 7.20.

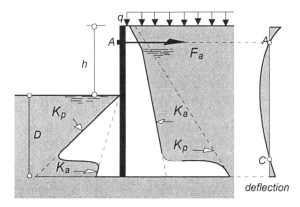

Figure 7.20: Actual lateral pressure distribution for deeply embedded sheet-piles.

The actual pressure distribution can be simplified by *assuming* a depth of embedment D' (smaller than the actual depth D as depicted in figure 7.21) throughout which the passive resistance of the soil is fully mobilised in front of the wall. Behind the wall, the pile is subject to the active thrust *and* to a concentrated load F_c resulting from both active and passive thrusts generated by the anticlockwise rotation of the toe of the pile.

The *net lateral pressure diagram* can thus be calculated then integrated:
- once to establish the shear forces distribution;
- twice to calculate the bending moments diagram;
- three times to compute the slope;
- four times to determine the deflection.

The associated boundary conditions at point C are as follows:
- the shear force is such that $S_c + F_c = 0$
- the bending moment $M_c = 0$
- the slope is *assumed* to be vertical $y'_c = 0$

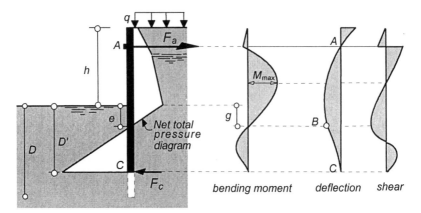

*Figure 7.21: Lateral pressure diagram related to the
assumed depth of embedment*

If the calculations yield a non-zero deflection at *C*, then another value of the depth of embedment is adopted, and the entire calculations are repeated following the same procedure. At convergence (*i.e.* when $y_c = 0$), the corresponding depth *D'* is then increased by 20% to ensure a factor of safety on embedment. This iterative procedure, though not suited for hand calculations, is very easy to program on a computer.

7.4.2 Blum equivalent beam method

This procedure, which is a *variation of the elastic line method*, was developed by Hermann Blum (see for example Blum (1931), (1951)) who undertook an extensive analysis of the behaviour of sheet piles that culminated in the formulation of the *equivalent beam method* which will be detailed shortly. However, the suitability of this method depends on how realistic its *assumptions* are in conjunction with soil conditions in which the pile is driven. In this respect, Blum's method assumes that *the point of zero net pressure and that of zero bending moment occur at the same depth* (that is *e = g* in figure 7.21); this assumption becomes arguable for non-homogeneous soil conditions (*i.e.* multilayered soils). Delattre *et al.* (1996) have shown that for *homogeneous* soils, the assumption can be justified provided that the ratio *e/h* is between 0.1 and 0.2 as depicted in figure 7.22, where *e* represents the depth below dredge level of the point of zero net pressure, *g* corresponds to the depth below dredge level of the point of zero bending moment, and *h* is the height of pile above dredge level (refer to figure 7.21). The error generated by assuming that *e = g* for ratios *e/h* < 0.1 *or* > 0.2 (*i.e.* outside the shaded area in figure 7.22) is on the *unsafe side* since the maximum bending moment will be, in this case, underestimated.

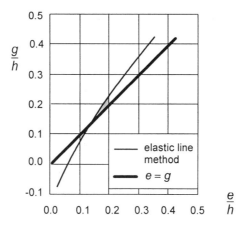

Figure 7.22: Relationship between the depth of zero net pressure and that of zero bending moment.

It is therefore recommended to restrict the use of Blum's method to the design of sheet piles, driven into *homogeneous* soils, and for which $0.1 < e/h < 0.2$. When applicable, the *modus operandi* of the equivalent beam method is as follows.

- Find the *net total pressure diagram* using the limiting conditions (*i.e.* a factor of safety $F = 1$ in conjunction with the coefficient of passive pressure K_p).
- Establish the *point of zero net pressure* (point B, figure 7.23(a)) and its depth e with respect to dredge level.
- Check that the ratio e/h is between 0.1 and 0.2.
- Consider the *two halves* separately (figure 7.23(b).
- Establish the equilibrium equation of horizontal forces in the *upper half*.
- Establish the equilibrium of moments with respect to the anchorage point A in the *upper half*.
- Solve these two equations and calculate the horizontal forces F_a and F_b.
- Establish the equilibrium of moments with respect to point C in the *lower half*.
- Determine the depth of embedment D'.
- Establish the *shear force diagram* and locate the depth z_m corresponding to zero shear force
- Calculate the *maximum bending moment* M_{max} occurring at the depth z_m.
- Calculate the total (safe) *depth of embedment* $D = e + 1.2(D' - e)$.
- Increase the anchorage force F_a by 15% to take into account any stress redistribution behind the wall.

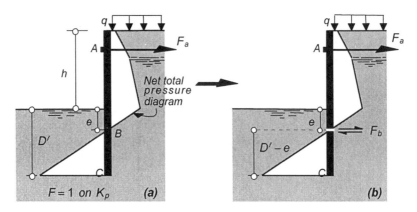

*Figure 7.23: (a) Determination of the depth of zero net pressure and
(b) separation of the pressure diagram.*

Example 7.3

To illustrate the potential pitfalls related to the use of the method, let us
apply it to the problem of example 7.1. The *net total pressure diagram* as
well as the position of the *zero net pressure* have already been established
and are depicted in figure 7.11(b). The corresponding ratio *e/h* is in this
case: $e/h = 0.458/7 \approx 0.07$. Now consider the two halves of the pressure
diagram as shown in figure 7.24.

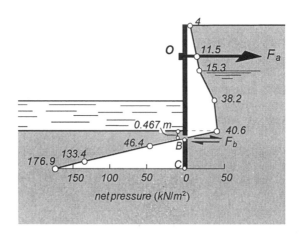

*Figure 7.24: Application of the equivalent beam
method to the net pressure diagram of example 7.1.*

Starting with the *upper half*, the equilibrium of horizontal forces is such that:

$$F_a + F_b = (4 + 11.5) \times \frac{2}{2} + (11.5 + 15.3) \times \frac{1}{2}$$

$$+ (15.3 + 38.2) \times \frac{2}{2} + (38.2 + 40.6) \times \frac{2}{2}$$

$$+ 40.6 \times \frac{0.467}{2} = 170.7 \, kN/m$$

The equilibrium of moments with respect to point O in the upper half implies that:

$$\Sigma M_o = 0 \quad \Rightarrow$$

$$-2 \times 4 \times 1 - \frac{2}{3} \times (11.5 - 4) \times \frac{2}{2} + \frac{1}{2} \times 11.5 \times 1$$

$$+ \frac{2}{3} \times (15.3 - 11.5) \times \frac{1}{2} + 2 \times 15.3 \times 2$$

$$+ \left(1 + \frac{2}{3} \times 2\right)(38.2 - 15.3) \times \frac{2}{2} + 4 \times 38.2 \times 2$$

$$+ \left(3 + \frac{2}{3} \times 2\right)(40.6 - 38.2) \times \frac{2}{2}$$

$$+ \left(5 + \frac{0.467}{3}\right) \times 40.6 \times \frac{0.467}{2} - 5.467 \, F_b = 0$$

yielding thus: $\quad F_b = 86.6 \, kN/m$

Hence: $\qquad F_a = 84.1 \, kN/m$

In the *lower half*, the equilibrium of moments with respect to point C yields the factor of safety F on embedment. Whence:

$$\Sigma M_c = 0 \quad \Rightarrow$$

$$-86.6 \times 2.033 + \frac{1}{F}\left[176.9 \times \frac{2.033}{2} \times \frac{2.033}{3}\right] = 0$$

or $\qquad \dfrac{121.86}{F} - 176.6 = 0 \quad \Rightarrow \quad F = 0.69$

The *shear force diagram* is determined in precisely the same way used in conjunction with example 7.1, and is shown in figure 7.25.

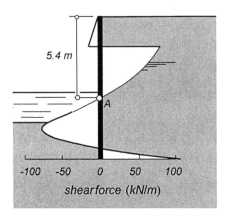

Figure 7.25: Shear force diagram.

The point of zero shear force occurs at a depth $z \approx 5.4\,m$; whence the maximum bending moment M_m, calculated with respect to point A in figure 7.25 is:

$$M_m^A = -4 \times 2 \times (1 + 3.4) - (11.5 - 4) \times \frac{2}{2} \times \left(\frac{2}{3} + 3.4\right)$$

$$+ 93.3 \times 3.4 - 11.5 \times 1 \times \left(\frac{1}{2} + 2.4\right)$$

$$-(15.3 - 11.5) \times \frac{1}{2} \times \left(\frac{1}{3} + 2.4\right) - 15.3 \times 2.4 \times \frac{2.4}{2}$$

$$-(38.2 - 15.3) \times \frac{2}{2} \times \left(\frac{2}{3} + 0.4\right) - (38.2 - 15.3) \times 0.4 \times \frac{0.4}{2}$$

$$= 142.7\,kN\,m/m$$

Comparing these results with the ones calculated with the *free earth support* (with $F = 1$ on K_p) in example 7.1, it emerges clearly that the equivalent beam method:

- produces a smaller anchorage force: $F_a = 93.3\,kN/m$ as opposed to $F_a = 101.4\,kN/m$ for the free earth support method;
- gives a smaller maximum bending moment: $M_{max} = 142.7\,kN\,m/m$ compared with $M_{max} = 169.7\,kN\,m/m$ from the free earth support;
- yields a factor of safety on embedment $F = 0.69$, thus necessitating a depth of embedment much larger than that calculated from the free earth support.

Although these findings do not diverge from the general trend, the difference in results will have been affected to a degree by the fact that, *in this instance,* the ratio *e/h* was outside the boundaries $0.1 < e/h < 0.2$. Nonetheless, it is seen that the fixed earth support method results in a longer pile with a smaller maximum bending moment, hence a lighter cross-section, which may be harder to drive to the required depth. Under such circumstances, driving can become *the* deciding factor as far as this design method is concerned; whence the need for a cautious approach when using the fixed earth support method to design such structures.

Example 7.4

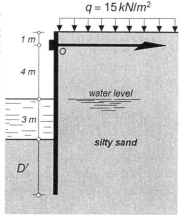

An anchored sheet pile is driven in a silty sand characterised by a bulk unit weight $\gamma = 19\,kN/m^3$, a saturated unit weight $\gamma_{sat} = 20\,kN/m^3$ and an angle of shearing resistance $\phi' = 30°$. The static water level is situated at a height of 3 *m* above dredge level as depicted in figure 7.26, and the angles of wall friction are $\delta_a = +2\phi'/3$ on the active side and $\delta_p = -2\phi'/3$ on the passive side.
Use the equivalent beam method, and determine the anchorage force, the depth of embedment of the pile as well as the maximum bending moment.

Figure 7.26: Pile dimensions and soil conditions.

In order to calculate the lateral pressure distribution on each side of the pile, the coefficients of active and passive pressure need to be known. Using Kerisel and Absi's tables (Kerisel and Absi, 1990), it can be seen that:

- on the active side:

$\beta/\phi' = 0,\ \delta/\phi' = 0.66,\ \lambda = 0,\ \phi' = 30°\ \Rightarrow\ K_a = 0.3$ (page 78)

$\phi' = 30°,\ \Omega = 90°,\ \alpha = 0,\ \delta_a = 20°\ \Rightarrow\ K'_a = 0.304$ (page 132)

- on the passive side:

$\beta/\phi' = 0,\ \delta/\phi' = -0.66,\ \lambda = 0,\ \phi' = 30°\ \Rightarrow\ K_p = 5.3$ (page 14)

Because there is no water seepage, only the *effective* lateral stresses need be calculated in the following way.

- *Active normal effective stress:* $\quad \sigma'_{an} = \cos \delta_a (K_a \sigma'_v + K'_a q)$

- *Passive normal effective stress:* $\quad \sigma'_p = K_p \sigma'_v \cos \delta_p$

The corresponding *net effective pressure diagram* is shown in figure 7.27, from which the depth of zero net pressure, as well as the ratio *e/h* can easily be calculated:

$$e = \frac{39.6}{46.98} = 0.843\,m \quad \Rightarrow \quad \frac{e}{h} = \frac{0.843}{8} = 0.105$$

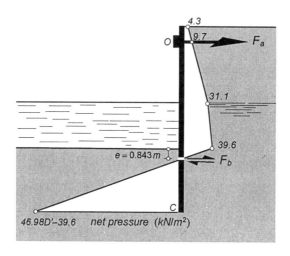

Figure 7.27: Net pressure diagram.

Now consider the equilibrium of moments with respect to the anchorage point in the *upper half* of the pressure diagram:

$$\Sigma M_{(o)} = 0 \quad \Rightarrow$$

$$-4.3 \times 1 \times 0.5 - (9.7 - 4.3) \times \frac{1}{6} + 9.7 \times 4 \times 2 + (31.1 - 9.7) \times \frac{4}{2} \times \frac{2}{3} \times 4$$

$$+31.1 \times 3 \times \left(\frac{3}{2} + 4\right) + (39.6 - 31.1) \times \frac{3}{2} \times \left(4 + \frac{2}{3} \times 3\right)$$

$$+39.6 \times \frac{0.843}{2} \times \left(7 + \frac{0.843}{3}\right) = 7.843 F_b$$

Hence a shear force: $\quad F_b = 114.7\,kN/m$

Next, the equilibrium of horizontal forces in the same *upper half* is such that:

$$F_a + F_b = (4.3 + 9.7) \times \frac{1}{2} + (9.7 + 31.1) \times \frac{4}{2} + (31.1 + 39.6) \times \frac{3}{2} + 39.6 \times \frac{0.843}{2}$$

yielding an anchorage force: $F_a = 96.6\,kN/m$

The depth of embedment is calculated from the equilibrium of moments with respect to point C in the *lower half*. Whence:

$$\Sigma M_C = 0 \quad \Rightarrow \quad (D' - e)F_b = (46.98D' - 39.6)\frac{(D' - e)^2}{6}$$

or $D'^3 - 2.53D'^2 - 12.51D' + 11.75 = 0 \quad \Rightarrow \quad D' \approx 4.67\,m$

Hence, the *actual* depth of embedment of the pile:

$$D = e + 1.2(D' - e) = 0.843 + 1.2 \times (4.67 - 0.843) \ = \ 5.43\,m$$

The depth at which the maximum bending moment occurs is determined from the shear force diagram depicted in figure 7.28 and corresponds to the depth of zero shear force (point A). Accordingly, the bending moment at A can be calculated in a straightforward way:

$$M^A_{max} = -4.3 \times 5 \times \left(0.5 + \frac{5}{2}\right) - (31.1 - 4.3) \times \frac{5}{2} \times \left(0.5 + \frac{5}{3}\right)$$

$$-31.1 \times \frac{0.5}{2} \times 0.5 - (32.5 - 31.1) \times \frac{0.5}{2} \times \frac{0.5}{3} + 96.6 \times 4.5$$

$$= 221\,kN\,m/m$$

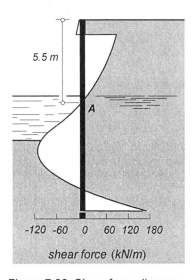

Figure 7.28: Shear force diagram.

If the same structure were designed using the *free earth support method* with a factor of safety $F = 1$ applied to the coefficient of passive pressure, then the net pressure diagram would be identical to that in figure 7.27 without separation (*i.e.* without the shear forces F_b). The critical depth of embedment would then be calculated from the moment equilibrium equation, established with respect to the anchorage point O in the following manner:

$$\Sigma M_{(o)} = 0 \quad \Rightarrow$$

$$-4.3 \times 1 \times 0.5 - (9.7 - 4.3) \times \frac{1}{6} + 9.7 \times 4 \times 2 + (31.1 - 9.7) \times \frac{4}{2} \times \frac{2}{3} \times 4$$

$$+31.1 \times 3 \times \left(\frac{3}{2} + 4\right) + [39.6 - 31.1] \times \frac{3}{2} \times \left(\frac{2}{3} \times 3 + 4\right)$$

$$+39.6 \times \frac{0.843}{2} \times \left(\frac{0.843}{3} + 7\right)$$

$$-(46.98D' - 39.6)\left(\frac{D' - 0.843}{2}\right)\left[\frac{2}{3}(D' - 0.843) + 7.843\right] = 0$$

or $D'^3 + 9.24D'^2 - 17.7D' - 49.7 = 0 \quad \Rightarrow \quad D' \approx 2.9\,m$

and the actual (safe) depth of embedment:

$$D = D'\sqrt{2} = 4.10\,m$$

Now that the critical depth is known, the precise net pressure diagram can then be drawn, from which the anchorage force is thereafter calculated using the equilibrium equation of horizontal forces. Thus, with reference to figure 7.29:

$$F_a = (4.3 + 9.7) \times \frac{1}{2} + (9.7 + 31.1) \times \frac{4}{2} + (39.6 + 31.1) \times \frac{3}{2}$$

$$+39.6 \times \frac{0.843}{2} - 96.6 \times \frac{2.057}{2} = 112\,kN/m$$

The corresponding shear force diagram is depicted in figure 7.30 which shows that the maximum bending moment occurs at a depth $z = 5.75\,m$ (point B in the figure). Calculating the moment at B, it follows that:

$$M_{max}^B = -4.3 \times 5 \times \left(0.75 + \frac{5}{2}\right) - (31.1 - 4.3) \times \frac{5}{2} \times \left(\frac{5}{3} + 0.75\right)$$

$$-31.1 \times 0.75 \times \frac{0.75}{2} - (33.2 - 31.1) \times \frac{0.75}{2} \times \frac{0.75}{3}$$

$$+112 \times 4.75 = 291.3\,kN\,m/m$$

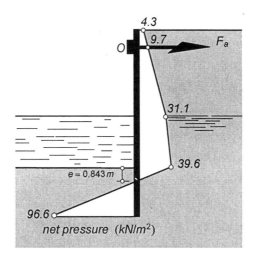

Figure 7.29: Net pressure diagram.

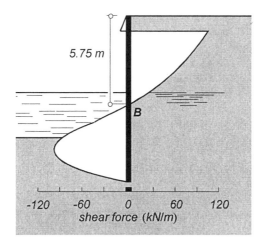

Figure 7.30: Shear force diagram.

These results confirm the findings of the previous example, the *trend* of which is represented diagrammatically in figure 7.31 (Delattre *et al.,* 1996). The figure represents the effect of the angle of shearing resistance of the (cohesionless) soil in which the pile is embedded on the ratios F_a/F_a^B, M_{max}/M_{max}^B and D/D^B where F_a, M_{max} and D are the anchorage force, bending moment and depth of embedment respectively calculated using the *free earth support method*, and F_a^B, M_{max}^B and D^B represent the same respective quantities resulting from the *elastic line method*.

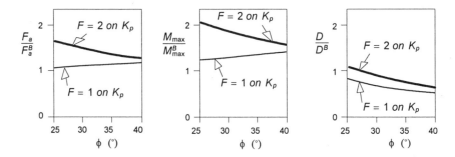

Figure 7.31: Comparison of results obtained using both free earth support and elastic line methods (Delattre et al., 1996). (Reproduced by permission.)

The figure depicts a trend and *should in no way be used for calculation purposes*. Yet, it is clear that the *elastic line method* (*i.e.* the equivalent beam method) underestimates both the anchorage force and the maximum bending moment while, in the meantime, it overestimates the depth of embedment of the pile. Moreover, the *free earth support method* that consists of using a reduced value of the coefficient of passive pressure K_p always yields an anchorage force and a maximum bending moment in excess of those calculated using the full K_p value. It is therefore essential that, prior to the selection of a design method, the designer should have a clear idea *vis à vis* the effects of parameters such as the angle of shearing resistance or the ratio *e/h* presented earlier on the outcome of calculations. Although experience plays an important part in the decision as to which method of design is most suitable, the usefulness of the graphs in figures 7.22 and 7.31 is indubitable.

7.5 Design of cantilever sheet-pile walls

Cantilever sheet pile walls are usually used when the height of retained soil does not exceed 5 *m*. From a behavioural view point, the pile is assumed to rotate about a point of fixity (point *C* in figure 7.32) so that the resistance to the *active load* is provided by a *passive thrust* developed in front of the wall as well as at the back due to the rotation. As in the case of anchored sheet piles, the pressure profile in figure 7.32 can be simplified without any loss of accuracy by assuming a depth of embedment D' through which the full passive resistance is mobilised, and by substituting the thrust F_c for the net total pressure below point *C* as depicted in figure 7.33. Based on these assumptions, the *elastic line method* can then be applied in precisely the same way used in conjunction with anchored sheet piles (refer to figure 7.21). Alternatively, the *equivalent beam method* can be applied in the knowledge that only the depth of embedment D' and the maximum bending moment need be calculated.

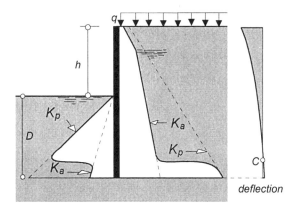

*Figure 7.32: Lateral pressure profile
around a cantilever sheet-pile wall.*

Thus, with reference to figure 7.33, the design of a cantilever sheet pile wall can be undertaken as follows.

- Determine the *net pressure diagram,* taking into account any water seepage when applicable.
- Solve the moment equilibrium equation with respect to point *C* and determine the critical depth of embedment *D'*.
- Calculate the actual (safe) *depth of embedment* $D = D' \sqrt{2}$.
- Establish the *shear force diagram.*
- Calculate the *maximum bending moment* in the pile which occurs at the depth corresponding to zero shear force.

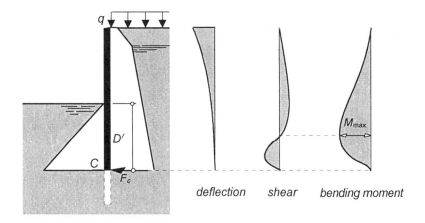

deflection   shear   bending moment

*Figure 7.33: Deflection, shear and bending moment
diagrams in the case of a cantilever wall.*

Notice that for cantilever walls in general, the resistance to any active thrust is entirely due to the passive resistance provided by the soil. Because passive thrusts depend on the angle of shearing resistance, piles driven in clays will require a *deeper* embedment. This can potentially lead to uneconomical design, in which case the use of anchors must be considered.

Example 7.5

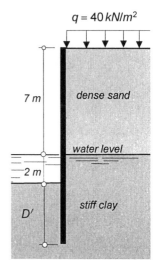

$q = 40 \, kN/m^2$

A steel sheet pile is driven into a thick layer of a stiff overconsolidated clay overlain by a dense silty sand. The following characteristics apply:
- *sand*: $\gamma = 19 \, kN/m^3$, $\phi' = 35°$,
- *cla*: $\gamma_{sat} = 19.5 \, kN/m^3$, $\phi' = 25°$, $c' = 5 \, kN/m^2$

The (static) water is situated at the same level on each side of the pile as depicted in figure 7.34. Allowing for an angle of wall friction $\delta_a = +2\phi'/3$ on the active side, $\delta_p = -\phi'/2$ on the passive side, and for a uniform pressure $q = 40 \, kN/m^2$ to be applied on the ground surface on the active side, calculate the depth of embedment and the maximum bending moment of the pile.

The active stress conditions are supposed to have been fully mobilised behind the wall. Also, Boussinesq theory is assumed to apply on both active and passive sides.

Figure 7.34: Wall dimensions and soil conditions.

Because the water level is static, only the effective active and passive stress distributions on both sides of the pile need be calculated. First, the relevant coefficients of active and passive earth pressure are evaluated using Kerisel and Absi's (1990) tables. Thus:

- *for sand*:

$\phi' = 35°$, $\delta = +2\phi'/3$, $\beta = 0$, $\lambda = 0$ $\Rightarrow$ $K_{as} = 0.247$ (page 78) (Kerisel & Absi, 1990)

$\phi' = 35°$, $\Omega = 90°$, $\delta = +2\phi'/3$, $\alpha = 0$ $\Rightarrow$ $K'_{as} = 0.250$ (page 150)

- *for clay on the active side*:

$\phi' = 25°$, $\delta = +2\phi'/3$, $\beta = 0$, $\lambda = 0$ $\Rightarrow$ $K_{ac} = 0.364$ (page 78)

$\phi' = 25°$, $\Omega = 90°$, $\delta = +2\phi'/3$, $\alpha = 0$ $\Rightarrow$ $K'_{ac} = 0.369$ (page 120)

- *for clay on the passive side*:

$\phi' = 25°$, $\delta = -\phi'/2$, $\beta = 0$, $\lambda = 0$ $\quad \Rightarrow \quad K_{pc} = 3.4$ $\qquad$ (page 21)

$\phi' = 25°$, $\Omega = 90°$, $\alpha = +\phi'/2$, $\delta = 0$ $\quad \Rightarrow \quad K'_{pc} = \frac{1}{0.304} = 3.289$ $\quad$ (page 120)

Note that the coefficients K'_a and K'_p are applicable to the uniform load q and to the cohesion of the clay. Accordingly, if the limiting conditions were used on the passive side (*i.e.* a factor of safety $F = 1$ in conjunction with K_p), both active and passive *normal effective stresses* can be calculated in the following way.

- *Throughout the sand layer.*

$$\sigma'_a = \cos \delta_s \, (K_{as}\sigma'_v + K'_{as}q)$$

- *Throughout the clay layer.*

$$\sigma'_a = \cos \delta_{ac}(K_{ac}\sigma'_v + K'_{ac}q) - c'\cot\phi' \, (1 - K'_{ac} \cos \delta_{ac})$$

$$\sigma'_p = \sigma'_v K_{pc} \cos \delta_{pc} + c'\cot\phi' \, (K'_{pc} \cos \delta_{pc} - 1)$$

σ'_v being the effective vertical stress due to the self weight of soil. The angles of wall friction are such that:

- for sand: $\qquad\qquad\qquad\qquad \delta_s = \frac{2}{3} \times 35 = 23.3°$
- for clay on the active side: $\qquad \delta_{ac} = \frac{2}{3} \times 25 = 16.7°$
- for clay on the passive side: $\delta_{pc} = -\frac{1}{2} \times 25 = -12.5°$

Whence the following values:

Active side

z (m)	$\sigma'_v \, (kN/m^2)$		$\sigma'_a \, (kN/m^2)$
0		0	9.2
2	19×2	$= 38$	17.8
7^-	19×7	$= 133$	39.3
7^+	133		53.6
9	$133 + 9.5 \times 2$	$= 152$	60.2
$9+D$	$152 + 9.5D$		$60.2 + 3.312D$

Passive side

$z\,(m)$	$\sigma'_v\,(kN/m^2)$	$\sigma'_p\,(kN/m^2)$
0	0	23.7
D	9.5D	23.7+31.534D

The corresponding *effective pressure diagram* is depicted in figure 7.35.

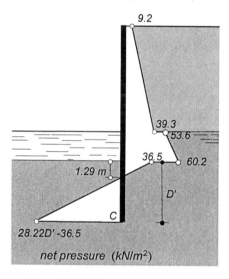

Figure 7.35: Net pressure diagram.

The equilibrium of moments with respect to point *C in*in Figure 7.35 can now be established:

$\Sigma M_{(c)} = 0 \quad \Rightarrow$

$$-9.2 \times 7 \times \left(\frac{7}{2}+2+D'\right) - (39.3 - 9.2) \times \frac{7}{2} \times \left(\frac{7}{3}+2+D'\right)$$

$$-53.6 \times 2 \times (1+D') - (60.2 - 53.6) \times \frac{2}{2} \times \left(\frac{2}{3}+D'\right)$$

$$-36.5 \times \frac{1.29}{2} \times \left(D' - \frac{1.29}{3}\right) + (28.22D' - 36.5)\frac{(D' - 1.29)^2}{6} = 0$$

or

$$D'^3 - 3.87D'^2 - 60.3D' - 196.2 = 0 \quad \Rightarrow \quad D' \approx 11\,m$$

Hence a safe depth of embedment: $D = D'\sqrt{2} = 15.55\,m.$

The ensuing shear force diagram is depicted in figure 7.36 where the shear force becomes zero at a depth $z = 15\,m$. The corresponding maximum bending moment, calculated at point A is hence:

$$M^A_{max} = -9.2 \times 7 \times \left(\frac{7}{2} + 8\right) - (39.3 - 9.2) \times \frac{7}{2} \times \left(\frac{7}{3} + 8\right)$$

$$-53.6 \times 2 \times (1 + 6) - (60.2 - 53.6) \times \frac{2}{2} \times \left(\frac{2}{3} + 6\right)$$

$$-36.5 \times \frac{1.29}{2} \times \left(6 - \frac{1.29}{3}\right) + 132.9 \times \left(\frac{6 - 1.29}{2}\right)\left(\frac{6 - 1.29}{3}\right)$$

$$= -2263.4\,kN\,m/m$$

This example gives a clear indication with regard to the cost effectiveness of design methods in conjunction with soil conditions and depth of retained soil, in that the excessive depth of embedment as well as the large maximum bending moment makes the use of a cantilever wall in this instance uneconomical. It also justifies why, in practice, cantilever walls are only used when the height of the retained soil is less than about 5 m.

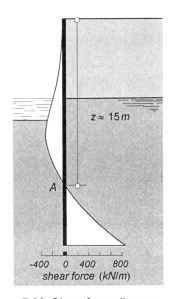

Figure 7.36: Shear force diagram.

Problems

7.1   Consider the anchored sheet pile with the dimensions indicated in figure p7.1. Knowing that the soil and loading conditions are the same as those used in example 7.5, and taking advantage of the then established net pressure diagram calculated using a factor of safety $F = 1$ on K_p, determine:
- the safe depth of embedment D,
- the anchorage force F,
- the maximum bending moment M_{max}.

Ans: $D = 5.97\,m$, $F \approx 187\,kN/m$, $M_{max} \approx 465$ $kN\,m/m$

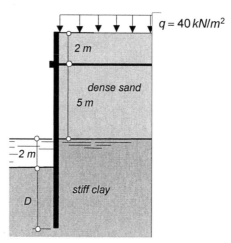

Figure p7.1

7.2   Rework problem *p7.1*, this time using the equivalent beam method.

Ans: $F_a \approx 182\,kN/m$, $D = 7.97\,m$, $M_{max} \approx 320\,kN\,m/m$

7.3   An anchored sheet pile cut-off wall is embedded in the soil strata depicted in figure *p7.3*. The loose sand has a bulk unit weight $\gamma = 19kN/m^3$ and an effective angle of friction $\phi' = 30°$, and the dense sand is characterised by a saturated unit weight $\gamma_{sat} = 20kN/m^3$ and an angle $\phi' = 40°$.

(a) Use the free earth support method, in conjunction with the limiting conditions on the passive side (*i.e.* $F = 1$ on K_p), and check the adequacy of the depth of embedment.

(b) Calculate the anchorage force F_a and the maximum bending moment M_{max}.

Ans: (a) *Factor of safety on passive resistance*: $F = 4.73$
(b) $F_a \approx 193\,kN/m$, $M_{max} \approx 234\,kN\,m/m$

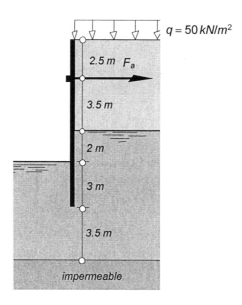

Figure 7.3

7.4   Use the free earth support method with a factor of safety $F = 2$ on K_p in conjunction with the sheet pile cut-off wall in problem p7.3 above, then apply Rowe's moment reduction method and estimate the reduced maximum bending moment M_c of the sheet pile.

Ans: $F_a \approx 188\, kN/m$, $M_c = 161.5\, kN\, m/m$

7.5   A diaphragm wall is embedded in a thick layer of a stiff clay overlain by a layer of clean sand (figure p7.5). The soil characteristics are as follows:
  - sand: $\phi' = 35°$, $\gamma = 18.5\, kN/m^3$
  - clay: $\phi' = 23°$, $\gamma = 19\, kN/m^3$, $\gamma_{sat} = 20\, kN/m^3$, $c' = 8\, kN/m^2$

The angle of wall friction can be taken as $\delta = 2\phi'/3$ on both sides of the wall. Using Boussinesq theory to determine the relevant coefficients of active and passive pressure, estimate the critical depth of embedment D' of the wall, and the maximum bending moment M_{max} as well as the depth at which it occurs.

Ans: $D' = 6.45\, m$, $M_{max} \approx -633\, kN\, m/m$ *occurring at a depth* $z = 7.8\, m$

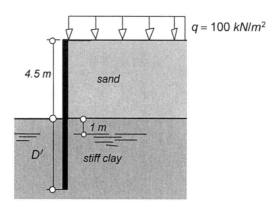

Figure p7.5

References

Azizi, F. (2007) *Physical Behaviour in Geotechnics*. 480 pp. Published by F. Azizi ISBN 978-0-9555996-2-0.

Blum, H. (1931) *Einspannungsverhältnisse bei Bohlwerken*. Wilhelm Ernest und Sohn Berlin, 27 pp.

Blum, H. (1951) *Beitrag zur Berechnung von Bohlwerken unter Berücksichtigung der Wandverformung, insbesondere bei mit der Tiefe linear zunehmender Widerstandsziffer*. Wilhelm Ernest und Sohn, Berlin, 32 pp.

British Steel (1997) *Piling Handbook*, 7th edn. British Steel Plc.

Delattre, L., Josseaume, H., Mespoulhe, L. and Delmer, T. (1996) *Comparaison des méthodes classiques de dimensionnement des écrans de soutènement ancrés*. Bulletin des Laboratoires des Ponts et Chaussées, 205, pp. 77–90.

Fleming, W. G. K., Weltman, A. J., Randolf, M. F. and Elson, W. K. (1992) *Piling Engineering*, 2nd edn. Wiley, New York.

Kerisel, J. and Absi, E. (1990) *Active and Passive Earth Pressure Tables*, 3rd edn. A.A. Balkema, Rotterdam.

Rowe, P. W. (1952) *Anchored sheet-pile walls*. Proceedings of the Institution of Civil Engineers, London, 1 (1), pp. 27–70.

Rowe, P. W. (1955).*A theoretical and experimental analysis of sheet pile walls*. Proceedings of the Institution of Civil Engineers, January, pp. 32–86.

Rowe, P. W. (1957) *Sheet pile walls in clay*. Proceedings of the Institution of Civil Engineers, London, 7, pp. 629–654.

Rowe, P. W. and Barden, L. (1966) *A new consolidation cell*. Géotechnique, 16 (2), pp. 162–170.

Skempton, A. W. (1951) *The bearing capacity of clays*. Proceedings of the Building Research Congress, London.

Terzaghi, K. (1954) *Anchored bulkheads*. Trans. ASCE, 119.

Tschebotarioff, G. P. (1973) *Foundations, Retaining and Earth Structures*, 2nd edn. McGraw-Hill, New York.

CHAPTER 8

Design of tunnels

8.1 The stability of cylindrical cavities: equilibrium equations

Consider the cross-section of a *circular tunnel* subjected to a uniform pressure σ_o at the top as depicted in figure 8.1. Within the circular area surrounding the tunnel opening, both *radial* and *circumferential* (or *hoop*) stresses are assumed to be principal stresses in the absence of any shear stress.

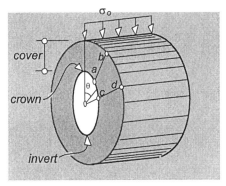

Figure 8.1: Cross-section of a circular tunnel.

Let us now analyse the equilibrium requirements of the curvilinear element *abdc*, whose axis is inclined at an angle θ with respect to the vertical. Using the different dimensions of the element shown in figure 8.2, and neglecting any shear stresses along the sides *ab* and *cd*, then the equilibrium equations can be established in a straightforward way.

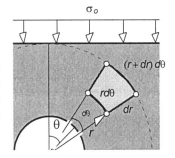

Figure 8.2: Dimensions relating to an elemental cross-section.

Thus, with reference to figure 8.3, the weight w of the element can be evaluated as follows:

$$w \approx \gamma \, r \, d\theta \, dr \qquad\qquad (8.1)$$

γ being the (relevant) unit weight of soil. Resolving the forces radially in the knowledge that $\sin \frac{d\theta}{2} \approx \frac{d\theta}{2}$, it follows that:

$$(\sigma_r + d\sigma_r)(r + dr)\, d\theta - \sigma_r r\, d\theta - \sigma_\theta \, dr\frac{d\theta}{2} - (\sigma_\theta + d\sigma_\theta)\, dr\frac{d\theta}{2} + \gamma \, r \, dr \, d\theta \cos\theta = 0$$

whence: $$\frac{d\sigma_r}{dr} + \frac{(\sigma_r - \sigma_\theta)}{r} + \gamma \cos\theta = 0 \qquad\qquad (8.2)$$

Now, resolving perpendicular to the radius:

$$\sigma_\theta \, dr + \gamma \, r \, dr \, d\theta \sin\theta - (\sigma_\theta + d\sigma_\theta)\, dr = 0$$

so that: $$\frac{d\sigma_\theta}{d\theta} - \gamma \, r \sin\theta = 0 \qquad\qquad (8.3)$$

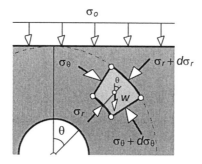

Figure 8.3: Stresses related to the elemental cross-section.

Both equations 8.2 and 8.3 represent the conditions of equilibrium of an element in the vicinity of the tunnel and, as can be seen from figure 8.3, the most unfavourable equilibrium conditions are likely to occur at the *crown* of the tunnel when $\theta = 0$. Under these circumstances, the equilibrium conditions are represented by equation 8.2 which, on substitution for $\theta = 0$, reduces to the following:

$$\frac{d\sigma_r}{dr} = \frac{\sigma_\theta - \sigma_r}{r} - \gamma \qquad\qquad (8.4)$$

8.2 Stress analysis related to circular tunnels in clays and sand

8.2.1 Circular tunnels in fine grained soils

In the short term, clays derive their strength from their *undrained cohesion* c_u. Hence, in accordance with equation 2.53 in section 2.5.3, the failure criterion in the *passive mode* (*i.e.* $\sigma_\theta > \sigma_r$) under undrained conditions is such that:

$$(\sigma_\theta - \sigma_r) = 2c_u \qquad (8.5)$$

Substituting for this quantity in equation 8.4, then integrating between 'the limits shown in figure 8.4, that is $\sigma_r = \sigma_a$ at $r = a$, and $\sigma_r = \sigma_o$ at $r = R$, it follows that:

$$\int_{\sigma_a}^{\sigma_o} d\sigma_r = \int_a^R \left(\frac{2c_u}{r} - \gamma\right) dr$$

or

$$\sigma_a = \sigma_o + \gamma(R - a) - 2c_u \ln\frac{R}{a} \qquad (8.6)$$

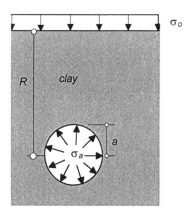

Figure 8.4: Circular tunnels in clays; boundary conditions.

Equation 8.6 yields the pressure σ_a needed in the *short term* to support an unlined tunnel in a clay with an undrained shear strength c_u and a unit weight γ; so that for example, in the case of a tunnel with a diameter $2a = 4\,m$ and a cover $R - a = 12\,m$, executed in a firm clay characterised by a unit weight $\gamma = 20\,kN/m^3$ and an undrained shear strength $c_u = 60\,kN/m^2$, the support pressure would be, in the absence of any surcharge ($\sigma_o = 0$):

$$\sigma_a = 20 \times 12 - 2 \times 60 \times \ln\frac{14}{2} = 6.5\,kN/m^2$$

This value of (short term) support pressure is in this case surprisingly low given the depth of the tunnel, and reflects a fact known as *stress arching*.

Example 8.1

A circular tunnel is to be excavated unlined in a firm clay having an undrained shear strength $c_u = 50 \, kN/m^2$ and a bulk unit weight $\gamma = 20 \, kN/m^3$. It is proposed to find the maximum tunnel opening a_{max} that does not require any support pressure (*i.e.* $\sigma_a = 0$) during excavation, if the ground pressure were $\sigma_o = 60 \, kN/m^2$.

Introducing the condition of zero support pressure ($\sigma_a = 0$) into equation 8.6, then rearranging, it is easy to show that:

$$a = \frac{2c_u \ln\left(\frac{R}{a}\right) - \sigma_o}{\gamma\left(\frac{R}{a} - 1\right)}$$

Accordingly, a graphical solution can be achieved by plotting the tunnel radius *a versus* the ratio R/a. The corresponding graph, depicted in figure 8.5 yields a maximum radius $a_{max} \approx 1.31 \, m$, corresponding to a ratio $R/a_{max} = 4$; whence a distance $R \approx 5.24 \, m$ (refer to figure 8.4).

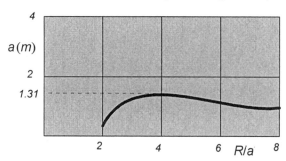

Figure 8.5: Graphical solution to the tunnel opening.

Technological advances achieved to-date led to a marked decrease in the cost of tunnelling, mainly through the use of specialised teams to whom such tasks are subcontracted. As a result, tunnels are in most cases excavated using tunnel boring machines (TBMs) which can concurrently excavate and apply linings to the tunnel walls. Moreover, TBMs can be made in different sizes, thus enabling the automated excavation of different size tunnels ranging from micro tunnels with diameters typically between 100 *mm* and 1000 *mm* (see section 8.4.3), to tunnels with diameters in excess of 10 *m* (examples include the 10 *km* long, 10.4 *m* diameter tunnel of the super-Périphérique orbiting Paris, the 12 *m* diameter tunnel under

Barcelona city centre for the rail link to Madrid). Alternatively, tunnels can be excavated using mechanical diggers in conjunction with the Sprayed Concrete Lining method discussed in section 8.5.1. In either case, the stability of the tunnel walls is an integral part of the excavation process. However, the stability of the tunnel face depends on the type of excavated soil, as well as the tunnel dimensions and depth. In particular, the short term stability of a tunnel face in the case of a cohesive soil is essentially linked to its undrained shear strength c_u through the equilibrium pressure equation:

$$\sigma^e = \sigma_v - T_c \, c_u \tag{8.7}$$

with: σ_v : the total vertical pressure at the centre of the tunnel face
T_c : an adimensional factor linked to the ratios H/D_e and P/D_e (H being the depth of the tunnel crown, P the length of the unlined tunnel section, and D_e the tunnel (external) diameter, as per figure 8.6).

The factor T_c can be cautiously estimated from the graphs in figure 8.6, established from a variety of measurements on a limited number of tunnels excavated in different sites (Atkinson & Mair, 1981). The use of equation 8.7 must be considered carefully, since only a positive equilibrium pressure σ^e implies the need for a support pressure to prevent the tunnel face from collapsing. Ideally, one aims at having a relatively small negative σ^e, as an excessive negative one can potentially cause surface heave.

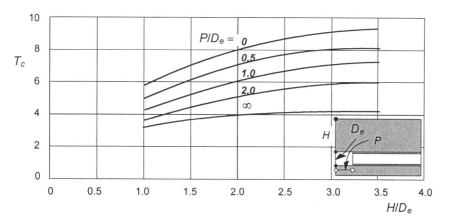

Figure 8.6: Effect of tunnel dimensions on tunnel face pressure coefficient

Example 8.2

A service microtunnel is excavated using the pipe jacking method in a very soft clay with an undrained shear strength $c_u = 8 \, kN/m^2$ and a saturated unit weight $\gamma_{sat} = 20\,kN/m^3$. The pipes have an external diameter $D_e = 950\,mm$, and the tunnel crown is at a depth $H = 2\,m$. In practice, a ratio $P/D_e = 0$ applies to micro tunnels excavated using this method. Consequently, figure 8.6 shows that for ratios $H/De = 2/0.95 = 2.1$ and $P/D_e = 0$, the tunnel face pressure coefficient is $T_c \approx 8.1$. Whence an equilibrium tunnel face pressure from equation 9.7:

$$\sigma^e = 20 \times 2.475 - 8.1 \times 8 = -15.3\,kN/m^2$$

implying the tunnel face is stable under short term excavation conditions.

Consider next, the case of a small diameter tunnel with $D_e = 4.3\,m$, excavated at a depth of $16\,m$ to the tunnel's centre. The tunnel lining lags some 4 m behind the tunnel's face, and the soil conditions consist of a thick layer of saturated firm clay with a unit weight $\gamma_{sat} = 20.5\,kN/m^3$ and an undrained shear strength $c_u = 40\,kN/m^2$. Hence from figure 8.6:

$$P/D_e = 4/4.3 = 0.93, \quad H/D_e = 13.85/4.3 = 3.2, \quad \text{and} \quad T_c \approx 6.9$$

The equilibrium face pressure is thus (equation 8.7):

$$\sigma^e = 16 \times 20.5 - 6.9 \times 40 = +52\,kN/m^2$$

implying that the tunnel face is unstable, and a pressure balance of around $60\,kN/m^2$ needs to be applied as the excavation proceeds in these soil conditions.

8.2.2 Circular tunnels in granular soils

For granular soils such as sand, an effective stress analysis is needed, and for a passive mode of failure, both radial and hoop effective stresses are related at failure through the coefficient of passive earth pressure defined as follows:

$$\sigma'_\theta = K_p \sigma'_r \tag{8.8}$$

$$K_p = \frac{1 + \sin\phi'}{1 - \sin\phi'}$$

In the absence of porewater pressure (i.e. dry soil), then $\sigma'_\theta \equiv \sigma_\theta$ and $\sigma'_r \equiv \sigma_r$. Thus substituting for the hoop stress σ_θ from equation 8.8 in the equilibrium equation 8.4, and rearranging:

$$\frac{d\sigma_r}{dr} = \frac{(K_p - 1)\sigma_r}{r} - \gamma \tag{8.9}$$

Using the following change of variables $r\xi = \sigma_r$, so that $d\sigma_r = rd\xi + \xi dr$, then substituting for the quantities σ_r and $d\sigma_r$ in equation 8.8, it is seen that:

$$\frac{dr}{r} = \frac{d\xi}{(K_p - 2)\xi - \gamma} \tag{8.10}$$

The limits of integration for the above equation are such that (refer to figure 8.4):

$$r = a \quad \Rightarrow \quad \xi = \frac{\sigma_a}{a}, \text{ and } r = R \quad \Rightarrow \quad \xi = \frac{\sigma_o}{R}$$

Thus:

$$\int_{\sigma_a/a}^{\sigma_o/R} \frac{d\xi}{(K_p - 2)\xi - \gamma} = \int_a^R \frac{dr}{r}$$

On integration, it is easy to establish that:

$$\sigma_a = \frac{a}{(K_p - 2)}\left\{\left(\frac{a}{R}\right)^{K_p-2}\left[(K_p - 2)\left(\frac{\sigma_o}{R} - \frac{\gamma}{(K_p - 2)}\right)\right] + \gamma\right\} \tag{8.11}$$

Example 8.3

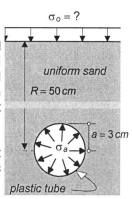

$\sigma_o = ?$

uniform sand

$R = 50\,cm$

$a = 3\,cm$

σ_a

plastic tube

A laboratory experiment is undertaken in a small transparent tank $0.5\,m \times 0.5\,m$ in cross section and $1\,m$ in depth, to simulate the collapse of a cylindrical cavity. The experiment consists of burying a thin plastic tube in a uniform sand having a unit weight $\gamma = 20\,kN/m^3$ and a friction angle $\phi' = 37°$. Considering the dimensions indicated in figure 8.7, and assuming the tube radial stiffness is equivalent to $\sigma_a = 0.3\,kN/m^2$, estimate the maximum static pressure σ_o needed to cause collapse of the tube.

Figure 8.7: Dimensions of opening.

The maximum pressure σ_o that would cause the opening to collapse is calculated from equation 8.11, which in the circumstances is rearranged as follows:

$$\sigma_o = \left(\left[(K_p - 2)\frac{\sigma_a}{a} - \gamma\right]\left(\frac{R}{a}\right)^{K_p-2} + \gamma\right)\frac{R}{(K_p - 2)}$$

with the coefficient of passive earth pressure: $K_p = \frac{1+\sin 37}{1-\sin 37} = 4.02$.

Substituting for the numerical values into the previous equation yields :

$$\sigma_0 = \left[\left(\frac{2.02}{0.03} \times 0.3 - 20 \right) \times \left(\frac{0.5}{0.03} \right)^{2.02} + 20 \right] \times \frac{0.5}{2.02} \approx 19.5 \, kN/m^2$$

This pressure is equivalent to a force $F \approx 478 \, kg$ applied across the top surface of the tank, indicating plainly that the collapse of very small openings in sand necessitates large static pressures. This is why vibration is used in conjunction with sand compaction to generate a state nearing *quick conditions* whereby the shear strength of sand is minimised, thus allowing the solid particles to be optimally positioned with respect to one another, reducing in the process the void ratio and hence increasing the density of sand.

It is essential to bear in mind that in practice, the support pressure for cohesionless soils must be provided by structural elements such as concrete or steel linings, since the application of an *air pressure* in this case would increase the total and porewater pressures equally, thus leaving the effective stresses unchanged. More importantly perhaps, *the use of large air pressures for tunnelling in clays at depth can potentially be a health hazard*. Under any circumstances, the air pressure should not exceed $350 \, kN/m^2$ (*i.e.* 3.5 *bars*), under which the maximum duration of work is limited to a mere one hour per day considering that, in this case, the time of decompression (about 50 *min*) is longer than the maximum time per shift (around 30 *min*) then, most importantly, a 6-*hour* rest interval is needed to recover physically (Tschebotarioff, 1973). Remember that an air pressure of $350 \, kN/m^2$ is equivalent to a 35 *m* head of water. In practice though, the air pressure used in conjunction with such a technique is usually limited to a safe *1 bar* ($100 \, kN/m^2$).

8.3 Tunnelling in rocks

Consider the general case of a tunnel with an elliptical cross-section, whose local x_1-axis is at angle β with respect to the horizontal as illustrated in figure 8.8. The geometry of the figure shows that at any point on the opening boundary, say point B for instance, the relationship between the angle α, which forms between the tangent at the point in question and the horizontal x-axis, and the angle θ between the normal at the point in consideration and the local x_1-axis is such that:

$$\theta = \frac{\pi}{2} - (\alpha - \beta) \tag{8.12}$$

or $\qquad 2\alpha = \pi - 2(\theta - \beta) \tag{8.13}$

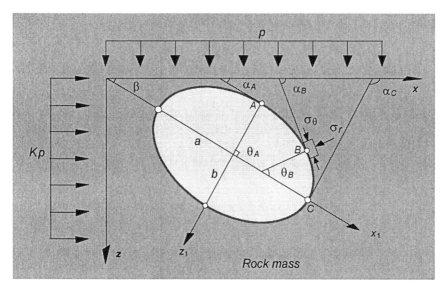

Figure 8.8: Elliptical opening in rock mass

Accordingly,

$$\cos 2\alpha = -\cos 2(\theta - \beta) \qquad (8.14)$$

and

$$\cos 2(\alpha - \beta) = -\cos 2\theta \qquad (8.15)$$

Analytical solutions to the stress distribution at any point in the rock mass do exist and reference can be made to Poulos and Davis (1974) or Jaeger and Cook (1979) in the first instance. However, these closed form solutions as well as being somewhat cumbersome and mathematically involved, cannot be extended to complex ground conditions (see Brady and Brown (1993), Timoshenko and Goodier (1970), Jaeger (1979)). For such complex ground and boundary conditions the stress analysis is usually undertaken numerically through finite element modelling (see for instance Mestat (1997), Smith and Griffiths (1998), Assadi and Sloan (1991), Zienkiewicz and Taylor (1991)).

Notwithstanding these limitations, the solution to the stress distribution at the walls of an elliptical opening is much more manageable, and It can readily be shown that for an elliptical opening of major and minor axes *2a* and *2b*, with a ratio $q = a/b$, having a major axis at an angle β with respect to the horizontal as per figure 8.8, the respective circumferential, radial and shear boundary stresses at any point of the tunnel walls are such that:

$$\sigma_\theta = \frac{p}{2q}\left\{(1+K)\left[(1+q^2)-(1-q^2)\cos 2\theta\right]\right.$$
$$\left.-(1-K)\left[(1-q^2)\cos \beta -(1+q)^2 \cos 2(\theta - \beta)\right]\right\} \qquad (8.16a)$$

$$\sigma_r = \sigma_{r\theta} = 0 \qquad\qquad (8.16b)$$

where p represents the overburden pressure, and K is the coefficient of lateral pressure. It must be appreciated that K in equation 8.16a bears no relation to the coefficient of lateral pressure at rest K_o which is an intrinsic parameter of the rock mass prior to tunnelling. Rather, K corresponds to the ratio of horizontal to vertical stresses at the tunnel walls that takes into account the stress relaxation generated by the excavation.

It is left to the reader to show that, were the elliptical opening to have a horizontal major axis (i.e. $\beta = 0$ as per figure 8.9), then the circumferential boundary stress calculated from equation 8.16a at points C and A in figure 8.9 are as follows:

- point C: $\beta = 0$, $\theta = 0$

$$\sigma_\theta = p(2q+1-K) \qquad\qquad (8.17)$$

- point A: $\beta = 0$, $\theta = \pi/2$

$$\sigma_\theta = p\left(K-1+\frac{2K}{q}\right) \qquad\qquad (8.18)$$

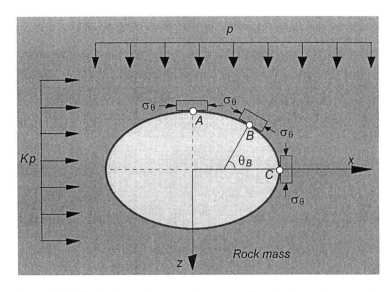

Figure 8.9: Elliptical opening in rock mass with a horizontal major axis

The general case of a circular tunnel of radius a, excavated in a rock mass and subjected to a biaxial stress field consisting of the overburden stress p and the lateral stress field Kp, (where K represents the lateral pressure coefficient as per equation 8.16a) is illustrated in figure 8.10. For a rock element, situated away from the tunnel walls a distance r from the centre of the tunnel, the complete solution to the stress and displacement distributions around the circular opening was established by Kirsch (1898):

$$\sigma_{rr} = \frac{p}{2}\left|(1+K)\left(1-\frac{a^2}{r^2}\right)-(1-K)\left(1-\frac{4a^2}{r^2}+\frac{3a^4}{r^4}\right)\cos 2\theta\right| \qquad (8.19a)$$

$$\sigma_{\theta\theta} = \frac{p}{2}\left|(1+K)\left(1+\frac{a^2}{r^2}\right)+(1-K)\left(1+\frac{3a^4}{r^4}\right)\cos 2\theta\right| \qquad (8.19b)$$

$$\sigma_{r\theta} = \frac{p}{2}\left|(1-K)\left(1+\frac{2a^2}{r^2}-\frac{3a^4}{r^4}\right)\sin 2\theta\right| \qquad (8.19c)$$

$$u_r = -\frac{pa^2}{4Gr}\left[(1+K)-(1-K)\left\{2(1-2v)+\frac{a^2}{r^2}\right\}\cos 2\theta\right] \qquad (8.20a)$$

$$u_\theta = -\frac{pa^2}{4Gr}\left[(1-K)\left\{2(1-2v)+\frac{a^2}{r^2}\right\}\sin 2\theta\right] \qquad (8.20b)$$

where G and v represent the shear modulus and Poisson's ratio of the rock mass receptively. Notice that the stresses in equations 8.19 represent the post excavation stress field, and the displacements of equations 8.20 are induced by tunnelling in the rock mass.

The boundary stresses on the tunnel walls are found by putting $r = a$ in equations 8.19, thus yielding:

$$\sigma_{\theta\theta} = p\left[(1+K)+2(1-K)\cos 2\theta\right] \qquad (8.21)$$

$$\sigma_{rr} = 0$$

$$\sigma_{r\theta} = 0$$

Interestingly, the reader may wish to check that the same equation 8.21 can be easily established from equation 8.16a by substituting for $\beta = 0$ (horizontal axis) and $q = a/b = 1$ (circular opening).

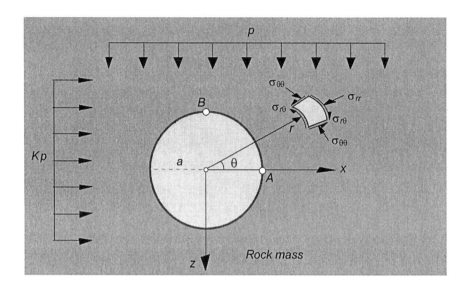

Figure 8.10: Circular tunnel in a rock mass

Finally, notice that It is common engineering practice not to take into account any tensile strength of a rock mass, and accordingly, the circumferential stress at the walls of a tunnel excavated in a rock mass having a compressive strength C should therefore be limited to the following:

$$0 < \sigma_{\theta\theta} < C \qquad\qquad\qquad (8.22)$$

As opposed to excavations in clays and sand, any support system to counteract a tensile stress in a rock mass is unlikely to alter significantly the state of stresses. Consequently, in the presence of a tensile stress, the design (*i.e.* the tunnel shape) must be altered.

Example 8.4

Consider the case of an unlined section of the channel tunnel excavated in the lower chalk marl at an average depth of 45 m below a 25 m deep seabed. The tunnel boring machine cut diameter is 8.36 m, and the chalk marl is characterised by the following parameters:
- unconfined compressive strength: $UCS = 3.5\,MN/m^2$
- saturated unit weight: $\gamma_{sat} = 23\,kN/m^3$
- shear modulus: $G = 2.4\,GN/m^2$
- Poisson's ratio: $\nu = 0.23$
- coefficient of lateral pressure: $K \approx 0.65$

The maximum and minimum circumferential stresses occur at the side wall (point A in figure 8.10) and at the tunnel crown (point B in figure 8.10) respectively, and are calculated using equation 8.21. Assuming points A and B are at a respective depth of 45 m and 41 m below seabed, and the overburden pressure p includes the pressure generated by the 25 m head of water of the *Dover Strait*, it follows that:

- at A, $\theta = 0$ and equation 8.21 reduces to:

$$\sigma_{\theta\theta}^A = p(3-K) = (45 \times 23 + 25 \times 10) \times (3. - 0.65) \approx 3020\, kN/m^2$$

- at B, $\theta = \pi/2$ and thus:

$$\sigma_{\theta\theta}^B = p(3K-1) = (41 \times 23 + 25 \times 10) \times (1.95 - 1) \approx 1133\, kN/m^2$$

Furthermore, the maximum radial displacement occurring at the tunnel's crown (point B) can be estimated from equation 8.20a:

$$u_r^B = \frac{pa^2}{4Gr}\left[(1+K)-(1-K)\left\{2(1-2v)+\frac{a^2}{r^2}\right\}\cos 2\theta\right]$$

since $r = a$ at point B, it follows that:

$$u_r^B = \frac{(41 \times 23 + 25 \times 10) \times 4.18}{4 \times 2.4 \times 10^6}[1.65 + 0.35 \times \{2 \times (1 - 0.46) + 1\}]$$

$$= 1.23 \times 10^{-3}\, m$$

This example indicates that the tunnel excavated in the lower chalk layer is everywhere in compression, meaning there is technically no need for any structural internal support for this section. Furthermore, the maximum settlement (or deformation) at the tunnel crown is too small to cause any concern, even after a time dependent deformation (or creep) is taken into account. No wonder that the experimental tunnels dug on either side of the *Dover strait* in 1881 are still standing unlined with no structural damage.

Example 8.5

In order to analyse the effect of tunnel shape on the circumferntial pressure distribution at the excavation walls, two elliptical openings are undertaken in a thick layer of unweathered hard sandstone. In either case, the overburden pressure at the tunnel crown (point B in figure 8.11) is generated by a $35\,m$ of rock having an unconfined compressive strength $C = 50\,MN/m^2$, a unit weight $\gamma = 27\,kN/m^3$, and a coefficient of lateral pressure $K = 0.3$.

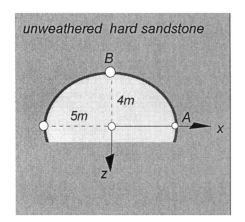 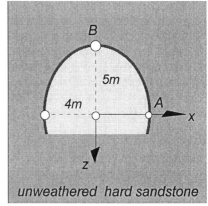

Figure 8.11: Circular tunnel in a rock mass

The tunnel on the left hand side of the figure is an ellipse of major and minor axes $10\,m$ and $8\,m$, and the circumferential stresses at A and B are calculated using equations 8.17 & 8.18 respectively:

$$\sigma_{\theta\theta}^A = P(2q + 1 - K) = (39 \times 27) \times \left(2 \times \frac{5}{4} + 0.7\right) = 3369.6\,kN/m^2$$

$$\sigma_{\theta\theta}^B = P\left(\frac{2K}{q} - 1 + K\right) = (35 \times 27) \times \left(\frac{2 \times 0.3 \times 4}{5} - 0.7\right) = -207.9\,kN/m^2$$

The shape of the tunnel on the right hand side of the figure is an ellipse of major and minor axes $8\,m$ and $10\,m$, and the circumferential stresses at A & B are thence:

$$\sigma_{\theta\theta}^A = (40 \times 27)\left(2 \times \frac{4}{5} + 0.7\right) = 2484\,kN/m^2$$

$$\sigma_{\theta\theta}^B = (35 \times 27) \times \left(\frac{2 \times 0.3 \times 5}{4} - 0.7\right) = 47.25\,kN/m^2$$

Although unweathered hard sandstone does have a tensile resistance of up to $5\,MN/m^2$, it is an engineering design practice to avoid having any tensile stress develop at the excavation walls. In this particular instance, it is seen that the tunnel on the left hand side of figure 8.11 develops some tensile stresses around the crown, whereas the mere fact of altering the tunnel shape to that of the right hand side ellipse generates a compressive stress field throughout the tunnel opening.

8.4 Calculation of settlement induced by tunnelling

8.4.1 Three dimensional settlement

The ground movement induced by tunnelling are an essential design feature since it can potentially generate excessive surface and subsurface settlements that can cause damage to services and structures. The settlement due to tunnelling can be subdivided into two categories:

- immediate settlement caused by the volume loss engendered by the excavation of the tunnel
- time dependent settlement due to the consolidation process triggered by the change in effective stresses as the excess porewater pressure generated by tunnelling dissipates with time.

In practical terms, the magnitude and effect of consolidation settlements are usually limited and can be controlled. However, there is a need to predict the immediate settlement with sufficient accuracy in order to take preventative measures if needs be to limit its effects on the built environment in the vicinity of the tunnel. The analysis of surface movements due to tunnelling is intricately linked, not only to the tunnel characteristics such as depth and dimensions, but more importantly to the method of tunnelling as well as the nature and state of soil in which the tunnel is excavated. Figure 8.12 shows a cross section of an homogeneous soil with an even ground surface.

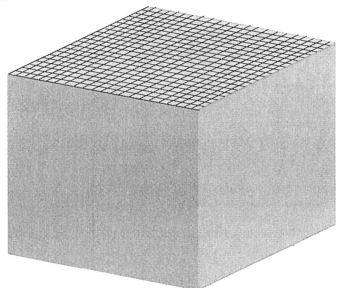

Figure 8.12: Soil mass prior to tunnelling

Figure 8.13 on the other hand, illustrates diagrammatically the deformation of the ground surface generated by the excavation of a tunnel of diameter D at a relatively shallow depth (less than 10 D) within the same soil mass.

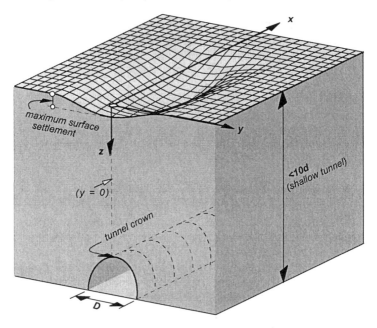

Figure 8.13: Post-tunnelling surface deformation

The cone of depression associated with the ground surface deformation in figure 8.13 is again plotted in figure 8.14 showing the soil movement into the tunnel due to stress relaxation generated by the stress redistribution as tunnelling progresses. The precise nature and extent of the ground surface settlement trough in both figures 8.13 & 8.14 depends on the stress redistribution around the tunnel, which are affected by the method of tunnelling as well as the type and state of soil. Thus, if the tunnel is excavated in a stiff overconsolidated clay for instance, using a sprayed concrete lining as temporary support, then the stress relaxation would result in a volume of soil excavated (per metre length of excavation) larger than the theoretical volume (per metre length) of the tunnel. The difference between these two volumes is known as the *volume loss* V_L (in m^3/m) that causes the ground surface above the tunnel axis to deform as per figure 8.13. On the other hand, if the tunnel is excavated in a soft plastic silt or clay containing soft pockets of weaker material, then it is likely that the soil would be grouted prior to tunnelling (to shore up its strength), and the opening would be structurally supported during excavation in order to prevent the tunnel walls from collapsing. Furthermore during tunnelling, the face of the tunnel is likely to be subjected to a pressure slightly higher than the in situ horizontal pressure due to the weight of soil at excavation level, so as to prevent the tunnel face from collapsing. The latter technique known as *Earth Pressure Balancing,* combined with grouting can in some instances cause the ground surface to heave generating a large bulge in figure 8.13 instead of a settlement trough, in which case the volume of soil excavated is actually smaller than the theoretical volume of the tunnel, and V_L corresponds in this instance to a volume gain.

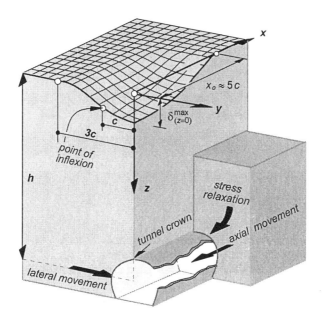

Figure 8.14: Stress realxation induced by tunnelling

From a mathematical point of view, the shape of the settlement trough can be represented reasonably well by a Gaussian distribution, and the volume of the trough per metre length of tunnel V_s (in m^3/m) can be calculated from the following relationship:

$$V_s = \int_{-\infty}^{+\infty} \delta_{(z=0)}^{max} \exp\left(-\frac{y^2}{2c_{(z=0)}^2}\right) dy \qquad (8.23)$$

where, with reference to figure 8.14:

- $\delta_{(z=0)}^{max}$ is the maximum (surface) settlement at depth $z = 0$
- $c_{(z=0)}$ is the distance from the tunnel centre line to the point of inflexion of the trough at depth $z = 0$ (see figure 8.14)

On integration, equation 8.23 yields:

$$V_s = \delta_{(z=0)}^{max} \, c_{(z=0)} \, \sqrt{2\pi} \approx 2.5 \, c_{(z=0)} \, \delta_{(z=0)}^{max} \qquad (8.24)$$

Experimental evidence supports the fact that the dimensions of the area of the surface settlement trough are limited to about $3c$ on either side of the tunnel centre line in the y-direction, and to $5c$ from the tunnel face in the x-direction of the tunnel axis as per figure 8.14. In theory, tunnels in clays are excavated under undrained (constant volume) conditions, and consequently, the volumes V_s and V_L should be identical. Practically however, the ratio V_L/V_s is affected by the method of tunnelling and the initial state of soil in which the tunnel is dug, so that:

- $V_L/V_s > 1$ for dense granular soils or stiff overconsolidated clays
- $V_L/V_s < 1$ for loose granular soils or soft clays:

Although the volume loss V_L is difficult to measure in practice, the limited data reported in the literature associated with different tunnelling projects seem to indicate that the normalised volume loss, that is the ratio:

$$p = V_s/A \qquad (8.25)$$

(A being the cross-sectional area of the tunnel) varies between 0.2 % and 3% depending on tunnelling methods. In this respect, Deane & Bassett (1995) and New & Bowers (1994) reported that the normalised volume loss p does not exceed 2% in the case of sprayed concrete lined tunnels. Mair et al. (1993) and O'Reilly & New (1982) have reported a ratio $p \approx 1.4\%$ associated with the subsurface settlements measured above the Centre Line tunnels in London clay, whereas Wood (2000) mentioned a ratio $p = 03.\%$ in the case of the Heathrow Cargo Tunnel. Furthermore, Mair et al. (1993) have established that the position of the inflexion point, and therefore the distance c, varies with depth as illustrated schematically in figure 8.15, showing the settlement above the tunnel crown increasing with depth (i.e. δ_z at depth z is larger than $\delta_{(z=0)}^{max}$). Based on data measured from different tunnelling sites, Mair et al. suggested that for clays, the maximum subsurface settlements above the crown of a tunnel with a diameter D can be cautiously estimated from the following equations:

$$\delta_{(z)} = \frac{pD^2}{4\,c_{(z)}}\sqrt{\frac{\pi}{2}} \approx 0.313\frac{pD^2}{c_{(z)}} \qquad (8.26a)$$

and

$$c_{(z)} = (h-z)\left|\frac{0.175 + 0.325\left(1-\frac{z}{h}\right)}{\left(1-\frac{z}{h}\right)}\right| \qquad (8.26b)$$

where h is the depth from the (undeformed) ground surface to the tunnel centre as per figure 8.15.

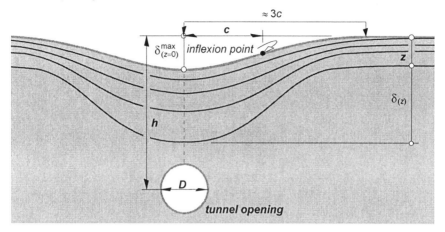

Figure 8.15: Gaussian distribution of tunnelling induced settlements

Accordingly, at the ground surface where $z = 0$, equation 8.26b reduces to:

$$C_{(z=0)} = 0.5 h \tag{8.27}$$

Thus substituting for c into equation 8.24 and rearranging, yields the following relationship for the volume of the surface settlement trough per metre length of tunnel:

$$V_s = \sqrt{\tfrac{\pi}{2}} \cdot \delta_{(z=0)}^{max} h \tag{8.28}$$

For tunnels excavated in granular soils or soft rock, the size of the trough and hence the distance c is somewhat smaller. Several empirical relationships have been suggested by various authors, and in the absence of measured values, c can be cautiously linked to the depth h through the following relationship:

$$c \approx 0.43 h + 1.1 \, (m) \tag{8.29}$$

The stage is now set for the calculation of surface settlements induced by tunnelling at any point on the surface of the trough in figure 8.14. The three dimensional nature of surface deformations is all the more important to predict so as to assess the effects of differential settlements on the built environment in the vicinity of the tunnel, due to the geometry of the trough's surface. To that effect, the following equation (Serratrice (1999, Serratrice &

Magnan 2002) can be used to calculate the settlement at any point within the space $(x, y, z = 0)$ in figure 8.14:

$$S_{(x,y)} = S_0 + 4\frac{\xi_1 r^2 h}{(h^2 + y^2)} \exp\left(-\frac{\xi_2 y^2}{(h+r)^2}\right)\left\{1 - \frac{h^2}{h^2 + (x - x_0)^2} \exp\left(-\frac{\xi_3 (x - x_0)^2}{(h+r)^2}\right)\right\} \quad (8.30)$$

where:

- $x_0 \approx 5c$: half the extent of the settlement trough in the direction of the tunnel axis (se figure 8.14)
- r is the tunnel's radius
- h is the depth from the (undeformed) ground surface to the tunnel centre

and according to Loganathan & Poulos (1998),

- $\xi_1 = (1 - v)p$ (8.31)

  v being the soil's Poisson ratio, and p is the normalised volume loss defined in equation 8.25.
- $\xi_2 = 1.38$
- $\xi_3 \approx 0.25$

As for the constant S_0 in equation 8.30, it reflects the effects of tunnel dimensions and depth, as well as the elastic characteristics of the medium through which the tunnel is excavated, and the method of tunnelling. Notwithstanding the difficulties of establishing a general relationship linking all these variables, S_0 can be estimated from the following equation based on a parametric study using finite element modelling of the behaviour of a circular horizontal tunnel excavated in a semi-infinite isotropic elastic medium, subjected to plane strain deformations (*i.e.* zero deformation along the tunnel axis: $\varepsilon_x = 0$) (Mestat 1994, Serratrice 2001, Serratrice & Magnan 2002):

$$S_0 = \lambda \frac{\gamma r^2 (3 - v)}{E}\left[K_0 - \left(\frac{h}{r} - 1\right)^{0.25}\right] \quad (8.32)$$

equation in which:

- γ is the unit weight of the medium through which the tunnel is dug
- r & h are the tunnel radius and depth of the tunnel centre, respectively
- E & v are the elasticity modulus and Poisson's ratio of the excavated medium, respectively
- K_0 is the coefficient of lateral pressure
- λ is the deconfinement ratio ($0 < \lambda \le 1$)

It must be appreciated that the coefficient K_o in equation 8.32 corresponds to the ratio of horizontal to vertical stresses at the tunnel walls that takes into account the stress release induced by the excavation.

Example 8.6

Consider the case of the *Toulon* tunnel in southern France linking the motorways *A50* (west of Toulon) and *A57* (east of Toulon). The 1800 m long tunnel was dug at an (average) depth of 34 m, and has a diameter $D = 11\,m$. The tunnel was excavated through a thick layer of sedimentary rock constituted mainly of limestone and sandstone, with the following average physical characteristics (refer to table 2.4, section 2.9 in chapter 2):

- elasticity modulus: $E = 2 \times 10^7\ kN/m^2$
- unit weight: $\gamma = 25\ kN/m^3$
- Poisson's ratio: $v = 0.25$
- Coefficient of lateral pressure: $K_o = 0.35$

The rock mass is characterised by a normalised volume loss (se equation 8.25) estimated at: $p \approx 1.3\%$, and a deconfinement ratio $\lambda = 1$. In some sections of the tunnel, the state of the (fractured) rock necessitated the use of temporary support consisting a shotcrete shells with horizontal rock bolts at the tunnel face, and 18 m long rock bolts inserted throughout the tunnel walls at an angle to the vertical as the excavation progressed, reducing markedly the excavation rate which in some instances was as little as 0.8 m per day. Based on these parameters, the 3-D settlement profile at the ground surface can be estimated from equation 8.30, in which:

$$h = 34\,m, \quad r = 5.5m, \quad c \approx 0.43h + 1.1 = 15.72\,m, \quad x_o = 5c = 78.6\,m$$

$$\xi_1 = (1 - v)p = (1 - 0.25) \times 0.013 \approx 10^{-2}, \quad \xi_2 = 1.38, \quad \xi_3 = 0.25$$

whence the constant S_o (see equation 8.32):

$$S_o = 1 \times \frac{25 \times 5.5^2 \times (3 - 0.25)}{2 \times 10^7}\left(0.35 - \left(\frac{34}{5.5} - 1\right)^{0.25}\right) = -1.2 \times 10^{-4}\,m$$

Equation 8.30 can now be used to calculate the settlement at any point (x,y) (see figure 8.14 for (x,y) directions) in the trough limited by:

$$-3c \leq y \leq 3c \quad \text{or} \quad -48\,m \leq y \leq +48\,m \qquad (8.33a)$$
$$0 \leq x \leq 5c \quad \text{or} \quad 0 \leq x \leq 79\,m \qquad (8.33b)$$

so that for instance, at the point $(x = y = 20\,m)$, the reader may wish to establish that the corresponding settlement is, according to equation 8.30:

$S_{(20,20)} = -1.2 \times 10^{-4} + 0.0159 \approx 0.0158\,m$

In particular, the surface settlement profile along the y-axis at $x = 0$ is established from the following expression derived from equation 8.30 with $x = 0$:

$$S_{(x=0,y)} = -1.2 \times 10^{-4} + \frac{35.163}{(34^2 + y^2)} \exp(-8.845 \times 10^{-4}\, y^2)$$

It is left to the reader to check the validity of the calculations at the following three points:

- $S_{(x=0,\,y=0)} = -1.2 \times 10^{-4} + 0.0304 = 30.28 \times 10^{-3}\,m$
- $S_{(x=0,\,y=20)} = -1.2 \times 10^{-4} + 0.0159 = 15.78 \times 10^{-3}\,m$
- $S_{(x=0,\,y=48)} = -1.2 \times 10^{-4} + 1.32 \times 10^{-3} = 1.2 \times 10^{-3}\,m$

Similarly, the settlement profile along the tunnel axis (that is $(x, y = 0)$ plan) is calculated from equation 8.30 with $y = 0$, and once more the reader may wish to check the validity of surface settlements at the following selected points:

- $S_{(x=10,\,y=0)} = -1.2 \times 10^{-4} + 0.0323 = 32.18 \times 10^{-3}\,m$
- $S_{(x=50,\,y=0)} = -1.2 \times 10^{-4} + 0.0173 = 17.18 \times 10^{-3}\,m$
- $S_{(x=60,\,y=0)} = -1.2 \times 0^{-4} + 9.674 \times 10^{-3} = 9.55 \times 10^{-3}\,m$
- $S_{(x=78,\,y=0)} \approx 0$

The above calculations indicate that the assumptions relating to the settlement trough dimensions of equations 8.33 are adequate.

8.4.2 Two dimensional surface and subsurface settlement

The 2-D settlement profiles illustrated in figure 8.15 can be determined using equation 8.30 with the variable $x = 0$. Alternatively, the maximum settlement at ground level $\delta_{(z=0)}^{max}$ can be calculated by combining equations 8.25 & 8.28 :

$$\delta_{(z=0)}^{max} = \frac{pD^2}{h} \sqrt{\frac{\pi}{8}} \tag{8.34}$$

where p is the normalised volume loss, D the tunnel diameter, and h the depth from the undeformed ground surface to the tunnel centre. Moreover, data amassed from field measurements indicate that for tunnels in clays, the shape of surface settlement profiles can be represented to a reasonable degree by a Gaussian distribution (Peck, 1969, Clough & Shmidt, 1980, Rankin, 1988, Mair et al. 1993). The surface and subsurface settlements can thence be calculated using the following 2-D equation:

$$S = \delta_{(z)}^{max} \exp\left(-\frac{y^2}{2c_{(z)}^2}\right)$$ (8.35)

where $c_{(z)}$ is calculated from equations 8.26b, 8.27 or 8.29 as appropriate, y is as per figure 8.14, and $\delta_{(z)}^{max}$ is calculated from equation 8.26a. Accordingly, the *surface* settlement profile along the y-axis in the previous example can also be calculated using equation 8.35, in which the maximum settlement at ground level is as follows (equation 8.34):

$$\delta_{(z=0)}^{max} = \frac{pD^2}{h}\sqrt{\frac{\pi}{8}} = \frac{0.013 \times 11^2}{34} \times \sqrt{\frac{\pi}{8}} = 0.029\,m$$

hence the ensuing *surface* settlements calculated using equation 8.35 at the three selected points ($y = 0$, $y = 20\,m$ & $y = 48\,m$):

- $S_{(y=0)} = \delta_{(z=0)}^{max} = 29 \times 10^{-3}\,m$

- $S_{(y=20)} = 0.029\exp\left(-\frac{20^2}{2 \times 15.72^2}\right) = 12.9 \times 10^{-3}\,m$

- $S_{(y=48)} = 0.029\exp\left(-\frac{48^2}{2 \times 15.72^2}\right) \approx 0.3 \times 10^{-3}\,m$

The surface settlement results calculated from both equations 8.30 & 8.35 are plotted in figure 8.16, which includes settlement points measured *in situ* at one of several strategic locations during the tunnel construction (Serratrice & Magnan, 2002). Clearly, the settlements calculated from equation 8.30 compare very favourably with the measured values, which indicates the validity of the 3-D approach to settlement analysis.

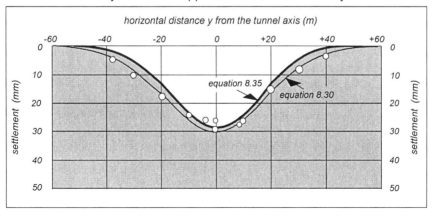

Figure 8.16 Calculated and measured settlements, Toulon tunnel

Example 8.7

The Channel Tunnel Rail Link (CTRL) includes a total of 17.5 km high speed London tunnel between St Pancras station and Dagenham as illustrated in figure 8.17. It also includes a 3.5 km long Thames tunnel excavated at a gradient of 1:40, reaching a maximum depth of 37.5 m under the *Thames* river.   Just outside Strattford, the London tunnel, excavated under an urban area, passes under two 4.6 m diameter cast iron Central Line tunnels of the London Underground.

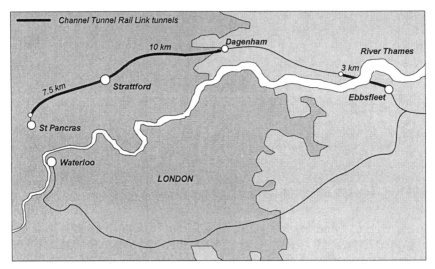

Figure 8.17 *Channel Tunnel Rail Link (CTRL) in London.*

The cover between the CTRL and the closest Central Line tunnel is a mere 4.3 m as illustrated in figure 8.18. During the tunnel boring machine operations, the Central Line remained in operation, albeit with a restricted speed. Furthermore, in order to accommodate any movement due to CTRL tunnel boring, every fifth ring of the Central Line's cast iron lining was loosened to enable some flexibility in an otherwise rigid structure. Careful *in situ* monitoring showed that the normalised volume loss achieved during tunnelling was limited to 0.3%.

The maximum settlement at the ground surface as well as the settlement at both Central Line tunnels crown and invert can now be evaluated. Since the CTRL tunnel is excavated in London clay, equation 8.34 can be used to calculate the maximum ground settlement at road level:

$$\delta_{z=0)}^{max} = \frac{pD^2}{h}\sqrt{\frac{\pi}{8}} = \frac{0.003 \times 8.11^2}{22}\sqrt{\frac{\pi}{8}} = 5.62 \times 10^{-3}\,m$$

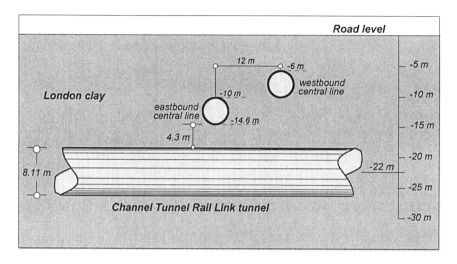

Figure 8.18 Channel Tunnel Rail Link (CTRL) near Strattford, London

Next, the settlement at depth z below the road level is calculated from equations 8.26. Hence at the crown of the westbound Central Line, the calculation parameters are such that (refer to figure 8.18):

$z = 6\,m$, $h = 22\,m$ and $c_{(z)}$ is calculated from equation 8.26b:

$$c_{(z=6m)} = (22 - 6) \times \left[\frac{0.175 + 0.325 \times \left(1 - \dfrac{6}{22}\right)}{\left(1 - \dfrac{6}{22}\right)} \right] = 9.05\,m$$

whence a crown settlement (equation 8.26a):

$$\delta_{z=6m} = 0.313 \times \frac{0.003 \times 8.11^2}{9.05} = 6.82 \times 10^{-3}\,m$$

The settlement at the invert of the same westbound Central Line tunnel is calculated in a similar way, knowing that in this case: $z = 10.6\,m$, and:

$$c_{z=10.6m} = (22 - 10.6) \times \left[\frac{0.175 + 0.325 \times \left(1 - \dfrac{10.6}{22}\right)}{\left(1 - \dfrac{10.6}{22}\right)} \right] = 7.555\,m$$

thus:

$$\delta_{(z=10.6m)} = 0.313 \times \frac{0.003 \times 8.11^2}{7.555} = 8.16 \times 10^{-3}\,m$$

The dimensions in figure 8.18 indicate that a similar settlement of $\approx 8\,mm$ would occur at the crown of the Eastbound Central Line tunnel. However, the settlement at the invert of the Eastbound tunnel is such that $z = 14.6\,m$ and:

$$C_{(z=14.6m)} = (22 - 14.6) \times \left[\frac{0.175 + 0.325 \times \left(1 - \frac{14.6}{22}\right)}{\left(1 - \frac{14.6}{22}\right)} \right] = 6.255\,m$$

Hence a settlement:

$$\delta_{(z=14.6m)} = 0.313 \times \frac{0.003 \times 8.11^2}{6.255} = 9.88 \times 10^{-3}\,m$$

8.4.3 Surface and subsurface settlement induced by microtunnelling

Microtunnels are shallow service tunnels with nominal diameters varying between $100\,mm$ and $1000\,mm$, though there are instances where the upper limit is exceeded. Given the small dimensions and the relative shallow depth, microtunnelling (which is also referred to in a rather austere way as trenchless technology) is a fully automated, remotely controlled technique consisting principally of installing a hydraulically operated jacking unit in a pre-excavated shaft, then jacking pipes towards a target pit. In so doing, the soil is either pushed aside to make room for the pipe, or excavated using a small size tunnel boring machine that removes the spoil through the jacked pipes. The drive length is dependent on the friction developed at the pipe/soil interface during jacking, as well as the loading of the pipe joints.

As in the case of excavation of larger deeper tunnels, microtunnelling induces settlements at and below the ground surface. The analysis of the stability of microtunnels faces on the other hand is mainly based on short term total stresses given the speed with which such excavations can take place. Although the surface settlement induced by a microtunnel is calculated using equation 8.35, the volume of the trough per metre length of tunnel V_s (in m^3/m) is, in this case, given by the following relationship:

$$V_s = \frac{\pi}{4}\left(D_e^2 - D_p^2\right) \tag{8.36}$$

where D_e represents the cut diameter of the microtunnel, and D_p corresponds to the internal diameter of the jacked pipe. According to equation 8.26, the maximum ground settlement generated above the crown of a microtunnel is thus:

$$\delta_{(z=0)}^{max} = \frac{V_s}{C_{(z=0)}\sqrt{2\pi}} \tag{8.37}$$

where the distance $c_{(z=0)}$ is calculated using equation 8.27 for pipes jacked in clays. Were the microtunnel to be excavated in sand or in soft rock, the following adjusted form of equation 8.29 is used to take into account the size of the tunnel:

$$c_{(z=0)} \approx 0.43\,h + D_p \qquad\qquad (8.38)$$

Example 8.8

A pipe of internal diameter $D_p = 900\,mm$ is jacked in a medium clay at a depth h. The microtunnel is excavated using a remotely controlled tunnel boring machine with a cut diameter $D_e = 950\,mm$. Calculate the depth h (from the ground surface to the centre of the tunnel) so that the maximum surface settlement above the tunnel crown is limited to $15\,mm$.

Using equation 8.27 and 8.36 to calculate $c_{(z=0)}$ and V_s respectively, the reader may wish to check that the depth h is such that:

$$h = \frac{\pi \times (0.95^2 - 0.9^2)}{4 \times 0.015 \times 0.5 \times \sqrt{2\pi}} \approx 3.86\,m$$

If the same pipes were jacked in a sandy soil under the same limiting conditions, then the depth h would be found with the help of equation 8.38, all other parameters being identical:

$$h = \frac{1}{0.43}\left[\frac{\pi \times (0.95^2 - 0.9^2)}{4 \times 0.015 \times \sqrt{2\pi}} - 0.9\right] = 2.4\,m$$

8.5 Tunnelling methods in soft grounds

8.5.1 The Sprayed Concrete Lining (SCL) design method

The short term stability of a tunnel (that is the stability of the tunnel walls during excavation) constitutes the most important aspect of a tunnelling project since it affects the safety of the working environment and the magnitude of settlement at the ground surface above the tunnel. Although tunnelling in hard grounds such as hard compact rocks does not require any support system during excavation, a permanent lining is always used to protect against water ingress or any unforeseen structural weakness of the rock mass.   However, tunnels dug in such grounds can stand safely unsupported for long periods of time so that the final lining can even be applied after the excavation is completed, although in practice segmental concrete lining is installed as the tunnel progresses. At the other end of the spectrum, tunnelling through soils such as saturated sands or silts with little or no cementation can lead to running ground conditions; in which case the tunnel excavation must be shielded by a steel tube and the face has to be supported using a closed shield with a narrow or adjustable slots that allow the spoil material to pass into the shield at a controlled rate.

Tunnelling through soft grounds on the other hand presents the engineer with a greater challenge in that a primary means of support for the tunnel walls must be provided *during* excavation to prevent collapse until more permanent support can be placed. The terms *soft grounds* are interpreted liberally in this context since they include hard overconsolidated stiff clays (with an average undrained shear strength in excess of $300 \, kN/m^2$ at typical tunnelling depths) and weak fractured rocks. The problem of tunnelling through such grounds in urban areas relates essentially to settlement of the built environment above the tunnel which must be kept to acceptable levels. To do so, one cost-effective engineering tunnelling method consists of applying closed rings of sufficient thickness of sprayed concrete and mesh or fibre reinforcement to the tunnel walls as excavation progresses. The method known as the *Sprayed Concrete Linings (SCL)* is sometimes referred to (inaccurately?) as the New Austrian Tunnelling Method (NATM). The SCL is a well established method which provides temporary support for tunnels dug in soft grounds in urban areas during the crucial period of excavation when the tunnel walls are affected by the change in stress field that can potentially cause them to collapse. Provided the design is properly undertaken, the SCL method can be applied safely, flexibly and cost effectively. Different stages of the method are illustrated in figure 9.19 with the cross section showing a primary lining used to stabilise the excavation walls which incorporate a drainage layer, thus allowing water seepage to take place and reducing the porewater pressure in the process; the final lining being applied with a waterproof geotextile fleece.

The spraying of the initial primary lining results in an immediate closure of the invert ring as the excavation progresses, whereas the application of the final lining aims at securing the long term stability of the tunnel walls. The initial lining in particular is crucial since it provides an immediate (short term) increase of stiffness of the excavation walls. The time within which a closed sprayed concrete ring is formed around the excavation walls is a design specification, and can vary between 8 and 24 hours from completion of an excavation advance depending on the type of excavated material. The variation with time of the sprayed concrete compressive strength C_s, illustrated in figure 8.20, shows that the SCL can potentially develop a compressive strength of up to $4 \, MN/m^2$, just one hour after being applied, thus enhancing markedly the stiffness of the excavation walls. The compressive strength of this temporary initial lining can reach $40 \, MN/m^2$ after 28 days, by which time a permanent lining would have to be applied.

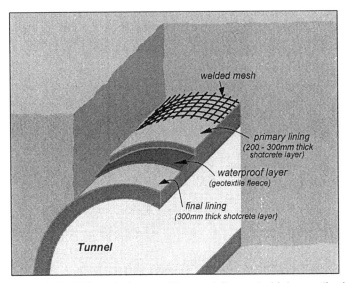

Figure 8.19: Different stages of Sprayed Concrete Lining method

term) increase of stiffness of the excavation walls. The time within which a closed sprayed concrete ring is formed around the excavation walls is a design specification, and can vary between 8 and 24 hours from completion of an excavation advance depending on the type of excavated material. The variation with time of the sprayed concrete compressive strength C_s, illustrated in figure 8.20, shows that the SCL can potentially develop a compressive strength of up to $4\,MN/m^2$ just one hour after being applied, thus enhancing markedly the stiffness of the excavation walls. The compressive strength of this temporary initial lining can reach $40\,MN/m^2$ after 28 days, by which time a permanent lining would have to be applied. In practice, the SCL is applied in two stages so as to have a primary lining followed by a final lining as illustrated in figure 8.19. The type of materials required for the initial primary lining consist generally of a welded mesh, fibre reinforcement , lattice arches, and sprayed concrete. Welded mesh made of $8\,mm$ steel wires at $200\,mm$ centres, or $6\,mm$ wires at $150\,mm$ centres are most commonly used in practice to provide a mesh on which concrete is sprayed until a design thickness is achieved. The sprayed concrete strength is enhanced by the use of up to $50\,kg$ of steel fibre per cubic metre of concrete (about 2% per weight). The plain or zinc-coated steel fibres are generally characterised by a length to equivalent diameter ratio (also known as aspect ratio) between 60 and 100. The use of lattice arches in conjunction with SCL not only provides a template for the excavation profile, but also helps secure the mesh reinforcement before the sprayed concrete is applied. Furthermore, lattice arches can provide support for any anchors should they be required to stabilise the ground in which the tunnel is excavated.

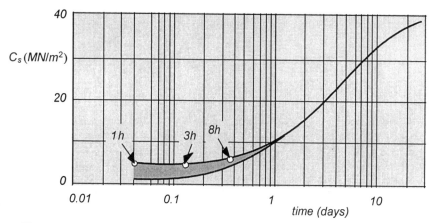

Figure 8.20: Variation with time of the Sprayed Concrete compressive strength

The sprayed concrete on the other hand consists of a mixture of cement, coarse and fine aggregates, as well as appropriate additives such as silica fume (pozzolnic material that enhances the concrete strength and density), accelerators (to increase the setting time of concrete), and inhibitors (to control the hydration of the shotcrete mix). The sprayed concrete is applied using one of two processes:

- a dry mix technique whereby water is added to the dry aggregates, cement, and additives at the delivery nozzle
- a wet mix process in which a wet ready-mixed concrete is supplied to the delivery nozzle where an accelerator is added if required.

Although the dry mix process yields a high strength concrete lining due to the lower water/cement ratio used, it can only be applied at a rate of circa $5\,m^3/h$ per nozzle, and most importantly, the process can be characterised by up to 30% rebound (i.e. up to 30% of sprayed concrete can potentially be lost). Furthermore, the rebound consists mainly of the coarser aggregate material, which leaves essentially a mortar pad at the soil/shotcrete interface. The wet mix concrete in contrast can be sprayed at a rate of up to $10\,m^3/h$ per hand-held nozzle and $20\,m^3/h$ per automated nozzle. The rebound in this case can reach 10%, although the achieved strength of the lining is somewhat lower than that of the dry mix process. In practice, the SCL method is by and large self regulatory since a poor quality shotcrete is usually characterised by a high percentage rebound. Moreover, the quality control is facilitated by the relatively straightforward inspection technique which consists of sounding the finished lining to check for any hollow or low adhesion areas which, if found, should be automatically demolished and resprayed.

8.5.2 Tunnel boring machines (TBMs)

Tunnel excavations are undertaken using either *full face tunnel boring machines* (TBMs), or partial face machines. A full face TBM is a machine with which circular cross-section tunnels are excavated. This type of machine sketched in figure 8.21 includes a circular cutterhead, with cutting tools mounted on (usually 8) radial arms designed to accommodate disc cutters or picks, or a combination of both depending on the ground's geology. Apart from the cutterhead, a full face TBM has a rear gripper unit which acts as a temporary anchor point while the front excavating section is thrust forward in small increments, facilities for erecting permanent tunnel lining which consists of either precast concrete or precast iron segments erected concurrently to the excavation, as well as a system for spoil removal and a shielded area that provides protection for the operating crew. The cost of a full face TBM increases proportionally to the tunnel diameter which can vary from under $1\,m$ for microtunnels, to over $12\,m$ for large diameter tunnels. Apart from microtunnelling, the capital and operational costs of a full face TBM are high, thus restricting the use of such machines to the excavation of tunnels longer than $1.5\,km$ (approximately 1 mile). From a practical perspective, a full face TBM can penetrate most types of soils (from clays to hard rocks), and given the length of the machine and its trailing gear, as well as the dimension of its cutterhead, $50\,m$ represents a typical minimum turning radius of a TBM. Furthermore, a permanent lining is always used concurrently to the excavation even when the ground in which the tunnel is excavated is completely self-supporting. The lining consists mainly of precast concrete segments assembled in situ, and designed in a way that incorporates knuckle joints so as not to transmit bending moments around the ring.

Tunnelling through highly fissured rocks or saturated sand and silts at depth is doubly challenging, given that the walls of the tunnel are liable to collapse, and the water ingress into the tunnel can occur at a very high pressure. Under such circumstances, not only the tunnel must be shielded by a steel tube, but also a closed face TBM with narrow or adjustable slots that allow the soil material to pass into the shield at a controlled rate should be used instead of an open face machine (see figure 8.21). Moreover, the total lateral pressure (including the porewater pressure) exerted at the tunnel face level should be balanced so as to prevent the face from collapsing into the cutterhead of the TBM. In such cases, and depending on ground permeability, either an *Earth Pressure Balance* TBM is used whereby pressurised water is injected into the tunnel face through the TBM cutterhead slots, or the tunnel excavation is undertaken using a bentonite slurry.

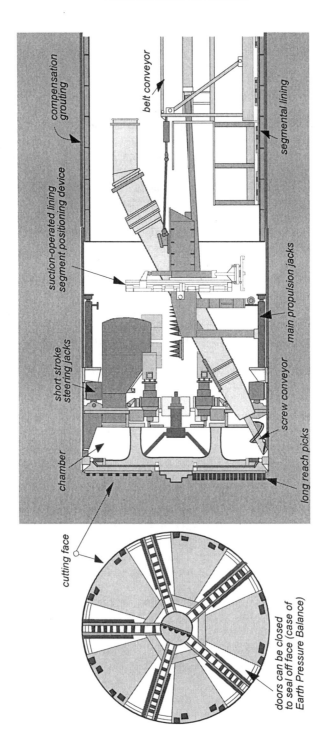

Figure 8.21: Full face tunnel boring machine (TBM)

Figure 8.22 delimits the areas (i.e. the type of soil) within which either technique can be used.

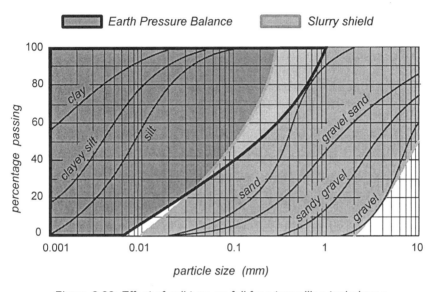

Figure 8.22: Effect of soil type on full face tunnelling techniques

Earth pressure balance TBMs with bentonite injection around the shield annulus were used in the excavation of the CTRL London tunnels (Channel Tunnel Rail Link illustrated in figure 8.17) where some 60% of the tunnels were driven through sand (Upnor and Thanet sands) with an average porewater pressure in excess of $300\,kN/m^2$ (i.e. 3 bars). Compensation grouting was systematically applied around the tail skin of TBMs to fill the annulus between the tunnel lining ring and the TBM excavation diameter, thus limiting the relative volume loss and reducing ground settlement markedly (refer to example 8.7). A large proportion of the French side of the *Channel Tunnel* (see the following section on the channel Tunnel case study) was excavated through a challenging terrain which included a number of fault lines, with some sections driven through the softer grey chalk layer which lays above the chalk-marl. Consequently, the stability of the excavation face was provided by earth pressure balance TBMs, where in some instances, these machines operated with a face pressure of 1 *MPa* (that is $1000\,kN/m^2$ or 10 bars).

Partial face tunnel boring machines consisting of a cutter head mounted at the end of a hydraulic boom allow for the excavation of a section of the tunnel face at a time, and are most commonly used in conjunction with sprayed concrete linings (SCL). Apart from stability (therefore safety) considerations, partial face boring machines present the advantage of being versatile, allowing for the cutting of right angle corners and the excavation of irregular tunnel cross-sections with any radius of curvature or invert slope. Although the excavation sequences used for partial face advance techniques in conjunction with SCL depend on ground conditions, the following four variations are most commonly used in practice:

A • *Crown, bench and invert excavation sequence:*
During this conventional partial face advance illustrated schematically in figure 8.23, the crown face is characterised by a domed profile so as to maximise the face resistance to any potential inward movement generated by the active lateral pressure at excavation level. Furthermore, the bench face should be inclined to generate a buttress effect, thus enhancing the stability of excavation. The sequence indicated in figure 8.23 starts with the crown heading, followed immediately by full width bench excavation. Although the distances *a* & *b* in the figure depend on the type of material excavated, *b* should not exceed 2.5 m, whereas *a* can reach a value of 20 m. However, these nominal values should only be used as a guide.

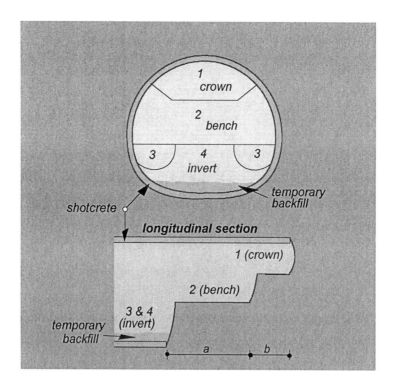

Figure 8.23: Crown, bench and invert excavation sequence

As each section advances, sprayed concrete is immediately applied (including mesh and lattice arch sections as appropriate). Most importantly, because of the temporary backfill in the invert section (see figure 8.23, the sprayed concrete wall should be thickened at bench level to provide adequate support to the arch during the final phase of excavation of the invert. Note that in practice, this technique is more suited to soft rock ground excavations.

B • *Twin sidewall drift excavation sequence*
During this sequence, the two sidewall drifts are driven concurrently maintaining a lag as illustrated in figure 8.24. Once more the distance *a* as well as the lag dimension are usually estimated on site by the excavation operator, but as a general rule, a distance $a \approx 20\,m$ for a typical $9\,m$ diameter tunnel is conducive to the overall stability of the excavation.

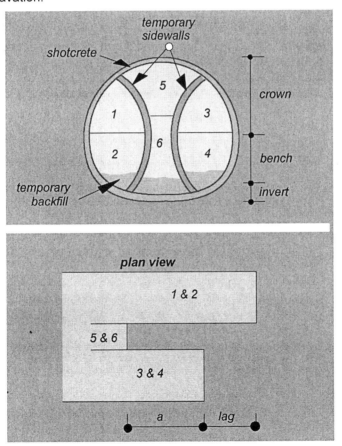

Figure 8.24: Twin sidewall drift excavation sequence

Sprayed concrete lining (with mesh, lattice arch sections) are applied to the outer walls as the excavation progresses. Concurrently, the inner walls of the drifts are sprayed with temporary concrete. The central core excavation is next undertaken as a heading bench and invert sequence, breaking in the process the temporary inner drift walls. The joints are thence cleaned, and the mesh and lattice arch sections extended, followed by the spraying of concrete. As in the previous case, because of the temporary backfill in the invert section in figure 8.24, the sprayed concrete wall should be thickened at bench level to provide adequate support to the arch during the final phase of excavation of the invert.

C • *Single sidewall excavation sequence*

This technique uses a single temporary sidewall and is illustrated in figure 8.25. It is essential for the sequence in the figure to be executed in that order in that the left hand side drift must be first excavated so as to maximise the resistance of the ground through the domed profile of inner wall which should be sprayed with temporary concrete as the excavation progresses.

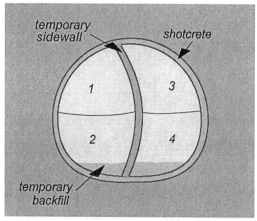

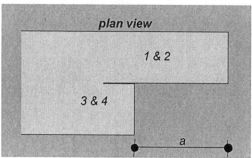

Figure 8.25: Single sidewall excavation sequence

On developing an adequate lag (once more $a \approx 20\,m$ for a typical $9\,m$ diameter tunnel), the right side drift is then excavated, making sure that sidewall is concurrently sprayed with temporary concrete on the right hand side. As the second drift advances the central wall is broken and the mesh & lattice arch sections extended then sprayed with shotcrete. Similarly, proper attention should be paid to the invert section during the final phase of excavation

D • *Pilot tunnels*
This technique illustrated in figure 8.26 offers many advantages. In particular, the excavation sequence does not lead to any jointing in the invert. The method consists of driving full face a circular (or near circular) tunnel, spraying the inside wall with temporary concrete, then enlarging the tunnel to the desired dimensions in such a way that the invert of the pilot tunnel is retained and is incorporated in the final lining of the enlarged tunnel. When applicable, this technique results in a faster execution time, and most importantly limits the settlement at ground level due to the marked reduction in volume loss.

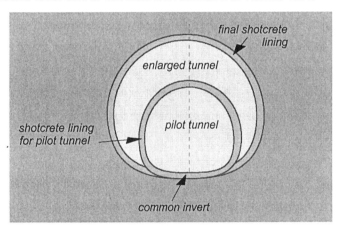

Figure 8.26: Pilot tunnel excavation technique

8.5.3 The *Channel Tunnel (Le tunnel sous la Manche)*: case study

The excavation of a tunnel underneath the Dover strait (*le Pas de Calais*) - which corresponds to the narrowest part of the English Channel (*La Manche*) - linking England to France dates back to the early 1880s when a circa $2\,m$ diameter tunnel was dug through the chalk-marl for a distance of about $2\,km$ on the French side, and a similar $1\,km$ long tunnel was excavated on the UK side. However towards the end of the nineteenth century, Europe was characterised by political turmoil, none more so than France where, in 1870, the Franco-Prussian war resulted in the defeat of

Napoleon III at the battle of *Sedan*, which precipitated the collapse of the French Empire and resulted in the creation of the third Republic. These political events occurred on the watch of Queen Victoria, whose reign over the British Empire was then at its zenith and unsurprisingly perhaps, the Channel Tunnel project was deemed a potential "conduit" for political and social unrest and was hence abandoned. This *grand projet* was never completely discarded, though it took the political establishments in both London and Paris more than 100 years to revive it. The scheme was relaunched in the early 1980s with a brief that consists - in its simplest form - of excavating two single rail track (with a standard 1.435 m gauge) running tunnels with identical internal diameters of circa 7.6 m, separated by a 4.8 m internal diameter service tunnel situated midway between the running tunnels and connected to them by cross-passages and pressure relief ducts at regular intervals throughout the length of the project.

The service tunnel was by far the most important component of the entire project for the following reasons:

- being excavated well ahead of the two running tunnels, it was used as pilot tunnel allowing for the undertaking of a more thorough in situ investigation of the geological conditions. It was used at different sections to carry out ground reinforcement through grout injection or anchor erection to improve the ground conditions before the excavation of the two running tunnels
- The service tunnel is central to the safety of the entire project since it is designed so that it can be accessed from the running tunnels at regular short intervals throughout their length. The design stipulates that the evacuation of both running tunnels under emergency conditions should take less than 90 min
- logistically, as well as providing a drainage channel, the service tunnel accommodates water and pumping mains, and acts as fresh air supply duct to the tunnel complex in normal operation. In order to prevent smoke ingress in the event of fire in one or both running tunnels, the service tunnel is designed to be kept under positive pressure in relation to the running tunnels in all conditions.

The two running tunnels on the other hand carry power supplies, secondary drainage, cooling pipes, walkways and auxiliary service. They are designed to act as the main air ducts for the additional ventilation system to control the smoke direction in the event of fire. Both tunnels were designed to accommodate fast passengers-only trains travelling at speeds of up to 200 km/h, as well as relatively slow shuttle trains which are specially designed to carry cars and all types of heavy goods vehicles the short distance between the two terminals at Folkestone and Sangatte (see figure 8.27). Due consideration was given to the track design so as to allow passenger trains to travel at high speed while minimising the track excessive wear that can be caused by the low speed shuttle trains especially on the low rail resulting from the use of a large cant on curved sections of the track. Consequently, all horizontal curves in both running tunnels are characterised by an absolute minimum radius of 4000 m, and all vertical curves are parabolic in shape with radii at the vertex of 15000 m (resulting in a vertical acceleration of 0.03 g at 200 km/h). Furthermore, safety considerations and drainage conditions resulted in the adoption of a maximum and a minimum gradients of 1.1% and 0.18% respectively in both running tunnels. The type of vehicles for which the service tunnel is designed and their relatively low speed (only rubber tyre vehicles running at a maximum speed of 80 km/h) led to less stringent design criteria for the tunnel resulting in minimum horizontal and vertical radii of 1000 m and 3000 m respectively, as well as a maximum gradient of 3.5%. The 7.6 m internal diameter running tunnels are excavated 30 m apart centre-to-centre, with the 4.8 m internal diameter service tunnel in the middle as illustrated in figure 8.27. Safety requirements are such that in the event of an emergency, total evacuation of both running tunnels should be achieved within 90 min. In order to satisfy these requirements, the running tunnels are connected to the service tunnel through cross-passages at 375 m intervals (see tunnels cross sections in figure 8.27). The 3 m internal diameter cross passages incorporate fireproof evacuation doors which may be operated in all working conditions. Furthermore, in order to alleviate the differential air pressures and aerodynamic resistance generated when trains travel at speed in a very long tunnel, 2 m internal diameter pressure relief ducts connecting the two running tunnels and crossing above the service tunnel were built at 250 m intervals (figure 8.27). The use of these pressure relief ducts reduces markedly the power needed to drive a train at operational speed, particularly in the case of shuttle trains characterised by a large ratio of train to tunnel cross-section, known as *blockage ratio*. Lastly for operational and maintenance reasons, four double crossovers were incorporated between Folkestone and Sangatte terminals, allowing the trains to cross from one running track to the other. Two of these lie close to the two terminals, and the other two are located under the sea dividing the tunnel length into three approximately equal sections. An intensive and somewhat expensive site investigation was undertaken in the Dover strait over a 30-year period (between 1958 and 1987), and after thorough analyses, the chalk marl layer was deemed most suitable for tunnelling, offering adequate short term stability during excavation. Chalk-marl formation consists of clayey carbonate mudstone strata with strength ranging from moderate in the case of carbonate beds to relatively weak for clay-rich layers.   The lower chalk-marl has a typical unconfined compressive strength (UCS) of 3.5 MPa and an undrained stiffness $E_u = 0.8 \, GPa$, as opposed to the upper and basal chalk marl which have a comparable average UCS of about 8 MPa and a typical $E_u \approx 1.5 \, GPa$.

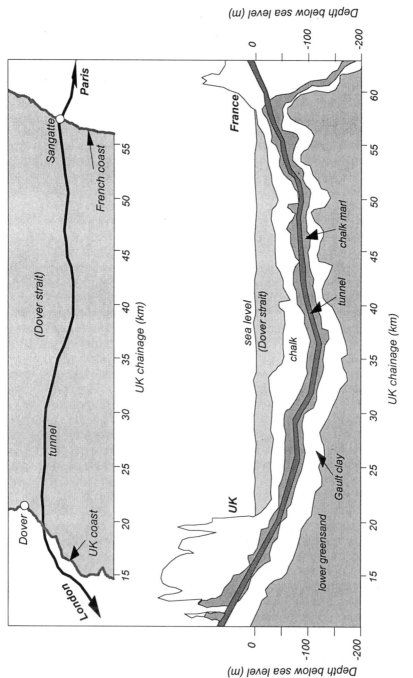

Figure 8.27: Channel Tunnel (Tunnel sous la Manche)

The mass permeability of the chalk marl varies between $4 \times 10^{-7}\, m/s$ and $2 \times 0^{-8}\, m/s$ with a typical value of $10^{-7}\, m/s$ (that is roughly $10\, ft/year$) for the lower chalk marl, making it practically impermeable. The tunnel, with a total length of $51\, km$ between the two terminals, was dug mostly in the lower half of the chalk-marl layer where the excavation depth in the UK side was kept at least $10\, m$ below the weathered rock, with an overall average depth of $45\, m$ below seabed. Consequently, the tunnel section under the seabed is $5\, km$ longer than the $33\, km$ Dover-Calais sea crossing. On the French side, the tunnels were excavated through a more challenging terrain which included a number of fault lines with some sections dug through the softer grey chalk layer which lays above the chalk-marl. Whence, the stability of the excavation face in the French side was provided by earth pressure balance (EPB) tunnel boring machines, where in some instances, these machines operated with a face pressure of $1\, MPa$. Furthermore, in order to counter the effects of water seepage due to the relatively high permeability as well as geological fault lines, watertight gasketed bolted linings were used during tunnelling in the French side.

The marine section of the running tunnels was excavated using two identical tunnel boring machines (TBM) characterised by an $8.36\, m$ cut diameter. The cutterhead of each TBM machine has a total of 198 picks mounted on 8 radial arms, designed to accommodate 60 disc cutters instead of the picks, or to use a combination of discs and picks. All in all on the UK side, some $84\, km$ of tunnels were excavated using a total of six open faced TBMs, each with a rear gripper unit acting as a temporary anchor point while the front excavating section is thrust forward in $1.5\, m$ increments. Tunnel lining was applied concurrently to excavation using precast concrete segments, and the overall average excavation (of all machines) was $150\, m$ per week. On the other hand, the geology along the $8\, km$ land tunnels to Folkestone terminal includes a series of old landslips which could have a detrimental effect on the short term stability of excavations. In order to alleviate these effects, the spray concrete lining method (SCL) was used in conjunction with the excavation of this section of running tunnels.

As indicated earlier, the service tunnel was excavated ahead of the two running tunnels, and was thus used to investigate closely the tunnel geology through probe holes drilled sideways. This in situ investigation showed that a $700\, m$ long section of the marine tunnels was characterised by a permeability ranging from 3 to 29 lugeons and was therefore deemed in need of grouting (1 lugeon unit = 1 litre per metre per minute at a pressure of $1\, MN/m^2$ or 10 bars, with grouting required for a permeability > 3 lugeons). Equally, in order to improve the ground conditions and to increase the safety of the working environment, it was decided to grout the last $500\, m$ of each of the two land running tunnel drives on the UK side. The ground treatment operation was achieved by drilling and grouting from the service tunnel in advance of both running tunnels. The grouting was undertaken using a *claquage* (hydrofracture) technique to penetrate the fine fissures of the ground during which a low viscosity silicate-based grout (20% bentonite/cement grout) was injected under a controlled pressure of $1.8\,MN/m^2$ or 18 bars (corresponding to the overburden pressure). The technique, introduced earlier in section 1.8 (chapter 1) , is based on the use of a *tube à manchettes* to induce a hydrofracture in the surrounding soil matrix.

This hydrofracture technique was applied to the last $500\,m$ of each of the two land running tunnel drives on the UK side so as to form a $3\,m$ annulus of treated ground around the upper half of both running tunnels with minimum interference with the service tunnel excavation. In all grouting instances, post-treatment packer tests indicated that the treated ground permeability had in most instances reduced to less than 1 lugeon, minimising the water inflow to the tunnels in the process. The tunnel connections including cross passages and relief ducts as per figure 8.26 were excavated by hand using pneumatic spades. The lining of these connections consisted of spheroidal graphite iron segments, except from the openings in the main tunnels where a hybrid concrete/cast iron lining was used. The UK undersea crossover, (located some $8\,km$ from Shakespeare cliff), consists of a large $164\,m \times 21\,m \times 15.4\,m$ chamber excavated using the sprayed concrete lining method. This was achieved by reducing the spacing between the two running tunnels from the standard $30\,m$ (figure 8.26) to just $10.5\,m$ centre-to-centre at the crossover head walls, while diverting the service tunnel some $40\,m$ to the north of the chamber. The French undersea crossover on the other hand was constructed by driving a number of $3\,m$ wide parallel adjacent headings and filling them with concrete, thus forming the permanent crossover walls on completion. Towards the end of excavation at the junctions of the British and French running tunnels, the British TBMs were diverted downwards on a $300\,m$ radius vertical curve, and once their carcasses were below the permanent tunnels line, the back-up equipment was removed and the TBMs were entombed in some $2000\,m^3$ of low strength concrete. This operation allowed the French TBMs to drive to a position within $1\,m$ of the last permanent lining segmental ring where they were dismantled leaving in place only their outer skin, so that the last section of each junction could be completed.

Problems

8.1 Refer to example 8.4 (section 8.3) concerning a section of the *Channel Tunnel* excavated in the lower chalk marl, at a depth of $45\,m$ below seabed. Using equations 8.19 & 8.20, calculate then plot the profile of radial and circumferential stresses as well as displacements induced by tunnelling in one quadrant of the tunnel.

8.2   A 4.8 m diameter tunnel is excavated in a thick layer of a saturated firm clay at a depth of 12 m, using a partial face boring machine in conjunction with the sprayed concrete lining method (see section 8.5.2). The ground surface is subjected to a uniform pressure $\sigma_o = 40\,kN/m^2$ over a wide area as per figure p8.2

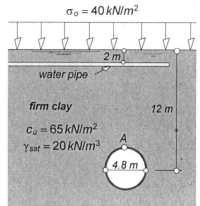

Figure p8.2

a • Check if the tunnel walls require any internal pressure during the tunnelling operation

b • Check the stability of the tunnel's face

8.3   a • Considering that the normalised volume loss measured during tunnelling in the previous problem *8.2* is $p = 0.8\%$, calculate the maximum settlement induced by tunnelling at the ground surface above the tunnel's crown.

b • Figure p8.2 shows a 55 *cm* water pipe buried 2 *m* below ground. In order to limit the structural damage of the PVC pipe, the tunnelling induced settlement should be limited to a maximum of 10 *mm*. Check if this condition is met

c • Calculate the settlement at the tunnel's crown (point *A*).

d • Using equation 8.35, calculate then plot the surface settlement profile corresponding to the tunnel cross section in figure p8.2.

Ans: a- $\delta_{z=0}^{max} = 9.6 \times 10^{-3}\,m$,   b- $S_{z=2} = 10.8\,mm$,   c- $S_{z=9.6} = 0.02\,m$

8.4   Use equation 8.35 to calculate then plot the settlement profiles at 2 m depth intervals relating to the tunnel cross section in figure p8.2.

8.5   Refer to figure *p8.5* which relates to the foundation of *Antonio Gaudi*'s famous Barcelona cathedral the *Sagrada Familia*.

Notwithstanding the poor quality of the artistic impression in the figure of the yet unfinished building (2007), its piled foundation is embedded in a saturated overconsolidated firm sand as illustrated. The final section of the high speed rail link between Madrid and Barcelona proved to be controversial, since this final leg from *Sants* train station to the city centre consists of a 12 *m* diameter tunnel. Although the tunnel is at a depth of 33 *m*, its route is adjacent to the foundation, and in order to protect the structure from any settlement effects induced by tunnelling, it is proposed to build a 42 *m* deep diaphragm wall just 1.75 *m* away from the foundation as indicated in the figure.

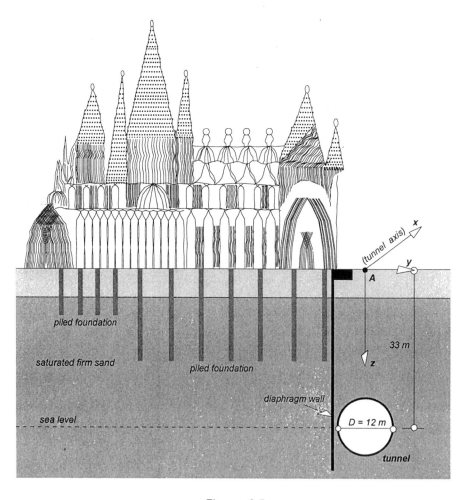

Figure p8.5

Assume the sand has the following average physical characteristics:
- elasticity modulus: $E = 48 \, MN/m^2$
- saturated unit weight: $\gamma_{sat} = 20 \, kN/m^3$
- Poisson's ratio: $\nu = 0.4$
- coefficient of lateral pressure: $K_o = 1.6$

Notice that K_o does not correspond to the coefficient of earth pressure at rest. Furthermore, the sand's normalised volume loss (see equation 8.25) is estimated at: $p = 1\%$, and the deconfinement ratio corresponds to $\lambda = 1$.

a • Using the 3-D equation 8.30, calculate the surface settlement $S_{(x=y=z=0)}$ at point A (refer to figure 8.14 for (x & y) co-ordinates), as well as at the point with co-ordinates $(x = z = 0, \, y = 10 \, m)$

b • Use the 2-D equation 8.35 to calculate the settlement at both previous points.

c • Write a computer routine based on equation 8.30, then calculate and plot the 3-D surface settlement profile.

Ans: a- $S_{(x=y=z=0)} = 25.4 \times 10^{-3} \, m$, $S_{(x=z=0, \, y=10m)} = 22.16 \times 10^{-3} \, m$
        b- $S_{(x=y=z=0)} = 27.3 \times 10^{-3} \, m$, $S_{(x=z=0, \, y=10 \, m)} = 22.04 \times 10^{-3} \, m$

8.6   Consider the *Toulon* tunnel analysed in example 8.6 (section 8.4) Write a computer routine based on equation 8.30, then plot the 3-D surface settlement profile induced by tunnelling.

8.7   Use equation 8.35 in conjunction with the *Toulon* tunnel in example 8.6, then calculate and plot the 2-D settlement profiles (as per figure 8.16) at 5 *m depth intervals.*

References

Atkinson JH & Mair R J (1981). Soil Mechanics aspects of soft ground tunnelling. Ground Engineering. Vol 14 (5). pp. 20-28

Clough G.W. & Shmidt B. (1980) Design and performance of excavations and tunnels in soft clay. Soft clay engineering , Elsevier, Amsterdam. pp 569-634.

Deane A P & Bassett R H (1995). The Heathrow Express Trial Tunnel. Proceedings of the institution of Civil Engineers, Geotechnical Engineering 113, pp. 144-156

Jaeger J. C. and Cook N. G.W. (1979). Fundamentals of rock mechanics. 3rd edn, Chapman and Hall London

New B M & Bowers K H (1994). Ground Movement model validation at the Heathrow express Trial Tunnel. Tunnelling'94, London. Chapman & Hall, pp. 301-326

Loganathan N & Poulos HG (1998). Analytical prediction for tunnelling induced ground movements in clays. Journal of Geotechnical & Geoenvironmental Engineering, ASCE, vol 124 (9) pp. 846-856

Mair RJ, Taylor RN, Bracegirdle A (1993). Subsurface settlement profiles above tunnels in clays. Geotechnique 43 (2) pp. 315-320

Mestat P H, 1994. Validation du progiciel CESAR-LCPC en comportement mécanique non linéaire. Volume 1: Fondations superficielles et tunnels. Laboratoire Central des Ponts et Chaussées, Collection Etudes et recherches des LPC, série Géotechnique. GT 58, 173 pages.

O'Reilly MP & New BM (1982). Settlements above tunnels in the United Kingdom: their magnitude and prediction. Tunnelling'82, pp. 173-181.

Peck RB (1969). Deep excavations and tunnelling in soft ground. Proceedings of the 7th international conference on Soil Mechanics. Mexico. Vol 3 pp. 225-290

Poulos H.G and Davis E.H. (1974). Elastic solutions for soil and rock mechanics. Wiley New York.

Rankin W.J. 1988. Ground movements resulting urban tunnelling. Proceedings of the conference on engineering geology. Underground movements, Nottingham. pp. 79-92

Serratrice J-F (1999): Suivi du plot Chalucet. Application à la prévision des tassements de surface. Tunnel de la traversée souterraine de Toulon. Journées de mécanique des sols et des roches des LPC, Aix en Provence. 31 pages.

Serratrice J-F, and Magnan J-P (2002). Analyse et prévision des tassements de surface pendant le creusement du tunnel nord de la traversée souterraine de Toulon. Bulletin de liaison des Laboratoires des Ponts et Chaussées. No 237. pp. 5-36

The Channel Tunnel. Part 1: Tunnels. Proceedings of the ICE, 1992

Wood AM (2000 Tunnelling: management by design. E & FN Spon, London

CHAPTER 9

Finite element modelling in geomechanics

9.1 Finite element modelling

This section aims at presenting the numerical modelling used in conjunction with geotechnical problems from a *practical perspective*. As such, it is not intended to develop in detail the mathematical formalisms of the finite element method, although its working will be explained succinctly. A thorough presentation of such a method of analysis is widely available, and reference should be made to Zienkiewicz and Taylor (1991), Bathe (1982, 1996), Hughes (1987), Stasa (1985), Griffiths and Smith (1991), Smith and Griffiths (1998), Reddy (1993) and Owen and Hinton (1980).

The finite element method is one of the most powerful approximate solution method that can be applied to solve a wide range of problems represented by ordinary or partial differential equations. The power of such a method derives from the fact that it can easily accommodate changes in the material stiffness which is evaluated at element level as will be explained shortly. Also, it allows for different boundary conditions to be applied in such a way that an acceptable global approximate solution to the physical problem can be achieved. Considering that closed form solutions cannot be elaborated for a large number of complex physical problems, due to the impossibility of satisfying the boundary conditions related to the corresponding equilibrium equations, the finite element method therefore provides an ideal alternative (approximate) solution method.
In its simplest form, the finite element method consists of:

- dividing a given structure or domain into a number of *elements* (hence the name *finite elements*); this process is known as *discretisation*. Elements are connected by *nodes* at the corners and sometimes at the sides as well;

- modelling the behaviour of the unknown variables at different nodes through the use of appropriate interpolation polynomials, better known as *shape functions*.

The *shape, size, number* and *type* of elements depend on the type of structure or domain, and also on the precision required in the solution, these points being further elaborated below.

In all cases, finite element modelling invariably leads to a matrix formulation that depends on the nature of the physical problem to be solved. Hence, steady-state problems (*i.e.* problems for which the unknown variables are independent of time) always consist of solving (numerically) the following matrix relationship:

$$[K]\{U\} = \{F\} \tag{9.1}$$

where $[K]$ represents the global *stiffness matrix* (that includes the material properties), $\{U\}$ is the vector of *nodal unknown variables* (for instance displacement or water pressure), and $\{F\}$ corresponds to the *vector of applied nodal loads*.

Based on the two basic principles stated above, a finite element procedure consists of the following steps:

(*a*) discretisation and selection of elements;
(*b*) selection of the stress-strain relationships;
(*c*) evaluation of element matrices;
(*d*) assemblage of elements matrices and introduction of boundary conditions;
(*e*) solution to nodal unknowns;
(*f*) computation of derived quantities, and *analysis of results.*

(*a*) **Discretisation and elements selection**

The elements used in conjunction with any discretisation process are selected with the view to obtaining sufficiently precise values of the nodal unknowns. Their *shape* and *type* depend therefore on the complexity of the boundaries of the discretised domain, and on the complexity of the physical behaviour to be modelled. In this respect, figure 9.1 illustrates the deformed shape of various one-, two-, and three-dimensional elements, each characterised by the *number of nodes* it contains. It is useful to mention at this stage that the number of variables at each node defines the number of *degrees of freedom per node* which are not necessarily identical for all nodes of every element in the mesh. Also, elements for which the *same* shape functions are used to define the unknown variable *and* the geometry of the element (*i.e.* its edges) are known as *isoparametric elements*. The (deformed) shapes are related to the type of the *shape functions*. Thus, *linear elements* are such that the unknowns vary linearly between any two connected nodes. The edges of a *quadratic element* on the other hand are curved since the corresponding shape functions consist of second-order polynomials. *Cubic elements* are generated using third-order polynomials.

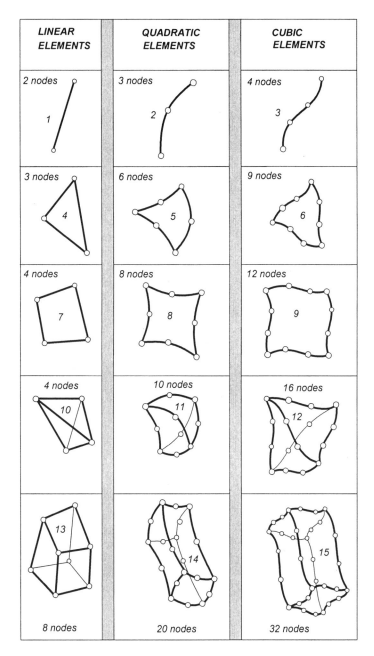

Figure 19.1: Selective types of elements.

While the list of elements depicted in the figure is by no means exhaustive, it contains however some of the most widely used elements in finite element modelling in geotechnics. Thus, the three-noded triangle (element 4 in the figure) is the simplest two-dimensional element. Because of its associated linear shape functions, the strains (and consequently the stresses) are constant within the element; for that reason, the element is usually referred to as the *constant strain triangle (CST)*. Although the *CST* is very easy to program, its use is limited to problems which do not involve the derivatives of the nodal variables such as computational fluid dynamics and seepage applications. Similarly, the same limitations apply to the four-noded rectangle (element 7 in figure 9.1). For these reasons, the six-noded triangle and the eight-noded rectangle (quadratic elements 5 and 8 respectively) are the two-dimensional isoparametric elements *par excellence*, although their performance depends on the integration rule used (see section 9.3) . Also, the 15-noded quadratic (cubic strain) triangle (element 6 with an extra node on each side and three extra interior nodes, figure 9.1) is another quite widely used element which is now incorporated in many finite element packages. These elements are particularly suitable for modelling plane strain and axisymmetric problems. Moreover, the quadratic nature of the associated shape functions makes it possible for domains with curved edges to be discretised in a precise way without the use of an excessive number of elements. It is perhaps worth mentioning that the shape functions associated with the eight-noded triangle are based on incomplete second-order polynomials (the straightforward mathematical details can be found in *any* book on finite elements) and, accordingly, the element is often referred to (in the jargon of finite elements) as a *serendipity triangle*.

When it comes to three-dimensional modelling in geotechnics, the two most widely used elements are the ten-noded tetrahedron and the twenty-noded serendipity hexahedron (elements 11 and 14 in figure 9.1). These quadratic 3-D elements can be used successfully to estimate displacement and stress fields. It must be borne in mind that the coding of mesh generation and output facilities for 3-D finite element analysis can be very complex. Accordingly, 3-D finite element modelling must only be used when neither plane strain nor axisymmetric conditions are suitable, or when the type of project justifies the cost of such a modelling (the case of the simulation of stresses and settlements beneath the foundation of a nuclear power plant for instance). It should be remembered that a finite element mesh consists generally of a combination of different types of compatible elements (*i.e.* nodes *common* to two elements must have the *same* degrees of freedom, and their shape functions must be characterised by polynomials of the *same* order). This may involve the use of transitional elements characterised by different shape functions on one side (to ensure a correct transition between elements) as illustrated in figure 9.2. More importantly, finite element modelling of soil structure interaction problems (examples include retaining, diaphragm or sheet-pile walls, laterally loaded piles, tunnels) may necessitate the use of interface elements to simulate the friction at the soil/structure interface (refer to figure 9.2).

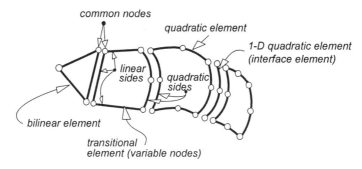

Figure 9.2: Use of transitional and interface elements.

(b) Selection of constitutive laws

The predictions based on the outcome of a finite element modelling depend to a large extent on how realistic is the stress–strain relationship used in the calculations. It is a fact that most engineers prefer to use simple linear relationships, and in some cases related to homogeneous isotropic soils, such assumptions can be justified. However, for more complex soil conditions corresponding to layered soils with different stiffness characteristics, the assumption of a unique stress–strain relationship, let alone a linear one, can be *markedly* erroneous. It is essential to realise that finite element modelling, with a however refined mesh and sophisticated elements, will not *per se* offset any shortcomings related to the use of inappropriate stiffness parameters (that is stress–strain relationships), and as such, it cannot be emphasised enough that the numerical analyst must have a good feel, if not a good grasp, of soil behaviour prior to embarking on expensive numerical modelling. Non-linear stress–strain relationships usually lead to iterative procedures in computation, increasing noticeably the cost of calculations. Such cost must therefore be justified at least in terms of obtaining reliable predictions of stresses and deformations.

(c) Evaluation of element matrices

In finite element modelling, element matrices are first formulated in terms of local co-ordinates, so that for each element in the mesh, the element stiffness matrix and vector of nodal forces are established using an integral method such as the *Galerkin weighted-residual method,* for instance, thus yielding:

$$[K]^e = \int_{V_e} [B]^T [D][B]\, dv$$

$$\{F\}^e = \int_{V_e} [N]^T \{F_v\}\, dv \tag{9.2}$$

$[B]^T$ being the *transpose* of the matrix $[B]$ which is derived from the shape functions $[N]$, and $[D]$ corresponds to the matrix of soil properties relating stresses and strains (refer to Hughes (1987), for example). The numerical integration of the element stiffness matrix is usually undertaken using the *Gauss quadrature method*, whose power is such that the integral in equation 9.2 needs only be evaluated at a few specific points known as *Gauss integration points*. It can be shown that using n points of integration in each direction of the space, this method can integrate exactly up to a $(2n-1)$-order polynomial. For instance, it can readily be shown that in the case of the eight-noded serendipity triangle (element 8 in figure 9.2), the integrand $[B]^T[D][B]$ in equation 9.2 is of the fourth order. Were the stiffness matrix for this element to be evaluated using nine integration points (that is 3×3 so that $n = 3$), an exact solution will be achieved since the use of $n^2 = 9$ integration points can integrate exactly up to a fifth order polynomial $(2n - 1 = 5)$.

(d) Assemblage of elements matrices and introduction of boundary conditions

Once all elements' stiffness matrices are evaluated in local co-ordinates, a global stiffness matrix is then determined by first expanding each element matrix so that it is expressed in terms of all nodal variables of the entire mesh, then summing all matrices in a straightforward manner, yielding in the process the now familiar equation 9.1:

$$[K]\{U\} = \{F\}$$

in which the vector $\{U\}$ contains all nodal variables (or degrees of freedom), and $\{F\}$ represents the (expanded) vector containing all nodal forces. The boundary conditions in terms of nodal forces are inserted into the global vector $\{F\}$ in a straightforward way. However, a prescribed nodal displacement can be introduced in many ways. For example, were the displacement at node i to be prescribed at $u_i = \delta$, then such a boundary condition can be satisfied if the diagonal coefficient in the stiffness matrix K_{ii} corresponding to node i is replaced by a large number ($M = 10^6$ for example) and the quantity $M\delta$ is substituted for the nodal force F_i. Notice that the global stiffness matrix is (usually) symmetric and has a dimension of $(m \times m)$ where m represents the total number of degrees of freedom contained in the entire mesh. For example a somewhat complex 2-D mesh for a tunnel having, say, 5000 nodes (which is not unusual) with only 2 degrees of freedom per node, yields a global stiffness matrix with a dimension of $(10,000 \times 10,000) = 10^8$. Storing such a colossal matrix in its entirety would undoubtedly cause few problems; fortunately, only a few of the 100 million coefficients in this case are *non-zero*. What is more, the non-zero coefficients are situated in and around the diagonal of the matrix, thus forming a *band*. It is only the width of this band that is of interest, because its storage is done according to a dynamic allocation of space that allows the corresponding coefficients (which may include zeros) to be stored in lines so that they are easily retrieved when required. This method is known as the *skyline storage method*, the details of which can be found in Zienkiewicz and Taylor (1991), for instance.

(e) Solution to nodal unknowns

This step consists of calculating the vector of nodal unknowns $\{U\}$ from the global equation 9.1. The obvious solution is to invert the stiffness matrix $[K]$ so that:

$$\{U\} = [K]^{-1}[F]$$

However, given the large size of $[K]$, its inversion is not practical. A more effective solution consists of applying the triangular decomposition method in conjunction with the stiffness matrix, then using the forward elimination and back-substitution method to calculate the unknown nodal variables. Based on the Gaussian elimination method, it can be shown that, provided $[K]$ is not singular (*i.e.* its determinant in not zero), it can always be written as the product of two matrices:

$$[K] = [L][S] \tag{9.3}$$

where $[L]$ is a lower triangular matrix in which the diagonal coefficients are unity, and $[S]$ is an upper triangular matrix, so that for example:

$$\begin{bmatrix} 2 & 4 & 8 \\ 4 & 11 & 25 \\ 6 & 18 & 46 \end{bmatrix} = \begin{bmatrix} 1 & 0 & 0 \\ 2 & 1 & 0 \\ 3 & 2 & 1 \end{bmatrix} \begin{bmatrix} 2 & 4 & 8 \\ 0 & 3 & 9 \\ 0 & 0 & 4 \end{bmatrix}$$

$$[K] \qquad = \qquad [L] \qquad \quad [S]$$

Thus, substituting for $[K]$ into the global relationship yields:

$$[L][S]\{U\} = \{F\} \tag{9.4}$$

which can then be solved in a very easy way using the forward elimination and back-substitution method (see Jennings and McKeown (1992), Hoffman (1992)) consisting of the following stages:

- *stage 1*: factorize $[K]$:

$$[K] = [L][S] \tag{9.5a}$$

- *stage 2*: use a forward substitution to solve for $\{Z\}$:

$$[L]\{Z\} = \{F\} \tag{9.5b}$$

- *stage 3*: use a back-substitution to solve for $\{U\}$:

$$[S]\{U\} = \{Z\} \tag{9.5c}$$

Notice that $\{Z\}$ in equations 9.5 represents a vector of intermediate variables.

Such a method of solution however, may quickly become unsuitable for 3-D finite element analyses, both on grounds of storage capacity and the number of calculations. Under such circumstances, iterative solvers such as the one based on the pre-conditioned conjugate gradient method (see Jennings and McKeown (1992)) can be very useful in terms of efficiency and precision.

(f) Calculation of derived quantities and analysis of results

Once the primary unknowns in equation 9.4 are determined, the *gradients* or derived quantities can then be established. For instance, the strains are derived from displacements, and the stresses are calculated from the stress–strain constitutive relationships. Perhaps the most important step in a finite element modelling consists of analysing the outcome of computation. Once more, it is worth reiterating that the finite element method is *only* a method of solution and, as such, it *cannot* make up for any deficiency related to soil stiffness parameters used in the calculations. It is naïve to consider a result acceptable simply by virtue of the fact that it was generated through a finite element modelling. The engineer must be in a position to question the very *raison d'être* of such a modelling in the first place. Is it needed ? If yes, then how can one get a reliable set of soil parameters (preferably measured in situ so as to minimise the effects of disturbance). Furthermore, it is essential that the soil/structure interaction mechanisms are well understood before embarking on time consuming expensive numerical modelling. It is also helpful if the working of the finite element method is understood, so that when it comes to the interpretation of results, any aberration can be attributed to its appropriate cause(s). In this respect, the following section contains some practical analyses related to the potential pitfalls of finite element modelling.

9.2 Effective stress analysis

Thus far, the term *stress* has been used indiscriminately. However, there is often a need during a finite element analysis of geotechnical problems, to dissociate (numerically) *effective stresses* from *porewater pressures* according to the effective stress principle (an important aspect in geotechnics). Although the specific details of such an analysis is beyond the scope of the present text (reference can be made to Naylor (1974) for example), it is worth mentioning that an effective stress formulation can easily be incorporated in a finite element program. The procedure consists of using an expanded matrix of soil properties relating stresses and strains (matrix [D] in equation 9.2) in the following manner (see Naylor *et al.* (1981)):

$$[D] = [D'] + [m][m]^T [K_f] \tag{9.6a}$$

$$\{\sigma\} = \{\sigma'\} + [m]\{u\} \tag{9.6b}$$

where $[m]^T$ represents the transpose of the column matrix related to the effective stress principle, $[D']$ is the soil skeleton modulus matrix, and $[K_f]$ corresponds to the bulk modulus of the pore fluid element. Note that all coefficients corresponding to shear stress components in $[m]$ are zero, the remaining coefficients being equal to 1.

All calculations involving element matrices, assembly and solution to the global system of equations thus formed are then undertaken as described previously. Once the strains are calculated, the ensuing stress increments are evaluated using the following relationships:

$$\{\Delta\sigma'\} = [D']\{\Delta\varepsilon\} \tag{9.7a}$$

$$\{\Delta u\} = [K_f]\{\Delta\varepsilon_v\} \tag{9.7b}$$

$\{\Delta u\}$ being the *excess* (i.e. load induced) porewater pressure, and $\{\Delta\varepsilon_v\}$ represents the volumetric strain change. Notice that a drained analysis amounts to setting $[K_f]$ to zero. More importantly, the effective stress analysis presented above does not apply to transient flow problems (i.e. consolidation problems).

Also, it should be mentioned that the critical state model (see Azizi, 2007) can be (and is often) successfully coupled to finite element programs. In this respect, reference should be made to Britto and Gunn (1986) and Naylor *et al.* (1981).

9.3 Finite element modelling of seepage and consolidation problems

Although seepage problems are steady state problems, their finite element solution is nonetheless elaborated in a slightly different way from the one developed earlier, since pressure heads are the corresponding primary unknowns. Seepage problems are represented by an elliptic equation, the two- dimensional form of which is as follows:

$$k_x \frac{\partial^2 h}{\partial x^2} + k_y \frac{\partial^2 h}{\partial y^2} = 0 \tag{9.8}$$

where k_x and k_y are the coefficients of soil permeability and h corresponds to the total head. Notice that for $k_x \neq k_y$, equation 9.8 is *not* a Laplace equation.

Whilst developing a closed form solution to such an equation can be fraught with difficulties, mainly because in many cases of flow, the corresponding boundary conditions are very difficult to satisfy, the finite element method can be applied in a straightforward manner. It can be shown that, irrespective of the nature of flow (i.e. confined or unconfined), the discretisation of equation 9.8 invariably yields a global relationship:

$$[K]\{H\} = \{Q\} \tag{9.9}$$

which is a familiar matrix relationship, since it is similar to equation 9.1. Here $\{H\}$ is the vector of nodal variables, which in this case correspond to the total heads, and $\{Q\}$ is the vector of nodal flow. It is interesting to mention that solving for total heads implies that each node has only one degree of freedom, in other words there is only one unknown quantity at each node.

The global stiffness matrix $[K]$ in equation 9.9 is obtained from the assembly of element matrices, each of which is calculated as follows:

$$[K]^e = \int_{V_e} [B]^T [P][B]\, dv \tag{9.10}$$

where $[B]^T$ corresponds to the transpose of matrix $[B]$ which is derived from the shape functions, and $[P]$ is the element permeability matrix (Naylor *et al.*, 1981):

$$[P] = \begin{bmatrix} k_x & 0 \\ 0 & k_y \end{bmatrix} \tag{9.11}$$

Notice the diagonal nature of $[P]$.

The numerical solution to equation 9.9 depends on the boundary conditions and therefore on the nature of seepage. Thus, in the case of confined flow as illustrated in figure 9.3, the corresponding boundary conditions are:

- *along AB*: $H = h_1 + d_1$

- *along CD*: $H = h_2 + d_2$

- *along EF*: $\dfrac{\partial H}{\partial y} = 0$ (impermeable side)

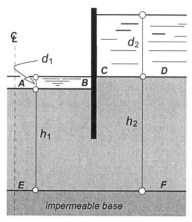

Figure 9.3: Boundary conditions related to confined flow.

For unconfined flow, on the other hand (see figure 9.4), the boundary conditions are:

- *along AB*: $H = h_1$
- *along BC*: $H = y$ and $u = 0$ (*u* being the porewater pressure)
- *along AC*: $\dfrac{\partial H}{\partial y} = 0$ (impermeable side)

in both cases, *H* is the *total head* expressed with respect to the datum represented by the impermeable base.

The *free surface* in the case of unconfined flow presents an additional problem as its location is not known à *priori*. The precise location can be found using iterative techniques such as the one suggested by Smith and Griffiths (1998), that consists of deforming the mesh until, eventually, its upper surface coincides with the free surface characterised by the boundary condition of a total head identical to the elevation head at any given point.

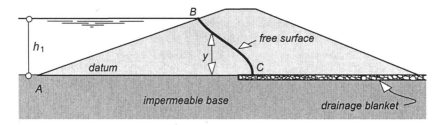

Figure 9.4: Boundary conditions related to unconfined flow.

Time-dependent problems such as consolidation are represented by a *parabolic equation*:

$$c_v\frac{\partial^2 u}{\partial z^2} = \frac{\partial u}{\partial t} \tag{9.12}$$

for which it can readily be shown that finite element modelling yields the following relationship:

$$[C]\left\{\frac{\partial U}{\partial t}\right\} + [K]\{U\} = \{F\} \tag{9.13}$$

where $[C]$ represents the matrix of soil consolidation characteristics. The nodal variables $\{U\}$ this time correspond to the porewater pressure; the remaining symbols having the same meaning as in equation 9.1.

A solution to equation 9.13 can be obtained through a combination of finite difference formulation (to discretise time) and finite elements (to discretise space). Consequently, using a forward difference operator:

$$\left\{\frac{\partial U}{\partial t}\right\} = \frac{1}{\Delta t}[\{U\}_{t+\Delta t} - \{U\}_t] \tag{9.14}$$

(Δt being the time increment), then inserting the latter quantity into equation 9.13 and rearranging, the following algorithm can easily be established:

$$\{U\}_{t+\Delta t} = \Delta t[C]^{-1}\left[\{F\}_t + \left(\frac{1}{\Delta t}[C] - [K]\right)\{U\}_t\right] \tag{9.15}$$

which can then be solved on a step-by-step basis. The convergence of the iterative process depends on the size of Δt. Furthermore, a stable solution may initially show some oscillations at one or more nodes. These oscillations, which only occur during the first few iterations, do not affect the convergence or the rate at which it occurs, and can be reduced by adjusting the size of elements or the size of time increment.

9.4 Practical aspects of finite element modelling in geotechnics

Finite element modelling of soil/structure interaction problems needs to be planned and undertaken carefully, so that any anomalies in the results can be spotted and remedied. The first step consists of discretising the domain, in other words generating a *mesh*. Although some finite element design programs contain mesh-generation pre-processors, it must be remembered that a mesh should always constitute a compromise between the computer capacity to store data and execute calculations (this capacity can in some cases be exceeded even by the standard of very powerful machines), and reasonable predictions in terms of outcome such as strains, stresses, porewater pressure etc.

Thus, a reasonable mesh should be refined (i.e. formed of smaller elements) near any applied load where the stress and displacement gradients are expected to be large, and around any geometric or material discontinuities (or singularities to use a finite element jargon) such as tunnel openings or excavations. Also, the mesh needs to be refined around the areas where changes in material properties occur, as in the case of different soil layers, or around a soil/structure interface (pile/soil, retaining structure/soil, tunnel/soil etc.). In such cases, interface elements are needed to simulate friction at the soil/structure interface, particularly when the structure surface is not relatively smooth.

Generally, the size of elements used in a mesh depends on the loading conditions and geometric discontinuities stated above. However, numerical evidence seems to indicate that the *aspect ratio* of an element (i.e. the ratio of the largest to the smallest dimensions of an element) must be kept within reasonable limits. In this respect, an aspect ratio smaller than 3 ensures satisfactory results in terms of stresses, unless the soil behaviour is markedly non-linear, in which case an even smaller ratio is required. As far as the shape of elements is concerned, and whenever practicable, triangles, rectangles and hexahedra used to generate a mesh should be as near as possible to equilateral triangles, squares and cubes respectively, so as to avoid any excessive distortion of these elements in the advent of large displacements. Notice that some sophisticated finite element programs offer the possibility of automatically regenerating the mesh while taking into account the level of deformation of different elements.

The size of elements should be increased gradually around the refined portions of the mesh in a way that ensures a smooth transition from small to larger size elements. This can be achieved if the ratio of the areas (or volumes in 3-D) of two adjacent elements does not exceed 2.

In any case, it is strongly advised (perhaps one should say it is logical) to avoid using distorted elements such as the ones illustrated in figure 9.5 when generating a mesh. The reason being that, once loaded, each of these elements can potentially deform to the point where the stiffness matrix becomes singular (i.e. with a zero determinant, so that it cannot be inverted) thus causing numerical instability. As a guideline, any angle α within an element must be such that $15° \le \alpha \le 165°$. Also, the middle node in a quadratic element should be situated within the middle third of the side as illustrated in figure 9.5 (Zienkiewicz and Taylor, 1991). Transitional elements (refer to figure 9.2 for the principle involved) are mainly used in conjunction with 3-D modelling.

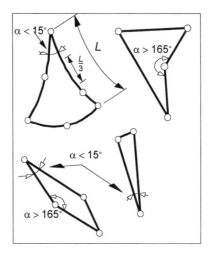

Figure 9.5: Unacceptable elements.

The type of elements used in a finite element modelling depends on the type of problem to be analysed. Nevertheless, one has to bear in mind that the strains and stresses are derived from displacements and, as such, using linear elements (i.e. elements characterised by linear shape functions) automatically yields constant strains and stresses within each element, which can be markedly erroneous, particularly in relation to stress distribution. Accordingly, the use of linear elements (refer to figure 9.1) is not advised. Quadratic elements on the other hand, especially the six-noded triangle and the eight-noded rectangle, are widely used to model different type of problems in geomechanics.

The calculation of strains and stresses is undertaken within each element at specific *integration points*. Often, the integration points used to calculate the strains (and hence the stresses) are fewer than those used to calculate the element stiffness matrix. For example, whilst the stiffness matrix of the eight-noded serendipity rectangle is calculated using 3×3 integration points, numerical evidence shows that in most cases, satisfactory results in terms of displacements are obtained from a *reduced integration* using 2×2 integration points. In fact in this case, an exact integration using 3×3 points yields an over-stiff response, so underestimating displacements. Situations might arise whereby a mechanism can occur as a result of a reduced integration using 2×2 points; however, these cases are extreme. As regards the six-noded triangle, a happy balance can be achieved using three (non-Gauss) integration points. On the other hand the use of four integration points in conjunction with the ten-noded tetrahedron (one of the most widely used 3-D elements) provides satisfactory results in terms of displacements. Interested readers can refer to the paper by Naylor (1994) on integration rules.

Once calculated at the integration points, the stresses are then extrapolated to the element nodes and, because each element has its own stiffness matrix, the magnitude of stresses resulting from each element at a common node such as the one depicted in figure 9.6 is generally different. This stress discontinuity can be smoothed by taking the *average* value at the node, so that the corresponding nodal stress results from the contribution of all adjacent elements. However, nodal averaging *should not* be used for stress and strain calculations at nodes connecting elements with *different stiffnesses* (for example elements corresponding to different soil layers). Such boundaries are characterised by a *stress discontinuity*, except for the stress component *normal* to the boundary. Numerical evidence shows that the stress field is not affected by the stress discontinuity provided that a refined mesh with smaller size elements around theses boundaries is used.

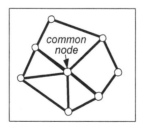

Figure 9.6: Stress calculation at a common node.

When using finite element modelling, special attention must be paid to the degree and type of anisotropy of the soil/structure material. For example the distribution with depth of the vertical stress generated by a uniform surface load within a thick homogeneous isotropic soil layer is *markedly different* in shape and in magnitude from that generated by the same load within a layered anisotropic soil.

As mentioned earlier, geometric or material discontinuities constitute singularities which are unavoidable for a large number of soil/structure interaction problems. This can generate inaccurate stress fields near the singularities (for example, an infinite stress beneath a point load is computed as a finite quantity). However, these effects can be minimised by using a refined mesh around the singularity, so that a right-angle boundary, for instance, can be transformed into a smooth curved boundary.

9.5 Practical aspects of a finite element mesh related to foundations

A finite element mesh related to a given problem in geomechanics must always take into account different aspects evoked previously and linked to elements type and size, and particularly to the nature of the problem (axisymmetry, anisotropy, drainage conditions, soil/structure interaction, geometric singularities, and nature of loading). Consequently, the following *guidelines* should be viewed with a sufficient degree of flexibility, so that local conditions are appropriately considered. As such, they should *in no way* be regarded as rules.

Based on the previous analysis, a finite element (axisymmetric) mesh in the case of a shallow foundation on an isotropic homogeneous soil, with a width B usually includes an area extending to about $5B$ laterally and $8B$ vertically as illustrated in figure 9.7; an area within which most of the stress variations are expected to occur. The conditions imposed at the mesh edges in figure 9.7 allow for a vertical movement (*i.e.* $u = 0$) along the vertical boundaries, while restricting any movement to $u = v = 0$ at the bottom horizontal boundary, where the stresses (and therefore the displacements) are expected to decay. Also, notice how the mesh is refined beneath and around the foundation, with increasing elements size as one moves away from the foundation in each direction. Were the soil conditions to be different as in the case, for example, of ansiotropic multi-layered and partially submerged soils, then the overall size of mesh as well as the size and type of elements would need to be altered drastically so as to reflect the markedly different characteristics of the problem. Hence the informative nature of the dimensions indicated in figure 9.7.

For a deep pile foundation, the mesh depends on the type of loading and the type of pile. Thus, for a single axially loaded pile with a length L embedded in an isotropic homogeneous soil, the mesh should ideally cover an area $3L$-deep and about 30-pile diameters wide as depicted in figure 9.8. The typical (axisymmetric) mesh in the figure consists mainly of eight-noded rectangles and a few six-noded triangles. The size of the elements reflects the stress distribution generated around the pile shaft and tip depicted in figure 5.28 (refer to section 5.5, chapter 5). The boundary conditions are of a similar type to the ones described previously in the case of shallow foundations. However, in this case, there is a need to use interface elements in order to simulate the friction developed along the pile shaft.

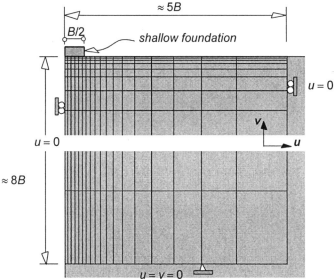

Figure 9.7: Typical (axisymmetric) mesh dimensions for an isolated shallow foundation on isotropic homogeneous soil.

It is interesting to notice that the mesh in figure 9.8 is used to simulate the behaviour of an *already* embedded pile. The numerical simulation of pile driving is very complex in nature, not least because soil failure around the pile shaft and tip has to occur every time the pile is struck with the driving tool, so that it can be driven to the required depth, or sometimes until the occurrence of a refusal.

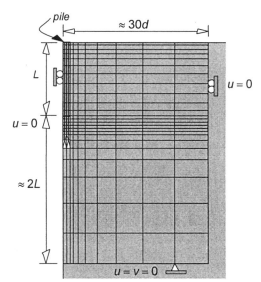

Figure 9.8: Typical (axisymmetric) mesh dimensions for a single axially loaded pile (isotropic homogeneous soil conditions).

A laterally loaded single pile, on the other hand, is characterised by a markedly different behaviour. This type of loading occurs especially in conjunction with bridges, flyovers and retaining structures founded on piles, and can be applied either actively or passively as depicted in figure 9.9. In both cases, the solution in terms of displacement, bending moment, shear stress and lateral pressure distribution with depth depends on soil/pile interaction, in other words on both soil and pile stiffness characteristics. This interaction is depicted in figure 9.10 whereby the resistance to the active load (a combination of a horizontal load and a bending moment applied at the pile head) is provided by the pile stiffness *and* the soil reaction per unit length (that is, the force per unit length induced within the soil mass by the active load as per section 5.7, chapter 5).

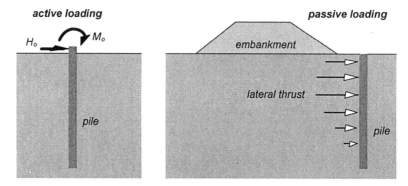

Figure 9.9: Active and passive lateral loading of piles.

While the pile stiffness can be assumed to be constant along the pile shaft, the soil stiffness, on the other hand, depends generally on the depth of embedment. Furthermore, figure 5..48 (chapter 5) shows that at a given depth z, the relationship between the soil reaction P and the lateral displacement y (i.e. the pile deflection) is non-linear, and that the nature of the relationship varies with depth.

The profiles of pile deflection, bending moment and soil reaction are also affected by the pile dimensions and the boundary conditions: a long slender pile behaves in a different way from a short rigid pile as illustrated in figures 5.51 and 5.52 (chapter 5) in the case of actively loaded piles embedded in an isotropic homogeneous sand. The figures also depict the difference in behaviour between a free head and a fixed head pile. Accordingly, a finite element mesh in the case of a laterally loaded pile should reflect the soil, pile and loading conditions. Because of the nature of the problem, no axisymmetry can be applied, and the mesh dimensions indicated in figure 9.10 should be applied sensibly.

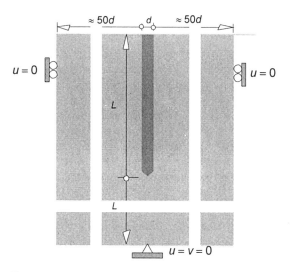

Figure 9.10: Typical mesh dimensions for a single laterally loaded pile (isotropic homogeneous soil conditions).

A pilegroup is much more difficult to model, especially in the absence of axisymmetry (which is generally the case). The difficulties are further illustrated by the fact that several modes of failure can potentially develop (a single pile failure within the group, a row of piles failing at the same time or a block failure en masse, refer to chapter 5). Under such circumstances, a three-dimensional mesh might become a necessity, with all the consequences elicited earlier concerning the potentially very large size of global matrices. However, notwithstanding the somewhat high cost that might be incurred in some cases, 3-D modelling of pilegroups is now becoming an almost routine operation.

Whenever the 3-D problem can be reduced to an axisymmetric problem, then a mesh such as the typical one depicted in figure 9.11 corresponding to a pilegroup embedded in an isotropic soil can be used. The dimensions of the area covered by the mesh extend to about $3L$ in depth, and at least a distance L outside the pile situated at the group's edge. Such a mesh should reflect the stress distribution generated within the soil mass by a pilegroup as per figure 5.28 (chapter 5).

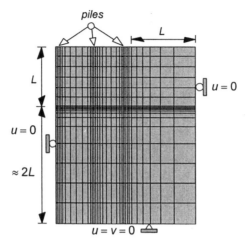

*Figure 9.11: Typical (axisymmetric) mesh dimensions
for an axially loaded pilegroup in an isotropic soil.*

9.6 Finite element mesh related to embankments, retaining structures and tunnels

The finite element modelling of soil loading through an embankment with a height H must be such that the mesh area covers most of the stress increase generated within the soil mass. Also, the area must take into account the possibility of a long term or a short term slope stability failure. Accordingly, for an isotropic homogeneous soil layer, the 2-D mesh should be characterised by a lateral dimension of at least four times the embankment length, and a minimum depth of $5H$ or the depth of stiff substratum, whichever is smaller (see figure 9.12). The mesh should be refined in areas where the maximum stress generated by the loading is expected to occur, and the size of elements should be increased gradually as one moves away from these areas. Note that were the depth of the stiff substratum to apply, then the boundary condition $u = v = 0$ indicated in the figure would correspond to a relatively small change in stiffness between the two layers. If the bottom layer were a rock, for example, overlain by a soft clay, then the boundary condition should be changed to allow for a lateral displacement, in which case $v = 0$. As regards a retaining wall with height H and base width L (see figure 9.13), the mesh should be wide enough to include not only the stress changes in the soil mass beneath the wall, but also the potential development of long term active and passive stress failures, as well as the possibility of a deep circular failure. Consequently, for a wall retaining an isotropic homogeneous soil, it is advised to use a mesh with a minimum lateral dimension of $2H$ in front of the wall and $3H$ behind the wall, depending on the type of soil. The mesh should extend a minimum depth of 6L or the depth of the stiff substratum, whichever is smaller as illustrated in figure 9.13. Also, interface elements may have to be used if the wall surface is relatively smooth.

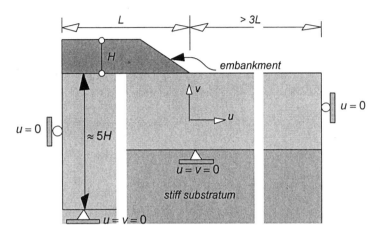

Figure 9.12: Typical mesh dimensions for an isotropic homogeneous soil loaded through an embankment.

The boundary condition related to the stiff substratum indicated in both figures 9.12 & 9.13 reflects the substantial change in stiffness between the two layers of soil.

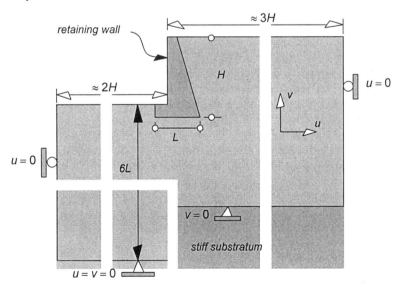

Figure 9.13: Typical mesh dimensions for a wall retaining an isotropic homogeneous soil.

Similar guidelines apply to diaphragm and sheet-pile walls (refer to figure 9.14).

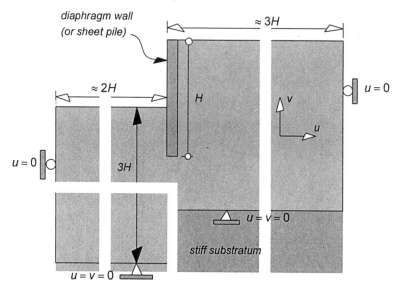

Figure 9.14: Typical mesh dimensions for a diaphragm wall retaining an isotropic homogeneous soil.

Finite element modelling of an underground cavity or a tunnel requires an engineering judgement as to how such a task can best be undertaken cost-effectively. Thus 3-D modelling is appropriate when there is a variation of soil stratification along the tunnel axis, or when stress conditions near the tunnel face need be studied. On the other hand, an axisymmetric analysis is suitable in the case of a vertical shaft when the soil stratification varies in the vertical direction only. There are instances in which plane deformations can be assumed to prevail, and therefore only a cross-section of the tunnel needs to be discretised. Under such circumstances, the area covered by the mesh must reflect the expected stress distribution and deformations around the opening.

As explained in the previous chapter, the *stress arching* that occurs around the opening is related to its depth and, accordingly, the dimensions of the meshed area should typically extend to a depth of around $5d$ beneath the *tunnel invert*, and should include the entire height of soil above the *crown*, unless the cover exceeds $10d$, in which case the soil thickness above the crown can be limited to $5d$ (Mestat, 1997). Laterally, the dimension of the meshed area should be extended to about $6d$ from the tunnel axis as illustrated in figures 9.15(*a*) and (*b*). Obviously, these dimensions only represent a guideline, and the engineer must always seek a compromise between reliable predictions in terms of stress–strain distribution, and cost. In so doing, the dimensions advocated above may need to be adjusted to suite the site conditions.

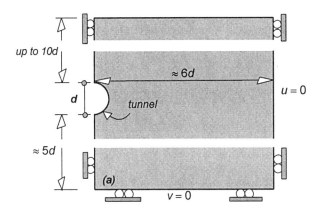

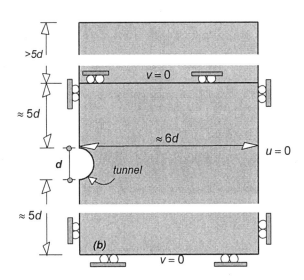

Figure 9.15: Typical mesh dimensions for (a) a shallow opening and (b) a deep tunnel (from Mestat (1997), by permission).

References

Azizi, F. (2007) *Physical Behaviour in Geotechnics.* 480 pp. Published by F. Azizi ISBN 978-0-9555996-2-0.

Bathe, K. J. (1982) *Finite Element Procedures in Engineering Analysis.* Prentice-Hall, Englewood Cliffs, New Jersey.

Bathe, K. J. (1996) *Numerical Methods in Finite Element Analysis,* 3rd edn. Prentice-Hall, Englewood Cliffs, New Jersey.

Britto, A. and Gunn, M. J. (1986) *Critical State Soil Mechanics via Finite Elements.* Ellis Horwood, Chichester.

Griffiths, D. V. and Smith, I. M. (1991) *Numerical Methods for Engineers.* Blackwell, Oxford.

Hoffman, J. D. (1992) *Numerical Methods for Engineers and Scientists.* McGraw-Hill, New York.

Hughes, T. J. R. (1987) *The Finite Element Method: Linear, Static and Dynamic Finite Element Analysis.* Prentice-Hall, Englewood Cliffs, New Jersey.

Jennings, A. and McKeown, J. J. (1992) *Matrix computation,* 2nd edn. John Wiley & Sons, Chichester.

Mestat, P. (1997) *Maillage d'élements finis pour les ouvrages de géotechnique: conseils et recommandations.* Bulletin de Laboratoires des Ponts et Chaussées, 212, pp. 39–64.

Naylor, D. J. (1974) *Stresses in nearly incompressible materials for finite elements with application to the calculation of excess pore pressures.* International Journal of Numerical Methods in Engineering, 8, pp. 443–460.

Naylor, D. J. (1994) *On integration rules for triangles.* Proceedings of the 3rd European Conference on Numerical Methods in Geotechnical Engineering, Manchester (ed. I. M. Smith), Balkema, Rotterdam.

Naylor, D. J., Pande, G. N., Simpson, B. and Tabb, R. (1981) *Finite Elements in Geotechnical Engineering.* Pineridge Press, Swansea, UK.

Owen, D. R. J. and Hinton, E. (1980) *Finite Elements in Plasticity: Theory and Practice.* Pineridge Press, Swansea.

Reddy, J. N. (1993) *An Introduction to the Finite Element Method.* McGraw-Hill, New York.

Smith, I. M. and Griffiths, D. V. (1998) *Programming the Finite Element Method,* 3rd edn. John Wiley & Sons, New York.

Stasa, F. L. (1985) *Applied Finite Element Analysis for Engineers.* CBS International Edition, New York.

Zienkiewicz, O. C. and Taylor, R. (1991) *The Finite Element Method,* (2 volumes) 4th edn. McGraw-Hill, London.

Subject index

Author index

The quadratic formula
The roots of the quadratic equation $ax^2 + bx + c = 0$ are given by:

$$x = \frac{-b \pm \sqrt{b^2 - 4ac}}{2a}$$

Determinants

$$\begin{vmatrix} a_1 & b_1 \\ a_2 & b_2 \end{vmatrix} = a_1b_2 - a_2b_1$$

$$\begin{vmatrix} a_1 & b_1 & c_1 \\ a_2 & b_2 & c_2 \\ a_3 & b_3 & c_3 \end{vmatrix} = a_1b_2c_3 + a_2b_3c_1 + a_3b_1c_2 - a_1b_3c_2 - a_2b_1c_3 - a_3b_2c_1$$

Laws of logarithms (where $\log_a x = y$ means $x = a^y$)

$$\log_a(M.N) = \log_a M + \log_a N, \qquad \log_a\left(\frac{M}{N}\right) = \log_a M - \log_a N$$

$$\log_a(M^x) = x.\log_a M$$

Analytic geometry
straight line: $y = mx + b$;   slope $= m = \dfrac{y_2 - y_1}{x_2 - x_1}$

Circle: $x^2 + y^2 = r^2$; $(x - h)^2 + (y - k)^2 = r^2$

Parabola: Vertical axis: $x^2 = 4ay$; $(x - h)^2 = 4a(y - k)$

Horizontal axis: $y^2 = 4ax$; $(y - k)^2 = 4a(x - h)$

Ellipse: vert major axis: $\dfrac{x^2}{b^2} + \dfrac{y^2}{a^2} = 1$; $\dfrac{(x - h)^2}{b^2} + \dfrac{(y - k)^2}{a^2} = 1$

hor. major axis: $\dfrac{x^2}{a^2} + \dfrac{y^2}{b^2} = 1$; $\dfrac{(x - h)^2}{a^2} + \dfrac{(y - k)^2}{b^2} = 1$

Hyperbola: vert. transverse axis $\dfrac{y^2}{a^2} - \dfrac{x^2}{b^2} = 1$; $\dfrac{(y - k)^2}{a^2} - \dfrac{(x - h)^2}{b^2} = 1$

hor. transverse axis $\dfrac{x^2}{a^2} - \dfrac{y^2}{b^2} = 1$; $\dfrac{(x - h)^2}{a^2} - \dfrac{(y - k)^2}{b^2} = 1$

Trigonometry
Area of a triangle: $A = \sqrt{s(s-a)(s-b)(s-c)}$ with $s = \frac{1}{2}(a+b+c)$

$a^2 = b^2 + c^2 - 2bc\cos\beta$

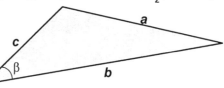

Pythagoras theorem: for $\beta = 90°$:
$a^2 = b^2 + c^2$

Trigonometry identities
$\sin(A+B) = \sin A\cos B + \cos A\sin B$ $\sin(A-B) = \sin A\cos B - \cos A\sin B$

$\cos(A+B) = \cos A\cos B - \sin A\sin B$ $\cos(A-B) = \cos A\cos B + \sin A\sin B$

$\tan A = \dfrac{\sin A}{\cos A}$ $\cot A = \dfrac{\cos A}{\sin A}$ $\sin^2 A + \cos^2 A = 1$

$\tan(A+B) = \dfrac{\tan A + \tan B}{1 - \tan A\tan B}$ $\tan(A-B) = \dfrac{\tan A - \tan B}{1 + \tan A\tan B}$

$\sin 2A = 2\sin A\cos A$

$\cos 2A = \cos^2 A - \sin^2 A = 2\cos^2 A - 1 = 1 - 2\sin^2 A$

$\tan 2A = \dfrac{2\tan A}{1 - \tan^2 A}$ $\sin\frac{1}{2}A = \pm\sqrt{(1-\cos A)/2}$

$\cos\frac{1}{2}A = \pm\sqrt{(1+\cos A)/2}$ $\tan\frac{1}{2}A = \dfrac{\sin A}{1+\cos A}$

$\sin A + \sin B = 2\sin\frac{1}{2}(A+B)\cos\frac{1}{2}(A-B)$

$\sin A - \sin B = 2\cos\frac{1}{2}(A+B)\sin\frac{1}{2}(A-B)$

$\cos A + \cos B = 2\cos\frac{1}{2}(A+B)\cos\frac{1}{2}(A-B)$

$\cos A - \cos B = -2\sin\frac{1}{2}(A+B)\sin\frac{1}{2}(A-B)$

$\sin A\cos B = \frac{1}{2}[\sin(A+B) + \sin(A-B)]$

$\cos A\sin B = \frac{1}{2}[\sin(A+B) - \sin(A-B)]$

$\cos A\cos B = \frac{1}{2}[\cos(A+B) + \cos(A-B)]$

$\sin A\sin B = \frac{1}{2}[\cos(A-B) - \cos(A+B)]$

Derivative formulae

$$\frac{d}{dx}(c) = 0 \qquad\qquad \frac{d}{dx}(x) = 1 \qquad\qquad \frac{d}{dx}[af(x)] = a\frac{d}{dx}[f(x)]$$

$$\frac{d}{dx}[f(x) \pm g(x)] = \frac{d}{dx}[f(x)] \pm \frac{d}{dx}[g(x)]$$

$$\frac{d}{dx}[f(x)\,g(x)] = f(x)\,g'(x) + g(x)\,f'(x)$$

$$\frac{d}{dx}\left[\frac{f(x)}{g(x)}\right] = \frac{g(x)\,f'(x) - f(x)\,g'(x)}{[g(x)]^2}$$

$$\frac{d}{dx}(x^n) = n\,x^{n-1} \qquad\qquad \frac{d}{dx}(u^n) = n\,u^{n-1}\frac{du}{dx}$$

$$\frac{d}{dx}\left[\log_a u\right] = \frac{1}{u}\frac{du}{dx}\log_a e \qquad\qquad \frac{d}{dx}[\ln u] = \frac{1}{u}\frac{du}{dx}$$

$$\frac{d}{dx}[a^u] = a^u\frac{du}{dx}\ln a \qquad\qquad \frac{d}{dx}[e^u] = e^u\frac{du}{dx}$$

$$\frac{d}{dx}[\sin u] = \cos u\,\frac{du}{dx} \qquad\qquad \frac{d}{dx}[\cos u] = -\sin u\,\frac{du}{dx}$$

$$\frac{d}{du}[\tan u] = \sec^2 u\,\frac{du}{dx} \qquad\qquad \frac{d}{dx}[\cot u] = -\csc^2 u\,\frac{du}{dx}$$

$$\frac{d}{dx}[\sec u] = \sec u \tan u\,\frac{du}{dx} \qquad\qquad \frac{d}{dx}[\csc u] = -\csc u \cot u\,\frac{du}{dx}$$

$$\frac{d}{dx}[Arc\sin u] = \frac{1}{\sqrt{1-u^2}}\frac{du}{dx} \qquad\qquad \frac{d}{dx}[Arc\cos u] = -\frac{1}{\sqrt{1-u^2}}\frac{du}{dx}$$

$$\frac{d}{dx}[Arc\tan u] = \frac{1}{1+u^2}\frac{du}{dx}$$

Integration formulae

$$\int u^n du = \frac{u^{n+1}}{n+1} + C \, , \qquad n \neq -1$$

$$\int u^{-1} du = \int \frac{du}{u} = \ln u + C$$

$$\int e^u du = e^u + C$$

$$\int u e^u du = e^u(u-1) + C$$

$$\int \sin u \, du = -\cos u + C$$

$$\int \cos u \, du = \sin u + C$$

$$\int \tan u \, du = \ln \sec u + C$$

$$\int \cot u \, du = \ln \sin u + C$$

$$\int e^{au} \sin mu \, du = \frac{e^{au}(a \sin mu - m \cos mu)}{m^2 + a^2} + C$$

$$\int e^{au} \cos mu \, du = \frac{e^{au}(m \sin mu + a \cos mu)}{m^2 + a^2} + C$$

$$\int \sec u \, du = \ln(\sec u + \tan u) + C$$

$$\int \csc u \, du = \ln(\csc u - \cot u) + C$$

$$\int \sec^2 u \, du = \tan u + C$$

$$\int \csc^2 u \, du = -\cot u + C$$

$$\int \sec u \tan u \, du = \sec u + C$$

$$\int \csc u \cot u \, du = -\csc u + C$$

$$\int \frac{du}{\sqrt{a^2 - u^2}} = \arcsin \frac{u}{a} + C$$

$$\int \frac{du}{a^2 + u^2} = \frac{1}{a} \arctan \frac{u}{a} + C$$

$$\int \frac{du}{\sqrt{u^2 \pm a^2}} = \ln\left(u + \sqrt{u^2 \pm a^2}\right) + C$$

$$\int \frac{du}{a^2 - u^2} = \frac{1}{2a} \ln\left(\frac{a+u}{a-u}\right) + C$$

$$\int u \sin u \, du = \sin u - u \cos u + C$$

$$\int u \cos u \, du = \cos u + u \sin u + C$$

$$\int u^n \ln u \, du = u^{n+1}\left[\frac{\ln u}{n+1} - \frac{1}{(n+1)^2}\right] + C$$

$$\int \sin^2 u \, du = \frac{1}{2}u - \frac{1}{4}\sin 2u + C$$

$$\int \cos^2 u \, du = \frac{1}{2}u + \frac{1}{4}\sin 2u + C$$

$$\int \tan^2 u \, du = \tan u - u + C$$

$$\int u \, dv = uv - \int v \, du + C$$